PRACTICAL
PRINTING AND BINDING

PREPARING FOR PRESS

Making final corrections before the formes are sent to the machine room. The job, consisting of type matter with illustration blocks inserted, is to be printed direct from type; otherwise, type-high metal furniture would have been utilized when imposing the formes for stereotyping or electrotyping. Patent quoins are in use, as shown in the foreground, where the compositor on the left is adjusting the quoins with the key in his right hand. The compositor on the right of the picture is shown lifting type from the forme in order to make a correction.

PRACTICAL PRINTING AND BINDING

A COMPLETE GUIDE TO THE LATEST DEVELOPMENTS IN ALL BRANCHES OF THE PRINTER'S CRAFT

Edited by
HARRY WHETTON
Editor of "The British Printer," 1900-1943

1946
ODHAMS PRESS LIMITED, LONG ACRE, LONDON, W.C.2

FOREWORD

THE Printing Industry today is of ever-increasing importance, for it touches every aspect in the life of the nation; and it is in order to give instruction covering the most recent technical developments in printing and its allied trades that PRACTICAL PRINTING AND BINDING has been prepared.

The aim has been to give, in a single volume, expert practical instruction in every branch of printing, so that apprentices, learners and craftsmen generally may increase their knowledge of the latest methods employed. Printers as a class are anxious to learn more of their craft than the work in which they are immediately concerned. The compositor wishes to know something of the machine-minder's work, and vice versa; the lithographer and the gravure printer appreciate the benefit of knowing something of the work of the departments which provide the material for transferring to plate or cylinder. The greater the sharing of knowledge among the numerous branches of the trade, the greater will be the efficiency of the industry; and it is believed that this book will be of great practical value in this connection.

Each of the thirteen sections, covering all sides of the industry, has been written by an expert; and the many illustrations have been selected to amplify the instruction given in the text. The colour section gives some idea of the variety of effects that may be obtained by various processes. Further valuable knowledge will be gained if craftsmen make their own collection of specimens of printing, noting on them particulars of the processes involved, the method and number of printings employed, and other details— information which can be obtained by reference to this book.

The Appendix on page 443 gives information in regard to Technical Education, and shows at a glance the location of Technical Schools in all parts of the British Isles. An inquiry to the Secretary of the College will bring full information as to the subjects taught in a particular school.

The leaders of the printing industry have never been lacking in enterprise, and they were pioneers in the field of scientific costing, a subject which is dealt with in Chapter Thirty. In research and experiment in connection with the many technical problems which confront the printer, the activities of the Printing and Allied Trades Research Association continue to provide very valuable results, and there is no doubt that future advances in science, as applied to printing, will provide opportunity for still further research.

The Editor holds no brief for any particular branch of printing, believing, as he does, that the future holds out prospects of important all-round developments. The vast growth of modern Publicity, for example, will lead to the use, to an even greater extent than at present, of all the latest developments in each process of the printing industry.

After a lifetime devoted to printing, the Editor believes that PRACTICAL PRINTING AND BINDING will prove to be of great value to those connected with the trade, and to all who handle print in any shape or form, and are interested in the progress of the craft.

H. W.

CONTENTS

THE PRINTED WORD

A view of part of a letterpress machine room which is typical of printing works in many parts of the world. A two-revolution machine, with automatic feed and delivery, is shown, producing its quota of printed sheets which are destined to be read by "all sorts and conditions of men." The machine minder is on the alert for any emergency, which may arise, such as a fault in the feeding of the sheets. By means of foot control, conveniently placed on the platform, the minder can instantly throw off the impression or stop the machine.

CHAPTER ONE

TYPE IN THE MAKING

FIRST MOVABLE TYPES. METHODS OF TYPE-CASTING. THE MATRIX. MAKING THE PATTERN. CUTTING AND STAMPING THE PUNCH. THE NODIS CASTER. THE POINT SYSTEM. TYPE BODIES AND THEIR APPROXIMATE POINT EQUIVALENTS. TYPE ALLOYS : PROPORTIONS OF METAL. NAMES OF TYPE PARTS. TYPE ALIGNMENTS.

THE inventor of printing from movable types in Europe is generally believed to be Johann Gutenberg of Mainz, Germany, who discovered, about the year 1450, that metal types could be cast in a mould. The Hollanders, however, claim the honour for Laurens Janszoon Coster and erected a statue to his memory in Haarlem. In 1823 the city celebrated the four-hundredth anniversary of his supposed invention.

Today it matters not so much whether it was Gutenberg, Coster or some mystic in the Orient who first practised the art of printing; what really matters is that it *was* invented.

Gutenberg was printing from movable types about 1450. In other words he was cutting punches, making matrices, and casting metal types in a mould. To obtain the type, the matrix was fixed on the top of the mould, the mould inverted, and molten metal poured in quickly to ensure a good cast.

First Type-casting Machinery

It was not until the latter half of the nineteenth century that machinery for casting types was introduced. Towards the end of the nineteenth century mechanical type-setting machines were invented. These would not have been practicable without an economical method of producing profuse supplies of *matrices*. The necessity was there, and the invention followed which made mechanical composition a commercial proposition and also revolutionized the art of typefounding, i.e. the invention of the punch-cutting machine.

Before proceeding to detail modern methods of production, however, it is worth reflecting that although the operations from the making of punches to the finished type are now almost fully mechanized we still find that some of the type designs of the pre-mechanization era are in great demand.

Tracing the Image

The initial stage in the making of a matrix is to trace an enlarged image of the letter on a sheet of drawing paper. The original from which this image is projected may be an artist's drawing, the print of a type, or an actual metal type—in which case an epidiascope is used. An epidiascope is a magic lantern which can be used for opaque as well as translucent objects. The traced image (Fig. 1) is the basis on which the drawing is constructed. The drawings are usually made at least nine or ten inches in depth so as to minimize chance of error in the later stages. The thickness of every stroke of the face is measured in units of one ten-thousandth of an inch.

The next stage is to make a pattern letter which acts as a guide on the punch-cutting machine. Methods for making the pattern vary. One method is to place the drawing and a piece of wax-coated glass in position, and the outline of the letter is cut by a pantograph (an instrument for copying, enlarging, or reducing) on the wax by means of a needle (Fig. 2). The wax core within the lines is taken away, the plate sensitized and placed in an electrolytic bath for a copper shell to be deposited. The shell is backed with type metal and completed. Thus the finished pattern is a plate about three inches square and a quarter of an inch thick, which has the character raised one-sixteenth of an inch on its upper side.

Another method of producing the pattern letter is as follows: two brass plates are sweated together with soft solder and, together with the drawing, are fixed in position on the pantograph machine. The operator traces the follower arm around the outline of the drawing, while the rapidly rotating routing tool cuts the same design—but on a smaller scale—on the brass plate. The routing tool is so adjusted that it cuts right through the upper plate but does not penetrate the lower plate. The engraver then inspects the work and corrects any irregularities. The next operation is to fix the part of the plate that is required—the character itself—to its base by means of rivets. The

surplus metal on the upper plate is removed by heating the lower plate until the solder runs.

In this way the character is left in relief on its backing plate.

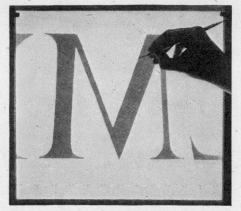

Fig. 1. *Tracing the projected image of the matrix. On this enlarged scale the image allows the draughtsman to distinguish clearly between what are accidental markings and what is the design proper.*

Cutting the Punch

Before the invention of the punch-cutting machine, punches were cut by hand—about one punch per day being the average output. A typefounder requires but one punch for each character because in all probability he will only require one matrix to be struck, whereas the type-composing machines require many matrices. It is essential, therefore, that an identical punch be made, as it may break the first time it is used. The punch-cutting machine (Fig. 3) is a vertical pantograph with a pendulum-like arm pivoted above the table where the pattern is mounted. The upper end of the pantograph carries the steel to be engraved, which is worked around a small cutting tool revolving at very high speed. The lower end of the pantograph is fitted with a roller, called the follower; this is traced around the edges of the large pattern of the character. This follower is then replaced by another of a smaller diameter, and so on until the engraved type on the steel punch is correctly formed. The cutting tool is four-sided and is ground with fine diamond dust. After cutting, the tool—not the punch—is examined through a microscope. If it is undamaged, the punch must have been perfectly cut. The soft punch is then hardened, justified and trimmed ready for its primary function—the stamping of matrices.

The next operation is to place the punch in the matrix-punching press (Fig. 4). The blanks are fed into the machine and the punch descends, leaving its impression of the character in each. The depth of the strike must be absolutely correct otherwise the resultant types will not be uniform as regards height to paper. The metal used for matrix making varies. For example, the typefounder uses copper and steel; Linotype matrices are made from brass; while the Monotype machine utilizes phosphor-bronze.

The matrices are finally tested by means of a special camera, where the face of each matrix is projected on to an etched ground glass which has limit lines of one ten-thousandth of an inch. The matrix is enlarged fifty times, and the rejection error is two ten-thousandth parts of an inch.

Casting the Type

In the early days each printer was his own typefounder. He was responsible for cutting the punches, making

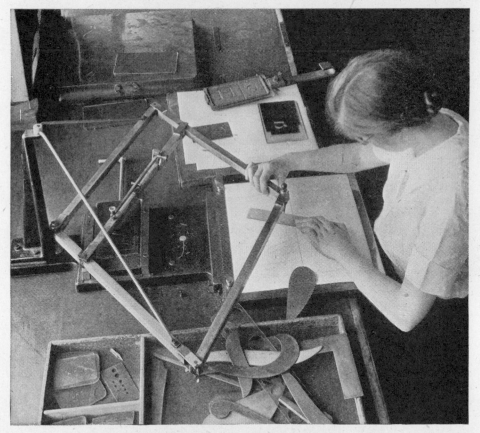

MAKING A WAX PATTERN

Fig. 2. *Use of the pantograph in type design. The illustration shows also (at top) pattern letters at three different stages: with wax partially removed; the electrotype shell in the holder (the pattern from which the punch is cut); and a completed pattern.*

P.T.G.—A*

The Monotype machines are used for casting the separate characters as composed lines ready for make-up into pages, or as individual letters for filling type cases for correcting the mechanically composed jobs, or for hand-set composition. Linotype and Intertype machines produce the lines of composed words as slugs, and any corrections therefore necessitate the line or lines being recast.

The type foundries use in the main two classes of casting machine. Firstly, the pivotal typecaster which casts letters at a rate of about 5,000 to 6,000 per hour for the smaller sizes and of course a lower rate for the larger sizes. The action of the machine is that a pivoted frame is

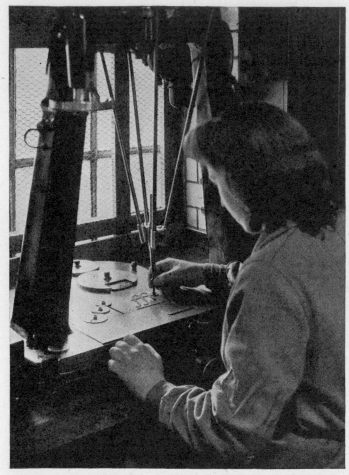

PUNCH-CUTTING MACHINE

Fig. 3. *Note how the lower end of the pantograph cutter follows the outline of the metal pattern. This machine has an accuracy of within one twenty-five thousandth of an inch.*

the matrices, mixing the metals, and casting the types. Probably he cast but one or two cases, and set up one or two pages at a time. These were printed, then the type was distributed back into the cases in order to carry on with the setting and production of the work.

Today there is a tendency to revert in part to the early practice. Every printing office of size has some machine for casting separate types or lines of type on one body (slugs).

worked in such a manner as to bring the mould to and from the nozzle of the metal pot, and in conjunction with this movement are combined movements for opening the mould and closing it, and also for tilting the matrix away. The moulds on the pivotal machines are not generally water-cooled, so it is necessary to stop the machine from time to time to allow the mould to cool.

The second class of casting machine used in the foundries has a water-cooled mould, constructed somewhat on the lines of the Mono-type mould, and delivers type in a continuous line at rates of over 10,000 letters per hour. The speeds vary according to the body size and set of the type being cast. The type is delivered from the mould completely finished, and ready for case. Generally speaking, a different mould is required for each body size, but some machines have moulds which are adjustable for other sizes.

The Nodis Caster

The Nodis is a simple and versatile machine for casting type. It occupies a space of only 2 ft. 6 in. square and, in addition to the Nodis matrices, those of Linotype, Intertype and Monotype machines—in fact, almost any other style of matrices—may be used. Two moulds are required for a full range of 5 to 72 point, and the difference in depth of strike in the matrices is allowed for by plates which are easily changed in a matter of minutes.

Leads, rules and borders can be cast in various lengths, and the attachment for these materials is fixed in a short time.

The following gives an idea of the

STAMPING MATRICES

Fig. 4. *After rolling to size and cutting to length, the matrix blanks are fed into the stamping machines. A turn of the wheel strikes one matrix. The matrices are made from a strip of copper alloy.*

range of production of the Nodis caster: type and spaces, 5 to 72 point; quads and logotypes, 5 by 72 point to 72 by 72 point; quotations, 24 by 72 point to 72 by 72 point; leads from 2 point; rules from 3 point; borders from 6 point.

The hardest type metal or the cheaper grades may be used with this machine. The metal is heated by a Funditor electric heater or by a specially designed, fumeless, gas-burner.

Power is supplied by a built-in $\frac{1}{2}$-h.p. motor with push-button starter.

THE POINT SYSTEM

FOR many years, little or no attempt was made to standardize the body sizes of types, and typefounders cast types to sizes based on their own dimensions.

In 1737, however, Pierre Simon Fournier, a Parisian typefounder, introduced a system for casting types to multiples of a fixed unit of measurement. Taking *approximately* 2 in. of the pre-metric French foot, he divided them into one hundred and forty-four equal parts which he termed points. The Fournier point measured ·0137 English inch and differs only slightly from the base unit of the present point system.

After the death of Fournier, another French typefounder, named François Ambrose Didot, advocated that Fournier's system should be based upon the legal foot measure of France. The Didot point measures ·0148 English inch, and the cicero—the Didot system equivalent of our pica—measures ·1776 inch. Didot rejected the old names of type bodies and gave to each a numerical name. His system is used in many continental countries.

Various other and later developments towards discarding the old names and substituting numerical or geometrical progression followed, but such systems failed to meet general acceptance. What was desired—a system common to all English-speaking peoples—seemed to be impossible on account of vested interests amongst typefounders and even printers themselves. But in 1871, the great fire of Chicago destroyed the type foundries of Marder, Luse & Co., and reconstruction provided a bold opportunity for scrapping old methods. Instead of formulating an entirely new system in accordance with the metric system, it was decided to take as the standard, pica—one which measured ·166044 inch. This, divided by twelve, provides the base unit of the present point system.

Finally, in 1898, the British typefounders as a body adopted the American standard, and the international value of this can scarcely be over-estimated.

With the advent of the point system, printers were faced with the problem of scrapping their existing supplies of type

Name	Point size	Name	Point size
Minikin	3½	English	14
Brilliant	4	Two-line brevier	16
Diamond	4½	Great primer	18
Pearl	5	Paragon	20
Agate (or Ruby)	5½	Two-line small pica (or double pica)	22
Nonpareil	6	Two-line pica	24
Emerald	6½	Two-line english	28
Minion	7	Two-line great primer	36
Brevier	8	Two-line paragon	40
Bourgeois	9	Two-line double pica	44
Long primer	10	Canon, or four-line pica	48
Small pica	11	Five-line pica	60
Pica	12	Six-line pica	72

ENGLISH TYPE BODIES AND THEIR POINT EQUIVALENTS

The above Table gives the old English names for type bodies and their approximate equivalents under the point system, which is now generally adopted in modern printing offices.

and starting again with new stocks of point-body type, or attempting to work with the old and the new. Many offices decided to scrap their larger types, but kept the smaller sizes of which they had large supplies. Consequently many printers still have cases of type cast on the old bodies. But it must be admitted that the reluctance to dispense with the old bodies has been the cause of a considerable amount of trouble and chaos in many composing departments. Compositors have been tempted to use brevier spaces with 8-point type or vice versa, often with disastrous results.

The old English names for type bodies and their *approximate* point equivalents are given on the opposite page.

TYPE ALLOYS

THE requirements of type alloys are as follows : they must be capable of being cast easily; give a solid, sharp casting, sufficiently strong to withstand distortion under reasonable pressure and long runs; impervious to oxidation; and must not tend to clog the small apertures in casting machines.

Lead-antimony-tin alloys meet these requirements fairly satisfactorily.

Lead forms the basis of printing metals. It is comparatively cheap, and melts easily. Types made entirely of lead, however, would be far too soft. Lead melts at 327 deg. C. or 620 deg. F. and has a specific gravity of 11·40.

Antimony is a bright crystalline and very brittle metal which is only very slowly tarnished by the air. It confers hardness and imparts its characteristic property of expanding on solidifying, thus facilitating fine sharp castings. Antimony melts at 630 deg. C. or 1,166 deg. F. and has a specific gravity of 6·71.

Tin, a bright metal which is not tarnished by the air, possesses the property of hardening the alloy, but not to the same extent as antimony. It is very ductile and malleable and produces toughness in the alloy. Tin also has the valuable property of making the alloy more fluid and easy-flowing at a low temperature, thus facilitating casting. Tin melts at 232 deg. C. or 450 deg. F. and has a specific gravity of 7·29.

Copper is sometimes added, in very small amounts, by the typefounders in order to increase the hardness of the alloy. It is a reddish-brown metal, tough, malleable and ductile. Copper melts at 1,085 deg. C. or 1,985 deg. F. and has a specific gravity of 8·79.

Proportions of Metals

Since the type-casting machines in the foundries generally cast at a slower rate than the mechanical composing machines, a metal with a higher melting point can be used. It follows, therefore, that a harder alloy may be used to obtain hard-wearing type which will have a longer life than the normal mechanically composed type. Such alloys contain from 10 to 25 per cent tin and from 20 to 30 per cent antimony. An addition of up to 1·5 per cent copper is sometimes made.

Metals for the slug-casting machines contain from $2\frac{1}{2}$ to 5 per cent tin, 10 to 13 per cent antimony, the balance being lead. The composition recommended for standard Linotype metal is 3 per cent tin, 11 per cent antimony, 86 per cent lead. The casting temperature for best results is 540 to 550 deg. F.

In order better to understand the characteristics of Linotype metal, a photomicrograph (Fig. 5) is reproduced. This was obtained from a 36-point Linotype slug. The dark patches are

Fig. 5. *Correctly cast Linotype metal* × *375 (2·9 per cent tin, 12·0 per cent antimony, 85·1 per cent lead). Note the needle-shaped arrangement of the lead. This photomicrograph was taken from a 36-point slug.*

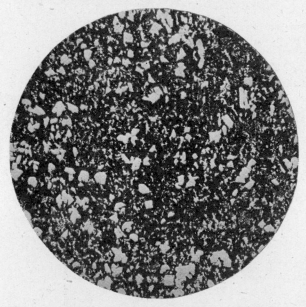

Fig. 6. *Correctly cast Monotype metal* × *375 (5·8 per cent tin, 15·9 per cent antimony, 78·3 per cent lead). Photomicrograph taken from a 24-point Mono character. Dark patches around the crystals consist largely of lead.*

crystals of lead, the groundmass is the eutectic alloy (i.e. an alloy which melts readily or at a low temperature). The eutectic alloy of lead, antimony and tin contains 84 per cent lead, 12 per cent antimony, 4 per cent tin, and melts completely at 239 deg. C., 463 deg. F.; this being the lowest melting temperature possible with lead-antimony-tin alloys.

The eutectic alloy is not suitable, however, for casting. Note the dendritic or needle-shaped arrangement of the lead and the very fine laminated eutectic. This field was typical of the structure throughout the entire slug.

For Monotype composition the alloy should contain from 6 to 10 per cent tin, 15 to 19 per cent antimony, and the balance lead. Many firms find it most convenient to have one grade of metal only for composition and case type. A specification for this purpose is 9 per cent tin, 19 per cent antimony, 72 per cent lead. The working temperature depends to some extent on the size of type being cast and the speed of casting and water cooling, and may range from 650 to 720 deg. F.

The photomicrograph in Fig 6 showing correctly cast Monotype metal affords an interesting comparison with Fig. 5. This photomicrograph was obtained from a 24 by 24-point Monotype character. In this case the structure consists of white antimony-tin crystals dispersed amongst the eutectic. The eutectic is comparatively soft, and these antimony-tin crystals confer hardness to the alloy. The cube-shaped (square) crystals contain 50 per cent tin and 50 per cent antimony. The more numerous irregular rectangular crystals consist mainly of antimony. The dark patches around the crystals consist largely of lead, due to absorption of antimony from the eutectic. The laminated eutectic is not very clearly defined. The regular distribution of the various small crystals in this field was typical of the structure throughout the piece of type.

Fig. 7 is a photomicrograph of an alloy used by typefounders. Note the large masses of antimony-tin crystals of both kinds, which give increased hardness and wearing qualities to the types.

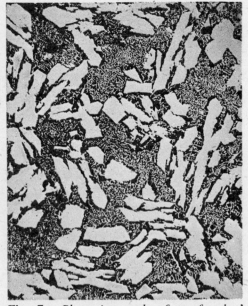

Fig. 7. *Photomicrograph of typefounders' type metal* × *150. The proportion of metals is : tin 12·02 per cent, antimony 23·88 per cent, lead 64·10 per cent.*

NAMES OF TYPE PARTS

IT is essential that the compositor should make a close study of the different parts of types and learn the names which have been given to them. By so doing, he will find that identification—both as regards method of casting and the name of type face—is often much simplified.

For simplicity and ease of understanding by the layman and apprentice the part names are arranged under four main parts: (1) THE FACE, (2) THE BEARD, (3) THE BODY, (4) THE FEET (Fig. 8).

(1) THE FACE is the entire printing surface of the type, and, according to design, may consist of the following parts:—

The *Main Stroke* is any straight main stroke of a letter, without the serif.

The *Serifs* are the small strokes normally at the tops and bottoms of the main strokes. The shapes and positions of the serifs, and the way they are bracketed to the stems are important factors in type face design. A skilled typographer can often identify a type face by its serifs. *Sans serif* is a term used to denote a type face having no serifs.

The *Counter* is that part of the type, immediately below the printing surface and normally between the main strokes. For example, in the letters O and e the counters are entirely enclosed. These counters, if too shallow, fill up quickly with ink and thereby cause trouble, and often print unsatisfactorily.

The *Kern* is the name given to any part of the face which overhangs the body. Italic and script types have a

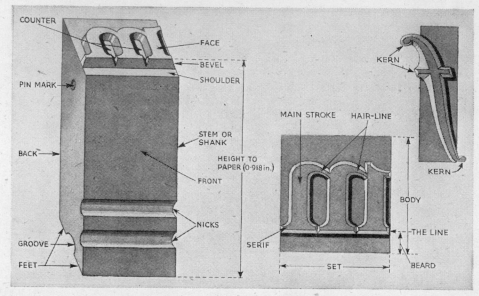

NAMES OF TYPE PARTS

Fig. 8. *The illustration shows the type body of a lower-case* m, *and an italic lower-case* f, *and names the various parts. The compositor reads type matter from left to right, but the letters and lines are of course inverted in the composing stick.*

larger number of kerned characters than the ordinary roman types.

(2) THE BEARD is the term used to describe the space from the bottom of the letter to the front of the body. Normally, this consists of:—

The *Bevel*, which is the sloping portion immediately below the face.

The *Shoulder*, which is the remaining horizontal portion to the front of the body, necessary to accommodate the descenders of the letters g, j, p, q, y.

The compositor is not concerned so much with the bevel and the shoulder as with the beard. The reason for this is that it is often necessary to adjust types of different body sizes or types and rules so that alignment is secured at the foot, as shown in Fig. 9.

Typefounders have simplified the work of the compositor by regulating the beard in nearly all cases to a specific number of points. To accommodate the descending strokes of the various

PRINTING AND BINDING

Name_____   Number_____

ALIGNMENT OF TYPE AND RULES

Fig. 9. *The above examples show the alignment of two different body sizes of type, and the alignment of rules with type. The adjustment is simplified when the types used have been cast with beards which are multiples of the point.*

type designs, three alignments have been found essential.

Point Common or *Standard Line*—for type faces with fairly short descenders. The body sizes and the beards of each are as follows:—

Type Body	Beard	Type Body	Beard
5 and 6 point	1 point	36 point .	7 point
7 to 10 point	2 point	42 point .	8 point
11 to 16 point	3 point	48 point .	10 point
18 to 20 point	4 point	54 point .	11 point
24 point .	5 point	60 point .	12 point
30 point .	6 point	72 point .	14 point

Point Title Line—with one or two exceptions used for capital letter founts only. As there are no descending characters, very little beard is needed.

Type Body	Beard	Type Body	Beard
5 to 16 point	1 point	30 to 48 point	3 point
18 to 24 point	2 point	60, 72 point	4 point

American Point Title Line:—

6 to 14 point, 1 point | 18 to 48 point, 2 point

Point Script (or *Art*) *Line*—is an alignment for script and other type designs which have longer descending strokes than those placed on point common line. In almost every size a third of the body is taken up by the beard. The actual sizes and their beards are as follows:—

Type Body	Beard	Type Body	Beard
6 to 8 point .	2 point	30 point .	10 point
10 point .	3 point	36 point .	12 point
12 point .	4 point	42 point .	14 point
14, 16 point .	5 point	48 point .	16 point
18 point .	6 point	60 point .	20 point
24 point .	8 point	72 point .	24 point

The American Type Founders Co. use the term art line. Three of their type faces cast on this alignment are Garamond, Bodoni and Cloister Old Style.

When aligning one body size with another the compositor subtracts the beard of the smaller size from that of the larger size and places the difference at the foot of the smaller size and the remainder at the head.

Thus, to align say 18-point Bodoni with 30-point Bodoni: the beard of the former is 6 point and the latter 10 point; the difference (4 point) would be placed at the foot of the 18 point and 8 point would be required at the head to make up to 30 point.

Unfortunately, however, there are still type faces on point body which are not on point line, and in this connection it may be as well to remind compositors that Monotype, Linotype, Intertype and Ludlow are not cast on point line, neither is founder's Caslon Old Face.

Self-lining Types (Fig. 10). Certain capital-letter founts (such as Spartan) much used for cards and letter headings are cast with as many as four sizes of face on one body—on one alignment. This method simplifies and speeds up composition as it eliminates the necessity of justifying different body sizes.

Point *Common* Line pgj
No. 1

Point *Art* Line p q g y j
No. 2

POINT TITLE LINE
No. 3

Art pj Common pj TITLE
No. 4

CAPS, SMALL CAPS, lower case
No. 5

SELF LINING TYPES AAAa BBBb CCCc
No. 6

Fig. 10. *Type alignments. No. 1 is 18-point Cheltenham Old Style. No. 2 is 18-point Bodoni (American Type Founders Co.). No. 3 is 14-point Goudy Title. No. 4 shows the three alignments compared—the body size being 14 point in each instance. No. 5 is 14-point Caslon Old Face, which is not cast to point line. No. 6 shows 6-point Spartan with four sizes of face on one body, all being cast on one alignment.*

(3) THE BODY—sometimes termed the *shank* or *stem*—consists of belly, back, sides, pin mark and nick (or nicks).

The *Belly* is the front of the type and parallel with the *back*. The distance between the two is referred to by printers as the body size and under the point system is always a specific number of points.

The distance between the *sides* of the type varies according to the width of the letter and is generally referred to as the *set*. Many have advocated that the set or width should (like the body) be governed by the point system. Where this has been done, the larger types have been cast to multiples of the point in width, while smaller sizes have necessitated a smaller unit—as low as a quarter of a point.

On one of the sides of typefounders' types is usually found what is termed the *pin mark*, which is a circular depression caused by the pin which ejects the type from the mould. It is utilized sometimes to indicate the body size of the type or perhaps the founder's name. There are no round pin marks on Monotype, but the body-size figure can be cast in the side if required.

The *Nick* is a groove across the belly. Monotype letters normally have one nick, but typefounders' types generally have two or three or even more. The nicks have definite functions and are very helpful to the compositor.

The Monotype Corporation, for example, utilize the nick in a most ingenious way. Moulds may be supplied which cast a very fine ridge on the *back* of the type. This ridge fits into the nick of the type immediately behind it and thereby prevents any spaces rising during printing. In Monotype composition all spaces and characters being cast from the same mould have identical (round or square) nicks. Typefounders'

spaces usually have no nicks. Some typefounders produce quads and spaces of the odd sizes such as 7, 9, 11 point with nicks at back and front. This is very helpful in distribution. Typefounders also make a narrow nick on the *back* of certain small capital letters, such as the O, S, V, W, X, Z, which may be easily confused with lower-case letters of the same fount.

The main function of the nick, however, is to facilitate speed in handsetting. The compositor sights the next type while his fingers are engaged placing the previous one, and the nick is a definite guide to the correct placing. As the nick is usually on the lower end of the belly it helps in the placing of the letter the face way up, and if the nicks are in line all the letters will be the right way round. As the nicks of founders' types are usually different for each series either in number or position, they also help the compositor to spot any wrong fount before justifying the line.

(4) THE FEET are the two projections at the base of the body and between them is the *groove*. When type is cast, a tang or jet is attached to the base. The older kind of mould delivers the types with the jets attached. They are broken off, and in order to eliminate the roughness caused by the break, the types are next placed in lines and a groove planed right along. Later moulds cast type with the jet in an existing groove. The jets are broken off and the types delivered from the machine ready for packing. The Monotype mould is so built that the jets are sheared off, the feet are thus flat and without a groove. Some Continental foundries plane down their types for sale to British and American printers. For example, type faces such as Erbar and Bernhard Cursive will often be found with flat feet and indications that they have been planed down to British height (·918 in.).

CHAPTER TWO

COMPOSING ROOM EQUIPMENT

FRAMES AND CABINETS. CASES. COMPOSING STICKS. TYPE SCALES. CORRECT MOVE-
MENTS IN TYPE-SETTING. THE ART OF SPACING. DISTRIBUTION. SPACING MATERIAL.
COMPOSING ROOM FURNITURE. CHASES. WOOD QUOINS AND SIDESTICKS. WEDGE-
SHAPED AND EXPANDING QUOINS. IMPOSING SURFACES.

FRAMES and cabinets of wood and metal are now in general use. The old-style wood frame with space between each case has been superseded by the so-called dust-proof type of frame (Fig. 1) in which all waste space has been eliminated. Certainly less dust and dirt can accumulate in the cases of this type of frame—but even so, they cannot truthfully be termed dust-proof. The dust factor has been lessened considerably through the attention now being given to flooring material, such as oiled parquet flooring and specially treated concrete.

It is a matter for debate which is the better material for frames—wood or metal. So far as damage by fire is concerned no doubt metal is preferable. On the other hand if a frame is damaged— say by a trolley running into it—there may be difficulty in sliding in the cases. Many claim that metal is much cleaner and helps to create an up-to-date, efficient atmosphere, while others, say it is cold and not so comfortable as wood. To sum up, it may be said that both types are much better than the old open-style wood frame.

Cabinet Units

Cabinets may be built up in units— which can be so arranged as to suit the particular work of the office. These cabinets usually comprise one case and two auxiliary units which may be fitted for galleys; drawers for copy, proofs and blocks; or bins for spacing material.

The manufacturers have given much thought and care to the planning, making, and utility of these units, and employers and overseers should study well their own particular requirements before deciding on new equipment.

Frames and Cases

Cases. Before the invention of mechanical composing machines, all type-setting was done by hand. It was essential, therefore, to have cases capable of accommodating a good supply of type. Two cases were used—one for the capitals and small capitals, and the other for the lower-case letters, points of punctuation and spacing material. These cases were and are still known as a pair of cases.

The pair of cases requires a frame and brackets—the names upper and lower case being derived from the fact of the lower case being placed below the upper case and nearer the compositor, while the upper case is placed on the brackets above and behind the lower case.

The average up-to-date composing department long ago discarded the pairs of cases. Hand-setting is now concerned primarily with the setting of display lines, corrections, and short texts, therefore it has been found more convenient to house the normal assortment of letters in one case, termed a double case. The arrangement for the different letters is termed the lay of the case.

DUST-PROOF METAL FRAME

Fig. 1. *Receptacles for spacing material are arranged along the top of the frame. The frame includes case and column galley units, together with serviceable cupboard and drawers.*

There is no standardized lay in this country although the variations are in the main only concerned with such characters as the ligatures (fi, ffi, fl, ffl, ff), figures, and lower-case k and q. The two best double cases are the California Job Case (Fig. 2) and the Improved Double Case. The sizes of cases used in this country are $32\frac{1}{2}$ by $14\frac{1}{2}$ by $1\frac{3}{4}$ in., and American-size cases, which are $32\frac{3}{16}$ by $16\frac{5}{8}$ by $1\frac{1}{2}$ in.

For the purpose of assembling the various types into words and lines, the compositor uses a composing stick.

CALIFORNIA JOB CASE

Fig. 2. *This is termed a double case and contains caps, lower-case, figures and punctuation points. This case is now generally in use in preference to pairs of cases. The small capitals are kept in separate cases which are about one-third the size of the case shown above.*

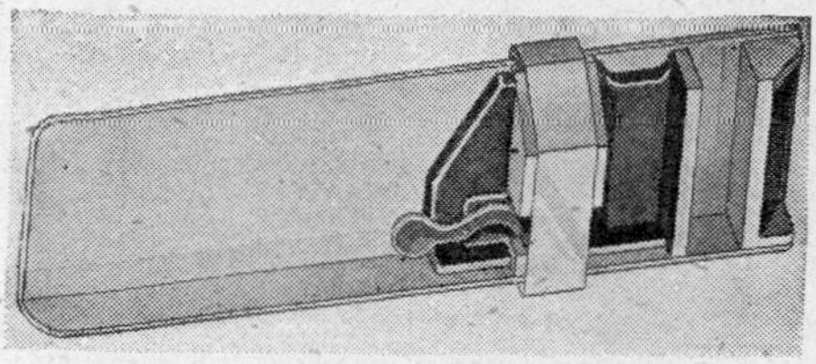

Fig. 3. *The "British" composing stick, made of stainless steel, with lever action for tightening the slide. This stick is much lighter to hold than other metal sticks.*

The modern composing stick is made of metal, usually stainless steel, and has a sliding head which is fixed by means of a thumb-screw or by lever action—the latter is to be preferred (Fig. 3).

Another type of composing stick is graduated in ens and ems of 12 points and can be quickly made up to the required measure without using a gauge (Fig. 4). These sticks can also be used with a micrometer gauge for setting any odd measure.

Making up the Stick. It is most important that the composing stick be made up very accurately to the required measure. In normal composition the measure is a specific number of ems of 12 point (or pica). The material used for making up the stick varies in different offices. For example, if the lines are to be included with some mechanically composed matter the stick should be made up to the lines as set on the machines. Otherwise, the stick may be made up to any accurate material or gauges available, such as em quads, or types turned sideways.

Type Scales are used for measuring type pages, etc., and are necessary items of equipment

for the compositor. The best kind of scale is made of steel and is graduated in points, ens and ems of the point system, in addition to inches (Fig. 5). Type scales are also made of wood, and in consequence much cheaper; while another kind is made of steel, to fold up, and is supplied in a leather case for convenience in carrying.

Correct Movements in Type-setting

Having made up the stick to the required measure and mounted the cases required, the compositor is ready to set up the type. He should work at case without coat and preferably with shirt sleeves rolled up, thus allowing free movement across the case. The stick is held in the left hand which should move in unison with the right as the types are lifted from the case (Fig. 6).

In order to facilitate composition a setting rule of the required length is placed in the stick. This is usually a piece of brass—more elaborate sets are chromium plated—which is the same height as type and about three points thick. At one end is a small projection or lip, while at the other end there should be a corresponding recess so shaped that the compositor can lift the rule over for the setting of the next line by simply lifting the rule from the lip end.

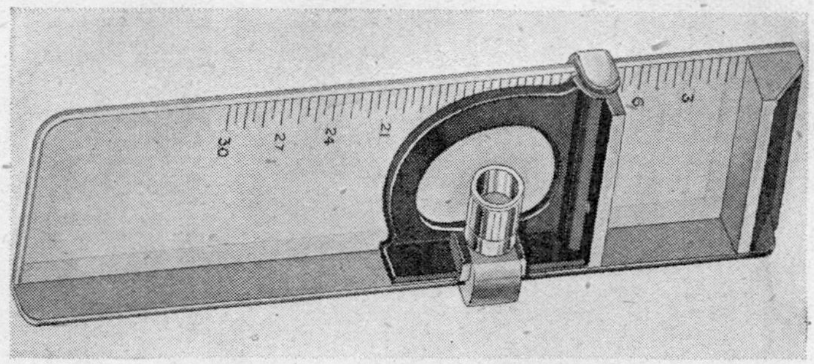

AUTOMATIC STICK ADJUSTMENT

Fig. 4. *The "Universal" composing stick, which is automatically adjusted to 12-point ems or half-ems. The locking device may be readily removed when any odd measures are required.*

Fig. 5. *Rustless steel type scale, graduated 1 point, and 5, 6, 8, 10 and 12 point ems, and inches.*

The compositor should stand upright in front of the case, place his copy in position convenient for his eyes, but not covering any of the boxes which he is likely to be using.

In starting to set type the letters are picked up one at a time with the forefinger and thumb of the right hand and placed in the stick. The eyes should travel ahead of the hands, sighting the next letter, noting the position of the nick, the fingers automatically turning the letter so that it is placed in the stick the right way, that is, with the nick to the front. *Thick* spaces are placed between the words as setting proceeds. Type lines must be spaced full out so that the printed matter shall end evenly. Therefore, the compositor has invariably to decide when approaching the end of his line whether (*a*) to increase the spacing between the words; (*b*) to decrease the spacing in order to get the last word in; or (*c*) to divide the word.

HAND COMPOSING

Fig. 6.   *The composing stick is held in the left hand, which moves in unison with the right hand in its movements to pick up the letters and spaces from the various boxes.*

There is real craftsmanship required if the compositor is to space his lines so that the spacing shall appear equal between the printed words. In order to achieve this desirable object it is necessary first to learn to recognize at a glance the thicknesses of the various spaces and their relative thicknesses individually and collectively as shown in the following Table:—

Description of spaces	Value expressed in sixtieths of the em
Thin space (5 to the em) . .	12
Middle space (4 to the em) .	15
Thick space (3 to the em) .	20
Two thin spaces . . .	24
One thin and one middle space .	27
En quad	30
One thick and one thin space .	32
One thick and one middle space.	35
Three thin spaces . . .	36
Two thick spaces . . .	40

Hair spaces, which vary in thickness according to body size from about eight to twelve to the em, are not normally used for spacing between words except in very short measures.

Spacing Out Lines

Assuming, for example, that the compositor in setting his line finds that one or two letters still remain over when the measure is full, he will reduce the thick spaces to middles in order to get the full word in. On the other hand, if only one or two letters of the last word come into the measure and four or five remain, he will increase the spacing between the words so that the complete word is taken over. If part of a long word comes at the end of the measure, the word will be divided at a suitable syllable and a hyphen placed at the end of the line.

The main point is: the spacing between words should *appear* equal; therefore, when spacing out in order to

justify the line full out, the compositor should note the shapes of the letters at the beginnings and ends of the words. For example, if slightly more space is required between the words in order to space full out, two thin spaces would be substituted for the thick spaces, priority being given to the places where the words begin and end with vertical strokes such as between words like "good boy." Words like "new violin" would require slightly less space between them. The space after a comma should also be slightly less than between words which commence or finish with vertical strokes.

It will be noted that the compositor reads type upside down and from left to right.

Every line must be justified to the same length, otherwise trouble will ensue when the job is locked up in the chase. The correct justification is achieved when the line can be pushed forward smoothly in the stick without falling down. The lines should not be too tight, otherwise there will be difficulty in lifting the matter safely from the stick.

After the type matter has been set up in the composing stick, it is lifted out as shown in Fig. 7 and placed on a flat tray called a galley.

Galleys are made in numerous sizes, the majority being column galleys. Square-shaped galleys are used for wide tabular and similar matter.

Make-up is the arrangement of the type into pages. For slug matter a special make-up galley is sometimes used as shown in Fig. 8.

After the page has been made up, it is tied up with page cord as shown in Fig. 9. The page is then safe for moving to the proofing press, imposing surface, or galley rack.

Distribution (Fig. 10) is the practice of returning type, leads and other

LIFTING TYPE FROM STICK TO GALLEY

Fig. 7. *With the setting rule at one side and a lead or clump at the other, the lines are gripped firmly in both hands, as shown, and placed in position on the making-up galley.*

materials utilized in composing a job back to their respective cases and racks. After printing and before distribution the type should be thoroughly cleaned with a type cleanser. Clean type is an aid to clean printing. It is advisable then to dissect the work, placing all types of the same series on one galley; leads, reglets and similar spacing material being separated to facilitate speed in distribution.

When typefounders' material and mechanical composition are combined in one job the dissecting must be done with care. All the Linotype or Mono-type materials can be dumped straight away into their respective bins, care being taken first to take out any founders' spaces or leads. Some firms distribute the larger sizes of Monotype —say over 14 point—back into case.

On the other hand some printers prefer the all-in distribution. In other words, mechanical composition is used throughout, and the spacing material, too, is cast on their own machines; therefore the entire job is relegated to the bin after printing. Undoubtedly this method has much to recommend it. But one word of caution: the all-in plan or the no-dis principle can only be adopted if facilities and machines are available to cast ample supplies of display type and spacing material. The various machines are dealt with in the chapter on Mechanical Type-setting.

Spacing Material

Leads are used for inter-line spacing and whiting out and grouping matter in display work. They are made—as the name implies—chiefly of lead, and are about ¾ in. high and made in four thicknesses as follows:—

One point (12 to pica) .	. .	1 point
Thin leads (8 to pica) .	. .	1½ point
Middle leads (6 to pica)	. .	2 point
Thick leads (4 to pica).	. .	3 point

In order to avoid mixing, some offices prefer to buy the 1-point and 2-point spacing material in brass. Leads may be bought in lengths of 18 or 36 in. or cut to sizes as required. Some offices prefer to buy leads cut to size and nicked at each end, the idea being that such leads are less liable to be cut and wasted.

Copper spacing material is used chiefly for letter spacing and is half a point thick, and supplied for the usual range of type sizes.

Clumps are leads cast to thicker bodies. They may be bought numbered for news work. The usual thicknesses are 6 and 12 point, but odd sizes and 18 point are available. Clumps are much more satisfactory in use than the wood spacing material known as

Reglets, which are strips of wood, from 6 to 18 point in thickness. These may be bought in various lengths or cut to sizes as required. The better qualities are made of hard wood and oil-soaked. Too many reglets in a job are liable to cause trouble when locking-up. They should not be used in foundry formes.

MAKING-UP SLUG MATTER

Fig. 8. *Showing a special make-up galley, adjustable as regards page depth. The cross-bar is removed after make-up to allow for tying up the page as shown in Fig. 9.*

TYING UP THE PAGE

Fig. 9. *Note the loop and the end of page cord, so arranged as to ensure speedy untying when the page is surrounded with furniture on the imposing stone, previous to locking up.*

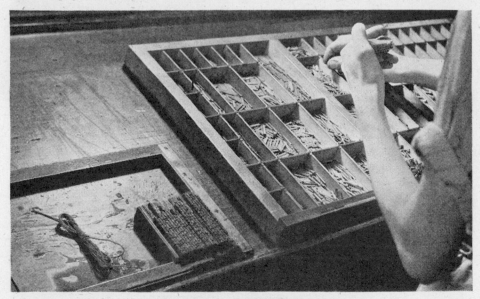

DISTRIBUTING FOUNDERS' TYPE

Fig. 10. *The type on the galley has been sprinkled with water, which facilitates safe handling. Mechanical composition has eliminated the necessity of distribution to a considerable extent.*

Quotations are cast with hollowed or cored centres and used in "whiting out." They are supplied from the founders in the following sizes in 12-point ems: 2 by 3, 2 by 4, 2 by 6, 2 by 8, 3 by 3, 3 by 4, 3 by 5, 3 by 6, 3 by 8, 4 by 4, 4 by 5, 4 by 6, 4 by 8, 5 by 5, 5 by 6, 6 by 6, 6 by 8, 8 by 8. Each piece is marked with the size in points. Quotations can also be cast on the Monotype super-caster.

Furniture is the name given to spacing material 24 point or more in width and can be obtained in wood, cast iron, or steel. The soft-alloy furniture is gradually becoming obsolete. In recent years, too, plastics have been utilized and no doubt Bakelite or similar products will become more popular. They have the advantage of lightness and accuracy— but are apt to be brittle. For spacing out catch-lines in posters, however, this material has proved most useful.

Wood Furniture is still widely used, probably because it is the most economical. Like reglets, it may be bought in lengths of 36 in. or cut as required and the sizes stamped at each end. The body sizes are as follows:—

24 point	72 point (Double Narrow)
30 point	84 point (Broad and
36 point (Narrow)	Narrow)
48 point (Broad)	96 point (Double Broad)
60 point	120 point

Cast-iron Furniture is preferable to wood because of its permanent accuracy, and is practically indestructible. Initial cost is the prime reason why it is not in universal use. It is 50 per cent lighter than lead furniture and particularly useful in making margins and locking up large formes. Cast-iron furniture is made in a wide range of sizes.

Interlocking Steel Furniture (Fig. 11) is very useful for building up blank pages speedily and accurately. Made in the following lengths: 8, 10, 12, 14, 16, 18, 20, 22, 24, 26, 28, 30, 32, 34, 36, 38,

Fig. 11. *Interlocking steel furniture. Useful for building up blank areas accurately.*

40, 42 ems (on 2-em body); 45, 48, 51, 54, 57, 60, 63, 66, 69, 72 ems (on 3-em body). When making up large blanks with this material it is advisable to bridge the short dimension with quotations or similar material so as to prevent unnecessary strain on the centre of the longer pieces of furniture.

Types of Chases

Chases are metal frames into which type and blocks are placed when made up into pages and thus made secure for handling. They are made in cast iron, wrought iron and steel. Steel chases are usually found the most satisfactory; they are made true and have perfectly square inner corners, and last indefinitely. Cast-iron chases, on the other hand, are rarely accurate and are liable to snap under pressure.

Book Chases (Fig. 12), as the term implies, are for bookwork. They are fitted with two crossbars which subdivide the chase into four, thereby making for greater strength and accuracy when locking-up a number of pages. The crossbars are dovetailed and slotted into the outer rim in the wrought-iron and steel varieties, but are cast with the rim in the cast-iron chases. The movable bars are marked, as also are the outer rims, to ensure the correct bars being used. Some book chases have

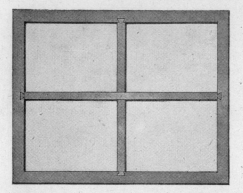

Fig. 12. *Steel book chase. It is a decided advantage to have the crossbars made to point-system dimensions as regards width.*

extra slots so as to enable the short crossbar to be moved two-thirds up the long side. This is necessary when imposing twelve pages as three rows of four for ordinary twelvemo. Book chases are made from foolscap to quad demy.

Jobbing Chases are made in a variety of sizes from foolscap 8vo to royal folio.

Machine Chases are made specially to fit the particular printing machine for which they are used—usually the platen type.

Foundry Chases are usually made type high and of steel. They are made in a variety of sizes and used for locking-up pages for stereotyping and for electrotyping.

Heading Chases are used for locking-up ledger and book headings, and are made in a number of sizes from about 19 by 6 in. to 41 by 6 in.

Long Folio Chases are made to accommodate jobs set for long folio sub-divisions—

from foolscap 19 by $7\frac{1}{2}$ in. to quad crown 41 by 15 in.

News Chases are made of steel and to fit the particular page of newspaper for which they are intended. They are made type high and have a special locking-up device fitted on two sides.

Broadside Chases are made to various measurements to accommodate full, double and quad-sheet sizes. They have no crossbars and are normally used for posters.

Card Chases are small chases used for visiting cards and other small jobs.

Folding Chases are used in pairs. They are preferred for large, heavy formes and make for safer and easier transport. One of the long sides is made thinner than the remaining sides and a short crossbar is fitted. Thus when two chases are placed together on the machine bed, the two thin rims are placed together while the short crossbars will be in the same position as the long crossbar in bookwork chases.

Another kind of folding chase has what are termed interlocking folds. In other words, the two sides which are placed together on the printing machine are rebated, as shown in Fig. 13.

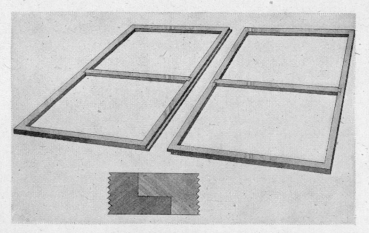

Fig. 13. *A pair of steel folding chases with interlocking folds; also section showing how they fit together when on the printing machine.*

USE OF WICKERSHAM QUOINS

Fig. 14. *Wickersham quoins are operated by means of a key inserted in the square hole of the cam. The turning of the key expands the quoin and thereby locks up the forme.*

Quoins (pronounced *coins*) are devices used to exert lateral pressure on the type, within the chase, so that the forme may be locked up and lifted from the imposing surface. Broadly speaking, there are two classes of quoins: (1) expanding and (2) wedge-shaped. The former are more satisfactory in general use and comprise the following makes.

Wickersham Quoins (Fig. 14), which consist of two side sections, a cam and two springs. Inside the side sections are raised bearings, two in one section and one in the other. On these bearings rotates the three-way cam. In the cam is a square hole to take the quoin key. The entire quoin is kept intact by the two small springs—one at each end.

The methods of use and operation are briefly as follows: the quoins are placed at side and foot of the page with furniture for "dressing." Sufficient space is left to allow quoins to be moved freely. If too much space is left the quoin will expand to its maximum (about 14 points) and then close, the side sections being drawn together by the two springs. If corrections are needed, do not take the quoins out—

simply turn them sideways which allows 6 points extra space.

When locking-up, insert the key in the square hole in the cam and turn clockwise. This expands the quoin, unless the cam has been reversed, when, of course, the key would have to be turned the other way. It would be better, however, to take off the side springs and place the cam the correct way up. A little oil on the cam sides and bearings will lengthen the life of these quoins considerably. The dimensions of the quoin are approximately as follows: length 12 ems, width $4\frac{1}{2}$ ems, height 4 ems.

A feature of this quoin is that, because of the central cam, it will adapt itself to a side not exactly parallel with its own sides—although, of course, straight metal furniture is advisable.

Notting Quoins (Fig. 15) are made of steel and consist of the following parts: two side plates, two guide pins, a screw and a wedge. Like the Wickersham, the quoin is operated by means of a key which fits into a square hole at the top of the screw. The turning of the screw, by means of the key, draws up the

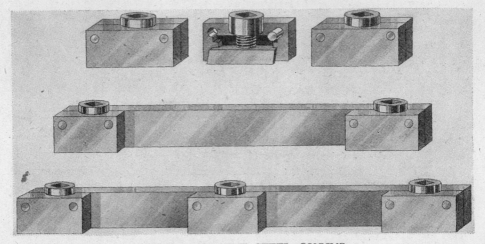

NOTTING PATENT STEEL QUOINS

Fig. 15. *Showing the single and combined arrangements of these quoins. The latter are very useful where space for lock-up is limited. The quoins are operated by turning a key.*

wedge, thus forcing apart the side pieces. The amount of expansion is 22 points.

The single Notting quoins are 8 ems long and 4 ems wide, whilst the height from the base to the top of the screw is approximately 4½ ems. Each quoin is self contained, has no springs or castings and is so constructed that the wedge cannot fall out.

Notting quoins are also made on steel bars and are available in the following lengths: 36 ems long with two screws, 48 ems long with three screws, and 60 ems long with three screws.

Notting Narrow-margin Quoins are very similar in pattern to the ordinary Notting quoin, but are manufactured for narrow margin and register work. They are made in one size only, 6 ems long by 2 ems wide, and have an expansion of 8 points. Instead of a key, they are operated by means of a screwdriver (Fig. 16).

Precision Register Quoins (Fig. 16) were designed for three-colour work and are very useful for locking up where space is limited. The quoin consists of a steel plate 4½ by 4½ ems and 6 points thick. This carries a screw on which revolves a steel disc. The quoin is

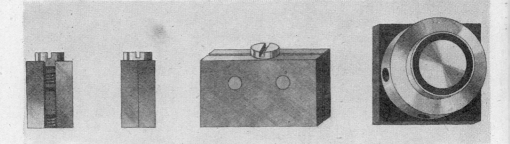

Fig. 16. *Notting narrow-margin quoins, for use in limited locking-up space, are shown in the three illustrations on the left. A precision register quoin is shown on the right.*

expanded by turning the disc on the screw by means of a tommy-pin which fits into the holes on the disc rim.

Hempel Quoins are double wedges made of metal and are for use with straight furniture. Each section is square on its outer edge and at an angle on the inside. On this inner side is a series of grooves, and when a pair of these sections is placed together a cogged key moves them so as to exert lateral pressure on the forme. There are two patterns of this quoin—plain and ribbed. In the latter the centre rib locks into the shoulder on each quoin and thereby prevents slipping when in use.

Sidesticks are wedge-shaped pieces of wood which are placed normally at the sides and feet of pages for purposes of locking-up. They are used in conjunction with wedges of wood (quoins) to tighten up the entire job within a steel frame or chase. Like ordinary wood furniture, sidesticks can be bought in lengths to cut up to required sizes. It is advisable, however, to have them cut to regular measures ready for use. The degree of taper varies and is thereby often a cause of trouble. A standardized taper of $\frac{1}{4}$ in. to the foot will be found to give a satisfactory result.

Wood Quoins should be tapered (one side only) to the same degree as the sidesticks, thereby ensuring that the outer surfaces of the two in combination will be parallel, while the tapered edge of the quoin will bind firmly along its whole length. A common practice is to duplicate wood quoins. This should be avoided, at least on small jobs. It is impossible to use two quoins to bind firmly along their full length.

Mallets. Used in conjunction with shooting stick for driving (locking-up and unlocking) wood quoins. Also used with planer for planing down the forme.

Shooting Sticks (Fig. 17) are available in several patterns and a variety

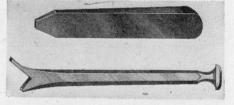

Fig. 17. *Xylonite and nickel-plated metal shooting sticks. The lower pattern fits on the wood quoin and does not contact the imposing surface, thus avoiding damage.*

of materials including hickory, box, xylonite, horn, metal-pointed (single or double ends), and nickel-plated wrought steel.

Planers (pieces of hard, smooth wood) should be used with great care. It seems incongruous that after every effort has been taken to ensure perfect printing surfaces, far too much ignorance is often displayed when planing down a forme. The planer should be used with wood quoins at finger pressure; and after the quoins are tightened gradually only very light usage of the planer is necessary.

Imposing Surfaces are made in a variety of sizes and consist usually of a smooth iron surface mounted on a frame which may be fitted to suit the work of the particular office. They are used primarily when locking-up the work after composing and correcting. The galley is placed on the imposing surface, the left hand holding the tied-up page while the galley is pulled sharply away with the right hand. For sliding type from stone to galley a groove or lip on one edge is provided.

A chase of suitable size is then placed around the type and the required furniture and quoins inserted between chase and job. This operation is known as dressing the forme. The page cord is then removed, the type planed down and the quoins tightened so that the locked-up forme may be safely lifted from the imposing surface or stone.

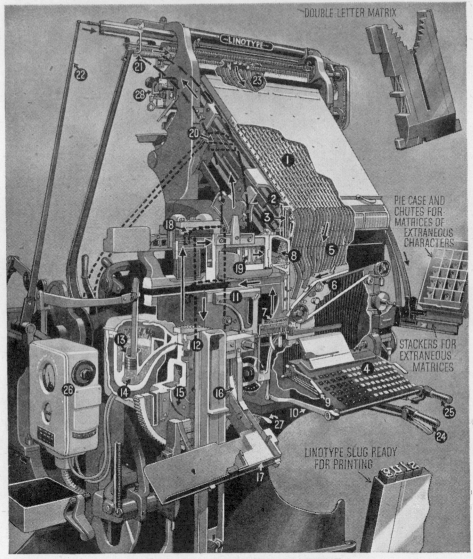

LINOTYPE COMPOSING MACHINE

Fig. 1. *(1) Inclined magazine storing matrices; (2) magazine escapements; (3) escapement rods to key levers; (4) keyboard; (5) matrix channels; (6) assembler belt; (7) matrices in assembler box; (8) spaceband box; (9) spaceband key; (10) assembler box lifting lever; (11) matrix slide to first elevator; (12) matrices in front of mould; (13) metal pot and plunger; (14) molten type metal; (15) revolving mould wheel; (16) cast slug being ejected; (17) trimmed slugs on galley; (18) transfer first to second elevator; (19) spacebands returned to box; (20) matrices lifted to distributor by elevator carrier; (21) matrices pushed on to distributor bar; (22) matrix pusher lever; (23) matrices returning to magazines; (24) magazine elevating arm; (25) handle for lifting assembler box; (26) electric heater for metal pot; (27) slug ejector lever; (28) distributor lift-box.*

CHAPTER THREE

MECHANICAL TYPE-SETTING

THE LINOTYPE : ITS MECHANISM AND OPERATION. THE INTERTYPE. THE TYPOGRAPH.
THE MONOTYPE : OPERATION OF THE KEYBOARD ; PERFORATING THE SPOOL ; SPACING ;
CASTING MECHANISM.   THE LUDLOW SYSTEM : GATHERING OF MATRICES ; CASTING
THE SLUG. THE ELROD CASTER. PHOTO-COMPOSING MACHINES.

MECHANICAL type-setting machines may be divided into two main groups: (1) slug-casting machines, which produce the lines as slugs—in other words an entire line on one body; and (2) the single-type casting machine—or Monotype—which produces the lines justified to measure, but with each character and space on a separate body.

The Linotype

As the name implies, the Linotype (Fig. 1) is a slug-casting machine. Introduced about 1886 it is now used in practically every newspaper office and also in many general printing offices. It is a one-man machine and the versatility of the product varies with the different models in use. The operator sits in front of the machine with the copy at the top of the keyboard. Having adjusted the machine for the required size and measure, with the metal heated to the correct temperature—about 550 deg. F.—he commences setting.

The manipulation of the key buttons actuates mechanism which releases the matrices. These are small pieces of brass in which the characters or dies are stamped. The matrices travel from the magazine channels where they are housed, by means of a miniature conveyor belt, into the assembler box or elevator. This assembler box is the composing stick of the Linotype. The slide is made up to the measure, just as the stick is made up normally to a multiple of 12-point ems. After each word the operator touches the space-band key which allows a spaceband to fall before setting the first letter of the following word. These spacebands are compound steel wedges and are used to spread out the line of matrices to the required width. When these spacebands have entered the assembler they are so positioned that their minimum width is between the matrices.

When the assembler is nearly full of matrices—about 2 ems from the end of the line—a bell rings. This warns the operator that he must decide whether to send the line away at the finished word; or, if the word is long and obviously will not come in the measure, just where to divide the word. As these decisions are made very speedily it is necessary for the operator to be expert in the correct dividing of words, otherwise corrections necessitating the re-setting of two new lines will have to be made at a later stage.

Justifying Spacebands

Having set the line of matrices and spacebands, the operator's function as regards the casting of the slug is practically finished. All that remains is for him to press a small lever and then carry on with the next line.

When the operator presses the small lever at the right of the keyboard the matrices are taken automatically by the delivery carriage into the first elevator head, the latter descending to a position

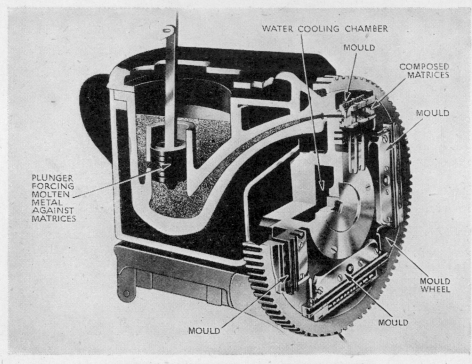

WATER COOLING CHAMBER

MOULD

COMPOSED MATRICES

MOULD

PLUNGER FORCING MOLTEN METAL AGAINST MATRICES

MOULD WHEEL

MOULD

MOULD

LINOTYPE METAL POT AND MOULD WHEEL

Fig. 2. *The illustration shows the composed matrices in position, forming a metal-tight joint exactly opposite the opening in the mould wheel. Molten metal is pumped in and the line is cast.*

opposite the mould wheel between the vice jaws, where the matrices and space-bands are justified to correct length of line. This is achieved by the justification block which pushes up the wedge-shaped spacebands until the matrices are spaced full out to measure.

The mould wheel (Fig. 2) moves forward and the justified line of matrices forms a metal-tight joint exactly over the opening or mould in the mould wheel. Molten metal is then pumped in from the pot behind the mould, and the line cast.

After the slug is cast, the mould wheel revolves, taking the mould with slug from the horizontal casting position to the vertical ejecting position. During this movement the slug is trimmed at the foot so that it will be the correct type height, namely, ·918 inch.

The Linotype slug is not cast directly to point dimensions as regards body. On the front of the slug is a series of slightly projecting ribs. When the vertical ejecting position is reached, the slug is pushed out of the mould by means of the ejector blade, between the trimming knives, which trim the slug to accurate body dimension, and finally the finished slug is delivered on to the galley.

But in the meantime, what of the matrices and spacebands? After the casting, they are taken first vertically by means of the first elevator and then laterally until the teeth of the matrices engage the ribs of a carrier bar attached to the second elevator lever. This lifts the line of matrices to the distributing mechanism at the top of the machine. The spacebands remain behind when the matrices are lifted to the distributor, and are brought back to their original position in the spaceband box ready to be used again.

The distribution of the matrices to their correct channels in the magazine is one of the most interesting functions of the Linotype. The matrices have teeth in their upper ends so arranged that as they are propelled along the intermittent seven-ribbed steel distributor bar just above the open upper ends of the magazine channels, they become disengaged when over their corresponding channels, and thereby fall into their correct places in the magazine ready for further use (Fig. 3).

Thus while the operator is assembling one line of matrices, a second is being cast, and a third line is being distributed back into the magazine. Therefore, the matrices which are normally used most frequently are placed to the left of the magazine, so that they will be distributed first; otherwise, a speedy operator may do what the hand compositor does quite often, run out of sorts.

The latest models of Linotype are the 48, 48 S.M., 50, 50 S.M. and the super-display model 50. The 48 and 48 S.M. are single distributor models. The 50, 50 S.M. and super-display 50 models have double distributors, thus making them ideal for mixed composition. These distributor bars are arranged one above the other, thereby allowing matrices from two main magazines or two main and two side magazines to be distributed simultaneously. The machines fitted with side magazines have two keyboards—one of ninety keys for the main magazines and the other of thirty-four keys for the side magazines.

The scope of the Linotype has been greatly extended in recent years by means of duplex matrices, which embody two different faces on one matrix.

Fig. 3. *Section of the Linotype distributor bar showing how the various matrices are returned into their own magazine channels.*

The maximum measure (specially ordered) is 36 ems; the standard maximum measure is 30 ems.

Decorative material in the shape of borders and dashes can be cast on the machine from unit or block matrices.

The Intertype

This machine (Fig. 4) is similar to the Linotype. Its capacity, like the Linotype, depends on the model, magazines and side units. These are designed to produce a wide variety of composition, in the form of slugs, to measures ranging from 4 ems up to 42 ems.

The type sizes range from 5 to 60 point.

There are two distinct models: (1) single distributor, and (2) mixer, or double distributor. The single-distributor model is for ordinary straight composition from one magazine only (main section) or from one main and one side magazine.

The mixer models have two distributor bars placed side by side. The matrices, after casting, are taken up by the elevator and then automatically

INTERTYPE COMPOSING MACHINE (C 3-S.M.)

Fig. 4. (A) *Twin-pig metal feeder;* (B) *elevator which carries matrices to distributor;* (C) *assembler guides control travel of matrices to assembler;* (D) *spaceband box;* (E) *composing stick attachment;* (F) *control knob for automatic centring and quadding;* (G) *matrix line assembly;* (H) *control wheel for rotation of mould wheel and change of body size;* (I) *micrometer adjustment of body size;* (J) *automatic casting and delivery of new type lines;* (K) *fast power-driven keyboards;* (L) *automatic distribution of matrices into magazines;* (M) *distributor;* (N) *magazines containing double-letter matrices;* (O) *magazines containing display matrices;* (P) *pie matrix chute;* (Q) *keyrods acting directly upon magazine escapements;* (R) *magazine change control handles;* (S) *additional magazines.*

sorted and passed on to the appropriate distributor bar. This means that matrices can be set from, and distributed to, two main magazines—one above the other; or two main and two side magazines. The mixer models are suitable for straight, display and mixed composition.

Borders, dashes and other ornaments can be cast on the machine.

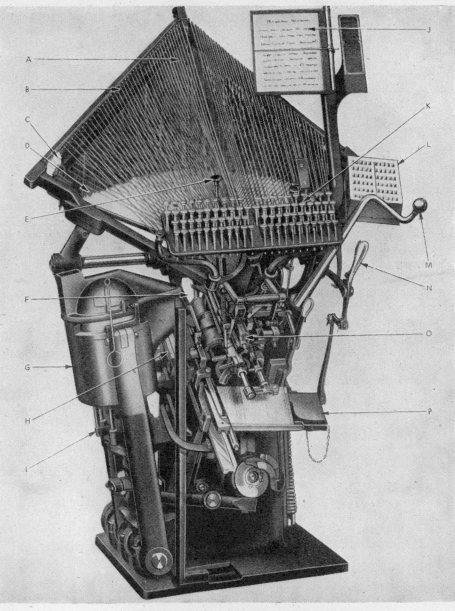

TYPOGRAPH COMPOSING MACHINE

Fig. 5. (A) *Connecting rods;* (B) *escapements;* (C) *guide wires;* (D) *matrices;* (E) *starting key;* (F) *upper jaw;* (G) *metal pot with pump;* (H) *mould;* (I) *gas burner;* (J) *copy holder;* (K) *keyboard;* (L) *container for sorts matrices;* (M) *handle for working machine by hand;* (N) *start and stop handle;* (O) *space ring shaft;* (P) *galley with slugs.* The *Typograph differs in several respects from other type-setting machines. The unusual method of returning the matrices to the magazine is described in the text; the spacing is by means of spacer rings with a tapering edge. The Typograph is a slug-casting machine.*

The Typograph

Consists essentially of two parts: the base containing spacing and casting mechanism, and the movable upper part or magazine unit comprising the matrices, keyboard, matrix guide rails and keyboard wires. Each key on the keyboard is connected by one of these wires to a releasing device at the top of the magazine. The matrices slide down the guide wires into the assembling channel (Fig. 5).

The method of spacing out the matrices is by means of spacer rings. These are disks with a tapering edge carried on a square shaft. They are released by depressing the spacer key and slide by gravitation—similar to the matrices—so that the narrow edge comes into position behind each word in the line on to the spacer shafts. These rotate until the wedging action of the spacer rings completely justifies the matrices to the measure. After a line of matrices has been composed the machine is caused to do its work of casting by lightly tapping the starting key. After casting, the upper portion of the machine is tilted back automatically and the matrices are returned to their position in the magazine.

The matrices carry two letters, the roman and italic or black character; the latter can be introduced as required in single words, lines, or paragraphs.

The matrix consists of a steel shank terminating in a movable eyelet and a brass body which bears the character.

The Typograph slug is cast and finished in a single operation. Its final dimensions are obtained from the mould, obviating the trimming of the sides and base—only the jet or tang formed in casting is removed, and as this is broken off slightly above the base the break does not affect the height to paper. Thus the Typograph slug has no ribs and is of point dimension in its entirety. This is advantageous when mixing the slugs with hand-set matter.

Normally, the machine is for sizes from 6 to 14 point, with measures up to 32 ems 12 point. There is also a special mould for large sizes up to 36 point. A wide selection of rules, dashes and borders can be produced.

The Monotype

The Monotype (Fig. 6) was invented by Tolbert Lanston, who was born in U.S.A. in 1844. After numerous improvements the machines were placed on the British market in 1897.

The Monotype consists of two units —a keyboard and a casting machine. The keyboard is operated by a compositor, whilst the caster attendant is—or should be—a skilled technician with a full knowledge of type and a flair for turning out the maximum production with the minimum of trouble to the hand compositor who will subsequently handle and correct the type.

The Monotype Unit System. In order to understand the fundamental differences between the slug-casting machines and the Monotype, which casts lines of single types and spaces, it is essential to know something of the Monotype unit system. Under this system all letters and spaces are cast, as regards width, to multiples of a fixed base unit. This unit is one-eighteenth of one point and measures ·0007685 in. Each em quad normally contains 18 units, therefore:—

·0007685 in. × 12 = ·0092220 in. = 1 unit of 12 set.

·009222 in. × 18 = ·1660 in. = 18 units of 12 set (or 12 points × 12 points).

The system is simplified by the fact that each character in a fount has a fixed unit value in proportion to the em quad or 18-unit size.

The Monotype "D" Keyboard. Unlike the Linotype operator, the operator on this keyboard (Fig. 7) sees nothing of

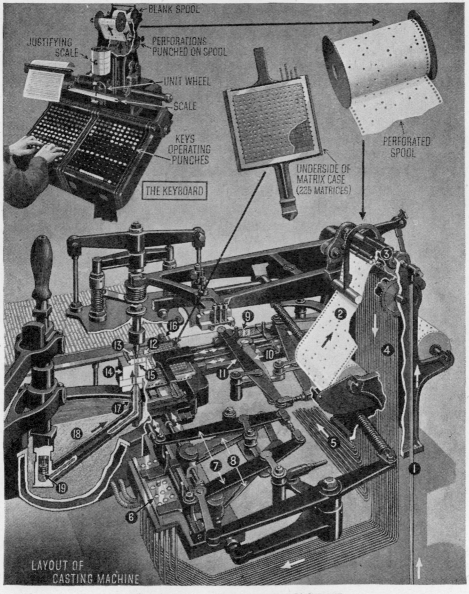

·MONOTYPE COMPOSING MACHINE

Fig. 6. *(1) Compressed air supply pipe; (2) perforated spool; (3) air escaping through perforations and operating stop-pins; (4) air pipes to position stop-pins; (5) air pipes to unit stop-pins; (6) fifteen stop-pins controlling movement of matrix case; (7) tongs controlling movement of stop rack; (8) tongs controlling movement of matrix case; (9) fifteen stop-pins controlling matrix case unit-wise; (10) tongs controlling movement of matrix case and normal wedge; (11) tongs controlling movement of stop rack; (12) matrix case; (13) centring pin; (14) mould; (15) cast type in mould; (16) cast types being assembled; (17) pump nozzle; (18) molten type metal; (19) type metal pump.*

MONOTYPE KEYBOARD

Fig. 7. *As each key is depressed the paper spool is perforated and moves on slightly. The punch holes later control the positioning of the matrix case on the casting machine.*

the matrices or the casting. His finished product is a spool of paper perforated with small holes. This spool of paper is next taken to the casting unit where, under the supervision of the caster attendant, it functions as the vital link in producing the thousands of individual letters and spaces in the form of justified lines of type (Fig. 8).

Before setting commences, a spool of paper is placed in position above the keyboard. This spool has a series of holes at each side for winding purposes. The measure is made up on the em scale—marked from 65 at the left to 0 at the right. This scale represents the ems of the set size in use. For example, if the job is to be 24 ems of 12 point measure and the type 6 point 6 set, the scale would be made up to 48 ems.

As tapping proceeds, a pointer moves along the scale from left to right. When approaching the end of the measure a bell rings to warn the operator, who then quickly decides where to end the line. Each character or space in the line is a definite number of units in width and the units are registered, or added, as the line proceeds. In ordinary composition the space between the words is first registered as four units ($\frac{4}{18}$ of the em), but when the last word of the line is tapped the remaining space is divided equally and added to the four-unit spaces—or "variables," as they are termed—in order to justify the line to the measure. All this is done automatically by means of the justification scale or drum. The operator simply notes the two numbers indicated on the drum by the pointer (anything from 1 to 15) and taps the corresponding keys on the two rows of red keys (numbered 1 to 15) at the top of the keyboard. He then presses a reversing key at the bottom of the keyboard, which moves the em rack pointer over to the left, ready for commencing the next line.

The Perforating Mechanism. As each key button is depressed the spool of paper is perforated—usually by one or two punches. When the key is released the paper moves on one marginal hole, ready for the next perforations. These perforations control the positioning of the matrix case over the mould when casting, the set width of every character and space, the starting and stopping of the pump, and the movement of the completed line of type to the galley.

The Monotype "DD" Keyboard. Similar to the ordinary keyboard with the

MONOTYPE CASTING MACHINE

Fig. 8. *Showing the casting of wide measure tabular matter. A metal ingot is being placed into the metal pot to replenish it.*

exception that it has two paper towers and two unit-registering mechanisms.

The advantages briefly are as follows: spools for the same matter are produced in two sizes of type at the same time. Rush work can be tackled without interfering with other work in hand. Measures from 60 up to 120 ems of 12 point can be produced by setting half the measure on each tower and combining the product from the caster. The "DD" keyboard can make duplicate perforated spools; set box headings for table work; and set footnotes for bookwork in different sizes from the body matter, with only one handling of the copy, by switching over to the other paper tower.

The Casting Machine

The main mechanism is mounted on a heavy base, and includes mould, matrix case, paper tower with air pipes leading to the pin blocks which govern the positioning of the matrix over the mould, a wedge which gives each type character its correct width, and two further wedges—one coarse, one fine—for controlling the width of the spaces between the words so that the lines are justified correctly.

Before casting from the spool, the attendant places the correct mould and type-sizing wedge on the machine, replaces the bridge over the mould and inserts the correct matrix case in the compound slide. The metal pot is swung round and raised until the nozzle of the pump fits in the orifice under the mould. An em quad (18 unit) is cast and sized up with the aid of a micrometer. The horizontal and vertical alignments are adjusted, the measure set to receive the lines, a galley fixed, and casting commences. The operation of changing over on the Monotype casting machine from one size to another for ordinary composition takes about fifteen minutes.

The spool starts on the caster where the keyboard operator finished. Therefore, the two perforations for justifying the line come first. As, on the keyboard, the paper travels one marginal hole per character, the first two revolutions are concerned with positioning the two wedges to give the correct space between the words in the line which follows. The pump is automatically cut out while the wedges are positioned. The composition now commences with the last letter of the line and so on until the next two justifying perforations, which also cause the completed line to be drawn from the type channel and pushed into the galley opening.

The Monotype Super-caster is about the same size as the ordinary composition caster, but designed specifically for casting type for case, also leads, rules, borders and spacing material.

The Ludlow

The Ludlow may be termed a semi-mechanical composing machine. There is a casting unit but no keyboard (Fig. 9).

The average installation consists of cabinets with cases containing matrices of the various type designs and sizes; universal spaces; matrix assembling sticks; one or more casting machines; super-surfacer for burnishing the larger type faces; profiler for eliminating beard or cutting-in letters; and trimmer-saw for cutting slugs in bulk to given measure.

The matrices are assembled and justified by hand in the Ludlow stick, automatically cast in the form of a slug, and then distributed back into case by hand.

The Ludlow is suitable for general jobbing and display work, and also for many kinds of stationery forms which have horizontal and vertical rules.

Ludlow machines are installed in many newspaper and publication houses. The fact that the same metal is used by composing machines saves any sorting of metals when the formes are dissected and the material returned after use to the foundry for melting and recasting into fresh ingots.

A distinctive feature of the Ludlow slug is that generally speaking only one measure is used and no matter what sizes of matrices are used the body dimension of the slug is normally either 6 or 12 point. Thus the machine is always ready for immediate casting. If two machines are installed it is usual to have one fitted with a 6-point mould and the other with a 12-point mould, in which case all matrices up to 12 point are cast on a 6-point slug while all matrices above 12 point are cast on a 12-point slug.

LUDLOW CASTING MACHINE

Fig. 9. *Showing self-feeding metal suspended at rear. The matrices are first set by hand and the lines cast in the form of slugs.*

The method of setting is shown in Fig. 10. The compositor *gathers* the matrices required (in display work all sizes are indicated on the layout) and places them in the Ludlow stick. The speed of assembling is much quicker than setting type inasmuch as a number of matrices are gathered and placed into the stick at one operation. The number varies according to the thickness of the matrices being used, but from three to eight is the approximate range. When all the matrices for the line have been placed in the stick, the spaces are placed between the words. This operation is facilitated by the markings in picas on the stick and also by the range of widths available in the Ludlow spaces —from ½ point, 1 point, 2 point, up to 36 point. Short lines need no justification.

Casting and Making Up the Slugs. The stick containing the line of justified matrices is put into a groove on the top of the machine and locked in position. A starting lever sets the mechanism in motion. The mould moves to the casting position, metal is pumped into the mould and the slug is cast. The

SETTING LUDLOW MATRICES

Fig. 10. *Note the compact case and cabinet. The handle is at side of the case which when pulled out is at a convenient setting angle. The lay is the same for capitals and lower case.*

stick is then taken off the machine and the matrices distributed. Meanwhile, the slug is trimmed at foot and finally delivered on to the galley. Any number of slugs may be cast from the same line of matrices by use of a repeat-casting lever.

When all the lines are cast they are made up by inserting shoulder-high slugs under the overhanging portions. Blank slugs and spacing materials in a variety of body widths are kept available for this purpose.

Stationery Forms. Many kinds of rule forms can be composed on the Ludlow, the repeat casting coming in very useful for this work. The difficulty of vertical alignment of rules has been overcome by an ingenious use of a special slug-aligning matrix. This produces a small lug on the front of the slug and a recess immediately behind. Thus when the slugs are made up they interlock and thereby ensure an accurate vertical alignment of the rules.

The Elrod Machine

This machine (Fig. 11) provides strip spacing material and borders of a high quality. Its range of product includes rules and spacing material from 1 to 36 point in thickness and it cuts the strips into any desired length from 6 to 144 ems of 12 point. The larger sizes have a cored body thereby effecting a saving in metal. The spacing material is also used to support overhanging portions of Ludlow slugs. The machine occupies a space of about six feet by two feet.

Photographic Type Composition

Although the existing mechanical composing machines are extremely versatile and fulfil their functions admirably, there is undoubtedly much scope for photographic type composition, especially in the photogravure and photo-litho printing processes. So far as type matter is concerned, these processes require only one good proof, and if this can be obtained without the use of type metal in the form of individual letters or slugs—which require to be set up, corrected, locked-up and carefully proofed—there are obvious and logical reasons for the further development of photographic and leadless type-composition methods and machinery. Experiments have been in progress now over a period of years and patents have been taken out recently for a number of machines.

Two machines which have achieved results which promise well for the future are the Uhertype and the Orotype.

The full Uhertype installation consists of three machines: the first is the setting unit, on which the matrix plate is hand-operated. The product of the setting unit is a film band, or negative, of the lines composed typewriter fashion and not justified. In order to make the lines full out, the second unit, the justifying machine, is used. After simple adjustments the unjustified lines on the first film are projected and exposed

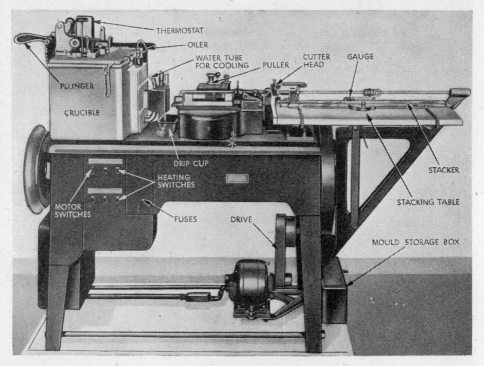

ELROD CASTER

Fig. 11. *The Elrod lead, slug and rule caster provides spacing material and borders of high quality, and cuts them into strips of any desired length from 6 to 144 ems of 12 point.*

word by word on to a second film for justification purposes. The film band can then be developed either as a positive or negative for either photogravure or offset-litho processes. The third unit is the photojobbing or Metteur machine by means of which a very wide range of display work, even of the most intricate nature, can be produced. Fig. 12 is a reproduction of a page of display work, on the Uhertype machines. Speeds up to 2,500 characters per hour have been accomplished on the hand-operated setting unit, but output is limited by the need for an additional process of justification. Improvements in the Uhertype are still being made.

The Orotype machine is similar in some ways to the Linotype, but instead of the matrices there are raised letters—termed patrices. These are assembled in lines by keyboard manipulation and justified by spring spaces. In place of the casting mechanism is a printing unit complete with inking rollers and cylinder. The justified lines of patrices are positioned and printed line by line on to cellophane

PHOTOGRAPHIC COMPOSITION

Fig. 12. *Reproduction of a display page which demonstrates the versatility of the Uhertype method of photographic composition. The original was printed in red and black on paper 5½ in. by 8½ in.*

film or Baryta paper as required. The patrices are distributed back to their respective channels in the magazine in a manner similar to that of the Linotype. The maximum speed of production is stated to be 14,000 letters per hour, but this depends, of course, on the skill of the operator. The machine occupies a space of about 5 ft. sq.

CHAPTER FOUR

BOOKWORK

PLANNING FOR BOOKWORK.   PAPER SIZES.   TYPE AREA DIMENSIONS.   ALLOCATING
MARGINS.   BOOK SUBDIVISIONS AND THEIR TREATMENT.   SELECTION OF TYPE SIZES.
TITLE PAGES.   HEADLINES.   FOOTNOTES AND SIDENOTES.   SIGNATURES.   COLLATING.

BOOK PRINTING is a specialized business and calls for careful planning, up-to-date machinery and equipment, and, just as important, craftsmen of high ability.

The vast bulk of bookwork is nowadays printed from mechanical composition. The Monotype, Linotype and Intertype machines are all highly suitable for the work. Some years ago, the Monotype was the most-favoured machine, but there has been a marked increase in the number of books set in Linotype and Intertype faces in recent years, and the number is still increasing.

Planning for Bookwork

Size of Paper Page. Some publishers have their own sizes for which they must give a special order to the paper maker. Others keep to the standard sizes. The sizes most used are as follows:—

Name and size of sheet	Name and untrimmed page size
inches	*inches*
Quad f'scap 27 × 34	Foolscap 8vo 6¾ × 4¼
,, crown 30 × 40	Crown 8vo 7½ × 5
,, demy 35 × 45	Demy 8vo 8¾ × 5⅝
,, royal 40 × 50	Royal 8vo 10 × 6¼

It will be noted that the ratios between width and depth are not constant. An eighth of an inch minimum should be allowed for trim at head, foot and fore-edge.

Type Area. The dimensions of the type page and the allocations for margins are very important details in the planning of a book. Generally speaking, cheap books have narrow margins and small-sized type, while *de luxe* editions have ample margin space, pleasingly proportioned, and a size of type face which is easy on the eye.

Allocating Margins

Three methods for deciding type-page dimensions and allocating margins are detailed below.

Method No. 1 (Fig. 1). In order to arrive at satisfactory proportions, allocate slightly less than two-thirds the trimmed paper width for the type area. Thus assuming the size of book to be demy 8vo and trimmed paper width 5½ in., or 33 ems of 12 point, the type measure should be 21 ems (1 em less than two-thirds the width). The margins for this class of work should be allocated on traditional ratios. Although slight variations are often adopted, the following proportions will be found to give a very satisfactory result: head, 2 units; fore-edge, 3 units; foot, 4 units; single back, 1½ units.

In planning, the *pair* of pages is taken as the unit. The measure of 21 ems or 42 ems for the pair of pages leaves 24 ems for the vertical spaces at the sides of the type pages. According to the ratios mentioned, the space would be allocated as follows: 8 ems for each fore-edge and 8 ems for the combined backs or 4 ems per page. The fore-edge (3 unit) margins measure 8 ems, therefore the head (2 unit) margins should be 5⅓ ems. To avoid using odd points in the formes allocate 5 ems to the head

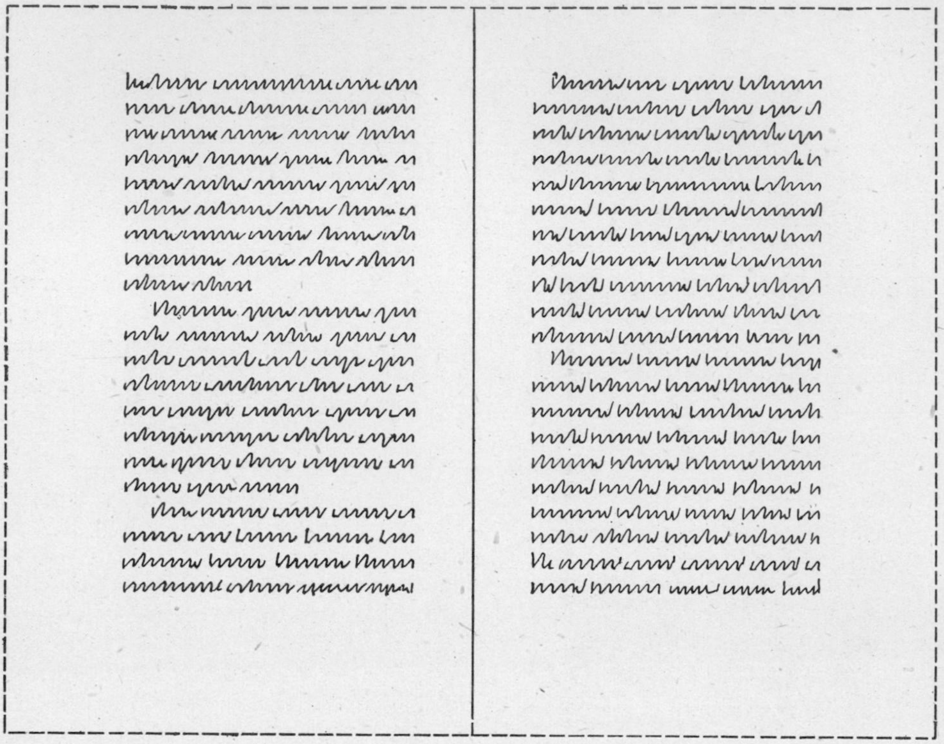

Fig. 1. *Type area and margins suitable for de luxe bookwork. The dotted lines represent paper size. The type measure is slightly less than two-thirds of the trimmed paper width.*

margin. The foot margin would thus be 10 ems while the depth of the type page would be 36 ems. A suitable size of type for this size and class of work would be 12 point; for 4to 14 point.

Method No. 2 (Fig. 2). Approximately three-quarters of the trimmed paper page width for type. Thus assuming the demy 8vo size is used, the measure would be 24 ems. Margins for this work are approximately uniform, with the exception of the foot which should be slightly more than the fore-edge. The margins could be allocated as follows: 4½ ems at back and fore-edge, 4 ems at head, and 5 ems at the foot. This leaves a type area of 24 by 42 ems. Sizes of type which are suitable for this page are 10 and 11 point.

Method No. 3 (Fig. 3). There are many who prefer something between the ample, finely proportioned margins as obtained from Method No. 1 and the ordinary effect obtained by Method No. 2. In order to determine the measure—find the widths as decided by Methods No. 1 and No. 2. In the case of demy 8vo, these were 21 ems and 24 ems respectively. For this method choose a measure between the two, say 23 ems. The margins should be allocated as follows: single back and head least, fore-edge a little more, and foot most of all. As with the measure, so with the ratios for margins—something between the traditional ratios of 1½, 2, 3, 4 and the uniform allocations. Thus a fairly logical allocation would be 4 ems single back, 4 ems head, 6 ems fore-edge and 8 ems at the foot. This would leave type page dimensions of 23 by 39 ems. A suitable type face for this page would be 10 or 11 point as in Method No. 2.

It should be noted that the size of type face is not always the same for each body size.

Parts of a Book. The average book is divided into two main parts: (1) the text or body matter, and (2) the oddments. The make-up of a book is arranged in the following sequence:—

1. Half-title
2. Frontispiece
3. Title
4. Printer's imprint, copyright note, etc.
5. Dedication
6. Preface
7. Contents
8. List of illustrations
9. Introduction
10. Text pages
11. Appendix
12. Glossary
13. Bibliography
14. Index
15. Colophon.

The pages which precede the text are termed preliminary pages, or prelims, and are often numbered in roman numerals separately from the text matter.

The *Half-title*, or bastard title as it is sometimes termed, is always a right-hand page, and consists usually of the name or title of the book. The type face should be the same character as used on the title page, but a size or two smaller. There should be no attempt to make the page unduly prominent by decoration.

The *Frontispiece* generally faces the title page. If it consists of a single or multi-colour half-tone illustration printed letterpress it is worked separately, usually on art paper, and pasted or guarded in the book afterwards. When

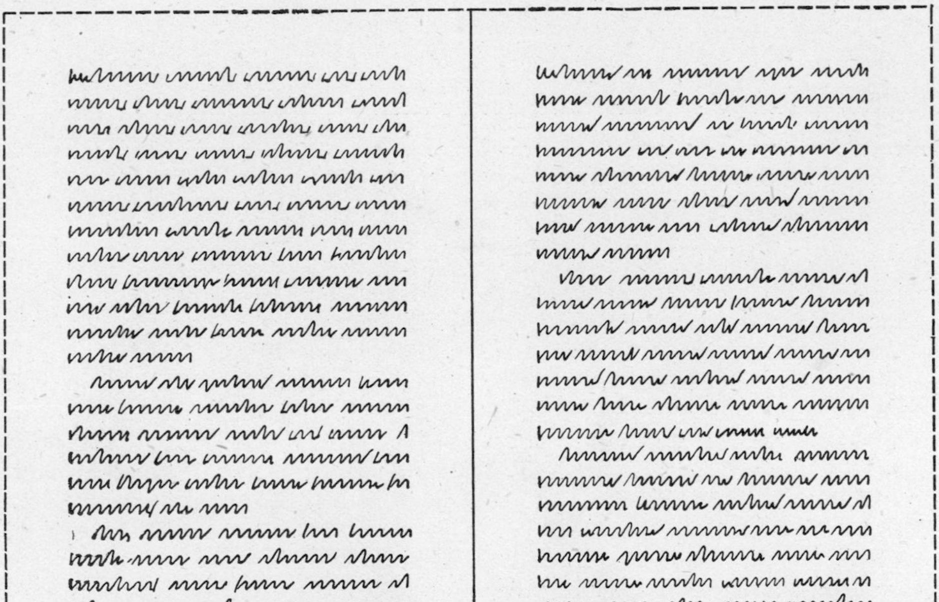

Fig 2. *Type area and margins suitable for the general class of bookwork. In the above example approximately three-quarters of the trimmed paper width is allotted to type area.*

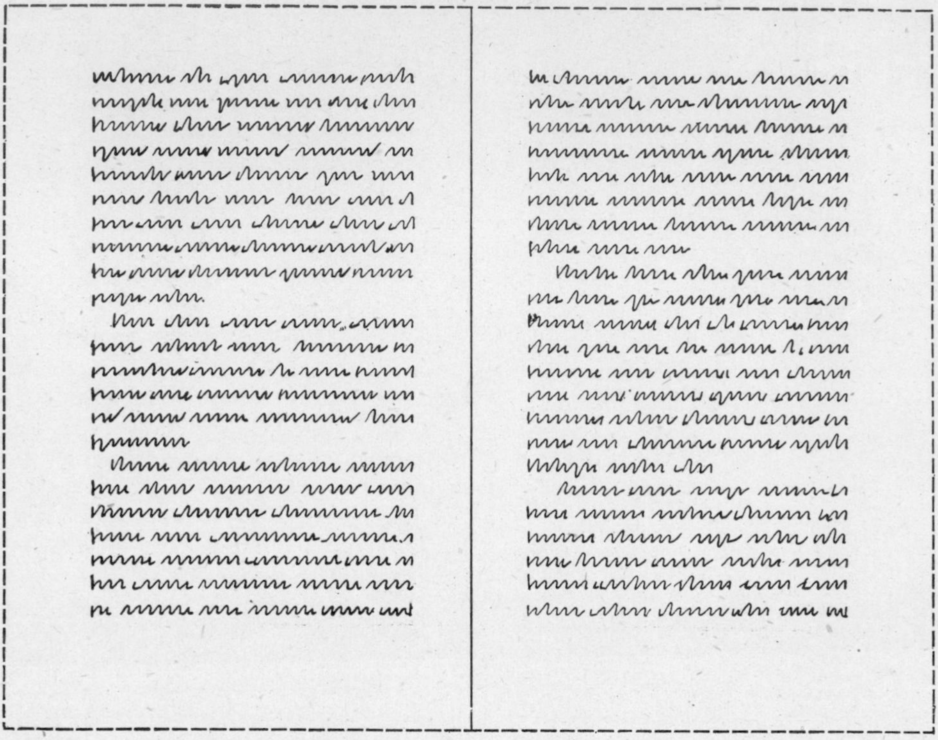

Fig. 3. *Type area and margins suitable for medium class of bookwork. The type area in the above example is a compromise between the type areas shown in Figs. 1 and 2. The margin proportions for back, head, fore-edge and foot are given on page 48.*

the picture is oblong or landscape, it should be inserted so that the caption reads from *foot to head.*

The *Title Page* (Figs. 4 and 5) is always a right-hand page. It should be designed with great care. The first essential is that the eye shall read the following three items: (1) the title of the book; (2) the name of the author; and (3) the name of the publisher.

There are various styles for setting title pages, but simplicity combined with dignity should be aimed at. The type face should be in harmony with the remainder of the book and the lines positioned with a view to registering perfect balance. Roman capitals are usually more suitable than italic or upper and lower case, although a long title may sometimes be set in upper and lower case. Unless the compositor is very highly skilled it is unsafe to venture far from these broad principles.

On the back of the title page it is customary to have the copyright notice, the printer's imprint, and the international requirement "Printed in Great Britain." The copyright notice is usually placed about three-eighths down the page. The other items are often placed at the bottom of the page.

The *Dedication* is always a right-hand page. Set in small caps and to the monumental style is most appropriate. The lines should be positioned about three-eighths down the page.

The *Preface* commences on a right-hand page. If it is the normal preface it should be set in the same size and face as the text matter. Italics may be used if the preface has been written by a person other than the author. If the book has both preface and introduction the former may be set in italics to mark the distinction. When the preface extends over two or three pages it is advisable to treat it as an introduction.

The *Contents Page* (Figs. 6 and 7) always commences on the right hand, and consists of a list of the chapter numbers and titles and the page folio upon which each begins. There are various styles of setting, depending to a great extent upon the length of the titles and other details. The chapter numbers are usually at the left, followed by the chapter titles in caps, caps and small caps, even small caps, or caps and lower case, and the page folio in arabic figures at the right.

If the book is the work of more than one author, the name of the author of each section or chapter is generally placed below the section or chapter title.

SKETCHES BY BOZ

ILLUSTRATIVE OF
EVERYDAY LIFE AND EVERYDAY
PEOPLE

BY

CHARLES DICKENS

WITH EIGHT ILLUSTRATIONS

LONDON
CHAPMAN & HALL, 193 PICCADILLY

Fig. 4. *A dignified and well-balanced Title Page, set in Caslon Old Face. The original was printed on antique paper, which is a particularly suitable paper for books set in Caslon type face.*

The *List of Illustrations* follows the contents pages and begins on a right-hand page. The typographical treatment is similar to the contents pages.

The *Introduction* follows the list of illustrations and commences on a right-hand page. The style of setting is the same size and face as the text matter. There are many who are not clear on the difference between a preface and an introduction. The preface is the author's personal remarks to the reader

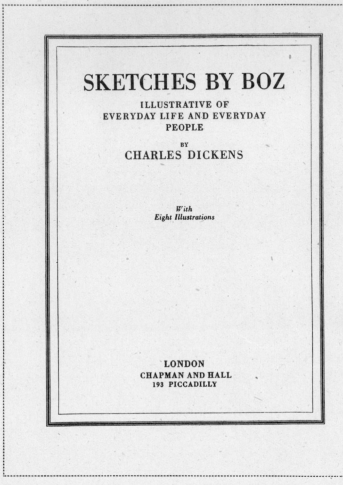

Fig. 5. *An alternative arrangement for the Title Page shown in Fig. 4. Set in Linotype Bodoni, with appropriate rule borders, also of Linotype material. Bodoni is suitable for antique or machine-finished paper.*

Legibility is one of the first considerations. The type face and its body go far to decide this. It is far easier to read lines of type if a little extra space is placed between them.

The following are a few type-size suggestions for ordinary bookwork: crown 8vo: 10 or 11 point face on 11 and 12 point bodies respectively; demy 8vo: 11 or 12 point face on 12 and 13 point bodies respectively; royal 8vo: 12 to 14 point face with thin lead (1½ points) between the lines.

The choice of type face is largely a matter of individual taste. There are many bookwork faces available. A few of these are shown in Chapter 7.

and these may be diverse in character and not necessarily connected with the text. On the other hand, the introduction should deal specifically with the subject of the book. The introduction is often written by a different author from the writer of the book.

The *Text Pages* (Fig. 8) are the most important in the book. Care must be taken, therefore, to ensure that all the little niceties which make or mar their appearance are given full consideration.

The dimensions of type areas and marginal spaces are most important in bookwork and have been explained.

Chapter headings may be dealt with in various ways. The high-class volume usually has every chapter starting on a fresh page with the possible addition of a decorative headpiece and initial (Fig. 8). The cheaper edition has what are termed run-on chapters, so saving space.

Headlines, too, must be given careful consideration. The usual style is to repeat the book title on the top of every page either in roman caps and small caps, or italic caps, or in letter-spaced even small caps. Another plan is to have the book title on the left-hand page and the chapter title on the right-hand page. Many publishers prefer to have on the right-hand page a headline descriptive of the contents of the actual page and to run the chapter title as a headline on the left-hand page.

The page numbers or folios may be at the head or foot of the type page. If at the head, they are placed in the headlines. The best position is on the outside or fore-edge.

Publishers have their own methods of dealing with the details of style and these often vary in accordance with the nature of the publication. Many publishers prepare from galley proofs a complete paste-up of every page in the book, including the placing of any illustrations and the captions for these. The make-up compositor follows the paste-up exactly; any adjustments are made in page proofs.

When *Footnotes* are used they are usually two or three sizes smaller than the text. One method of indicating footnotes is by the reference marks. These are as follows:—

1. * Star (or asterisk)   4. § Section
2. † Dagger   5. ‖ Parallel
3. ‡ Double dagger   6. ¶ Paragraph.

The reference mark should follow the word to which reference is made and the same mark precedes the note at the foot of the page. Footnotes are usually

CONTENTS

VOLUME ONE

Fig. 6. *Conventional and pleasing arrangement for a Contents Page. Linotype-set in Granjon Old Face. Note proportions of the margins.*

CONTENTS

Volume One

Chapter One	How Mr. Oxenham saw the White Bird .	*Page* 1
Two	How Amyas came home the first time . .	*page* 22
Three	Of two Gentlemen of Wales, and how they hunted with the Hounds, and yet ran with the Deer	*page* 59
Four	The two ways of being Crost in Love . .	*page* 80
Five	Clovelly Court in the Olden Time . . .	*page* 108
Six	The Coombes of the Far West	*page* 138
Seven	The true and tragical history of Mr. John Oxenham of Plymouth	*page* 148
Eight	How the Noble Brotherhood of the Rose was Founded	*page* 195
Nine	How Amyas kept his Christmas Day . .	*page* 215
Ten	How the Mayor of Bideford baited his hook with his Own Flesh.	*page* 254
Eleven	How Eustace Leigh met the Pope's Legate	*page* 266
Twelve	How Bideford Bridge dined at Annery House	*page* 286
Thirteen	How the "Golden Hind" came Home Again	*page* 317
Fourteen	How Salvation Yeo slew the King of the Gubbings	*page* 328
Fifteen	How Mr. John Brimblecombe understood the Nature of an Oath	*page* 356

Volume Two

Sixteen	The most chivalrous Adventure of the Good Ship "Rose"	*page* 1
Seventeen	How they came to Barbados, and found no Men therein	*page* 20

Fig. 7. *An alternative treatment for a Contents Page. Set in Caslon Old Face caps and small caps, with chapter numbers in italic, a style which is in keeping with the period of the book "Westward Ho!"*

separated from the text above by a blank (or white) line. Occasionally, full width or short medium face rules are used. If short rules are used they should be placed to the left after type matter.

Many offices now prefer to use superior figures instead of the reference marks. Superior figures ($^{1\ 2\ 3}$) are small figures cast on the upper part of the body. When footnotes are numerous there is no doubt that superior figures are preferable. References are sometimes used consecutively throughout a chapter and listed collectively at the end under the corresponding number used in the text.

Reference Bibles use a combination of figures and the alphabet, and sometimes place their references in a narrow column down the centre of the page.

Side or *Marginal Notes* are printed on the fore-edge margin of the page and should be so arranged that the first line of each note aligns with the line of text to which it refers.

Shoulder Notes are printed in the fore-edge margins of the pages on a level with the first line of the text. There is only one shoulder note to each page and it may consist only of the chapter title.

Cut-in Notes are set in narrow measure in type smaller and usually heavier than the text. They are inserted in the outside edges of the text pages and should be surrounded at top, side and foot by an equal amount of white space. If possible, the lines immediately above, below and at the side of cut-in notes should be full out and not indented,

The *Appendix* comes after the text pages and should commence on a right-hand page. It should be set in the same type face as the text but a size smaller.

The *Glossary* is usually a list and explanation of abstruse, obsolete, dialectal, or technical terms, and should commence on a right-hand page. The size of type depends on the nature of the work, but generally speaking two sizes less than the text will be found suitable.

The *Bibliography* consists usually of a list of book titles with the names of the authors to which the writer of the work has referred for information. It may be treated similarly to a glossary. A short bibliography referring to the date of printing and number of editions is often printed on the back of the title page.

The *Index* should commence on a right-hand page. There are varieties of style as regards arrangement, and care should be exercised to select a style which will suit the text matter of the book. An index is normally set in

8-point type and made up in double or treble column pages, according to the number and length of the entries.

Folding and Collating

The sizes of sheet used for bookwork naturally vary according to the size of page of the work. For a crown 8vo novel probably quad- or eight-crown sheets would be used. Thus each quad-crown sheet would produce sixty-four pages, i.e. thirty-two on each side of the sheet.

CHAPTER III

OF TWO GENTLEMEN OF WALES, AND HOW THEY HUNTED WITH THE
HOUNDS, AND YET RAN WITH THE DEER.

"I know that Deformed; he has been a vile thief this seven year;
he goes up and down like a gentleman : I remember his name."
Much Ado about Nothing.

MYAS slept that night a tired and yet a troubled sleep; and his mother and Frank, as they bent over his pillow, could see that his brain was busy with many dreams. And little wonder; for over and above all the excitement of the day, the recollection of John Oxenham had taken strange possession of his mind; and through all that long evening, as he sat alone in the cool bay-windowed room where he had seen him last, Amyas was recalling to himself every look and gesture of the lost adventurer, and wondering at himself for so doing, till he retired to sleep, only to renew the fancy in his dreams. At last he found himself, he knew not how, sailing westward ever, up the wake of the setting sun, in chase of a tiny sail which was John Oxenham's. Upon him was a painful sense that, unless he came up with her in time, something fearful would come to pass : but the ship would not sail. All around floated the sargasso beds clogging her bows with their long snaky coils of weed; and still he tried to sail, and tried to fancy that he was sailing, till the sun went down and all was utter dark. And then the moon arose, and

71

Fig. 8. *A page of text from " Westward Ho! " with chapter heading and decorative headpiece and initial. Set in Linotype Granjon Old Face.*

The eight-crown sheet would produce one hundred and twenty-eight pages, i.e. sixty-four pages on each side of the sheet.

The folding of these sheets is generally done on folding machines, which deliver them usually as sixteen page or thirty-two page sections. To fold a sheet of quad-crown size down to crown 8vo would require five folds.

When all the sections of a book have been gathered it is necessary to have some means of checking to ensure that all the pages of the book are in correct sequence. The checking is termed collating—and in order that this operation may be done speedily, it is the usual practice to use signatures.

Signatures

Signatures are small capital letters or figures placed alphabetically or numerically at the foot of the first page of each section. The best position is in the white line immediately below the text and indented 1 em from the beginning. Apart from their importance in the binding department the signatures also facilitate the work in the composing and machine departments. They serve to designate the various formes. For example, it is much easier to find a forme say of a specified signature than to look for page numbers. In books of which the prelims consist of only one section no signature is used as the title itself serves to identify it—and a printed letter would appear unsightly. If the prelims run into two or three sections italic lower-case signatures are often used. If it is undesirable to have the letters or figures on the printed pages they may be placed so as to print at the extreme head or foot of the untrimmed sections. They are then removed when the edges of the book are trimmed.

Another style of signature which has become popular in bookwork offices

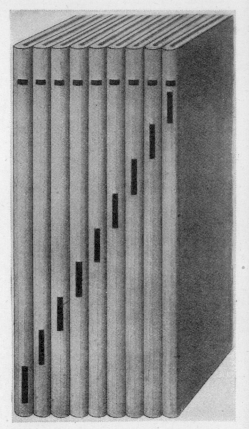

Fig. 9. *The black-step method of collating. A missing or misplaced section would be noted at a glance, by the missing step.*

is known as the black-step method.

The method is simple and effective. A piece of rule, about 6 points thick and 24 points long, is placed between the first and last pages (or spine) of each section. As these two pages are placed side by side in the forme the method incurs little or no trouble. For the first section the rule would be positioned opposite the top line of text. The next section would have the rule stepped down, say 24 points, and so on through the sections. The appearance of the folded sections from the rear is shown in Fig. 9. The rule at the lower left-hand corner is level with the last line of text.

CHAPTER FIVE

IMPOSITION

STANDARD PAPER SIZES. ORDINARY SUBDIVISIONS. LONG AND IRREGULAR SUB-
DIVISIONS. FOLDING MACHINES. MARGINAL TERMS EXPLAINED. FOUR-PAGE SCHEMES.
SHEET WORK AND HALF-SHEET WORK. EIGHT-PAGE SCHEMES. SIXTEEN-PAGE SCHEMES.
TWELVE-PAGE SCHEMES. OFFCUTS AND FOLDERS.

THE term *imposition* means liter-
ally *in position*, and as applied to
the locking-up of formes means
the placing of the pages so that when
locked-up, printed and folded, the pages
will fall in the required sequence.

A necessary preliminary to the study
of imposition is a knowledge of paper
sizes and subdivisions.

The British Standards Institution has
issued the following British standard
sizes for paper, which were drawn up in
1937 by a committee representative of
paper suppliers and users in Great
Britain and the Dominions.

WRITINGS AND PRINTINGS—ALL CUT EDGES

Name			Size, in.
Crown, Double			20×30
,, Quad			30×40
Small Demy			$15\frac{1}{2} \times 20$
,, ,, Double			20×31
,, ,, Quad			31×40
Demy			$17\frac{1}{2} \times 22\frac{1}{2}$
,, Double			$22\frac{1}{2} \times 35$
,, Quad			35×45
Small Foolscap			$13\frac{1}{4} \times 16\frac{1}{2}$
,, ,, Double			$16\frac{1}{2} \times 26\frac{1}{2}$
,, ,, Oblong Double			$13\frac{1}{4} \times 33$
,, ,, Quad			$26\frac{1}{2} \times 33$
,, ,, $1\frac{1}{3}$ Sheet			$13\frac{1}{4} \times 22$
,, ,, $1\frac{1}{2}$ Sheet			$13\frac{1}{4} \times 24\frac{3}{4}$
Foolscap			$13\frac{1}{2} \times 17$
,, Double			17×27
,, Quad			27×34
,, $1\frac{1}{3}$ Sheet			$13\frac{1}{2} \times 22\frac{1}{2}$
,, $1\frac{1}{2}$ Sheet			$13\frac{1}{2} \times 25\frac{1}{2}$
Imperial			22×30
,, Double			30×44
,, $1\frac{1}{2}$ Sheet			22×45
Medium			18×23

Name			Size, in.
Medium, Double			23×36
Post			15×19
,, Double			19×30
Large Post			$16\frac{1}{2} \times 21$
,, ,, Double			21×33
Small Royal			19×24
Royal			20×25
,, Double			25×40
Large Royal			$20\frac{1}{2} \times 27$
,, ,, Double			27×41
Elephant, Double			27×40

Note.—All double and quad sizes in the
above table are exact multiples of the standard
sizes. The above designations also apply to
cover papers, the sizes of which are, however,
slightly larger.

WRAPPINGS AND CASINGS

Name			Size, in.
Imperial			$22\frac{1}{2} \times 29$
,, Double			29×45
,, Double Double			45×58
Saddleback			36×45
*Casing			36×46
,, Extra Large			40×48
Bag Cap			20×24
Crown, Double			20×30
,, Quad			30×40
Medium, Double			23×36

* In the Irish Free State and Northern Ireland
36×48 casing is used.

BOARDS—TRIMMED

Name			Size, in.
Royal			20×25
Postal			$22\frac{1}{2} \times 28\frac{1}{2}$
Imperial			$22\frac{1}{2} \times 30$
,, Large			$22\frac{1}{2} \times 32$
Index			$25\frac{1}{2} \times 30\frac{1}{2}$

In the course of the inquiry it was found that
there were some sizes which could not be
omitted, not necessarily on account of the
extent of their use, but due to the fact that
official and other publications have for a great

number of years been issued in one or other of those sizes. It will be recognized, however, that they can only be obtained if a sufficiently large order justifies their being made. They are given below:—

WRITINGS AND PRINTINGS

Name	Size, in.
Copy	$16\frac{1}{2} \times 20$
„ Double	20×33
Super Royal	19×27
Pott, Quad	25×32
„ „ Double	32×50
Antiquarian	30×53
Atlas	$26\frac{1}{2} \times 34$
Columbier	$24 \times 34\frac{1}{2}$
Foolscap, Quad $1\frac{1}{2}$ Sheet	$34 \times 40\frac{1}{2}$
Pinched Post	$14\frac{1}{2} \times 18\frac{1}{2}$
„ „ Double	$18\frac{1}{2} \times 29$
Small Post	$14\frac{1}{2} \times 18$
„ „ Double	18×29

WRAPPINGS AND CASINGS

Name	Size, in.
Bag Cap	19×24
Imperial Casing	23×33
„ „ Double	33×46

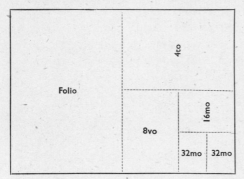
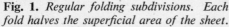

Fig. 1. *Regular folding subdivisions. Each fold halves the superficial area of the sheet.*

Ordinary Subdivisions. It will be noted from Fig. 1 that each fold halves the superficial area, but alters the measurement in one direction only. Thus: demy, $17\frac{1}{2}$ by $22\frac{1}{2}$ in.; demy folio, $11\frac{1}{4}$ by $17\frac{1}{2}$ in.; demy 4to, $8\frac{3}{4}$ by $11\frac{1}{4}$ in.; demy 8vo, $5\frac{5}{8}$ by $8\frac{3}{4}$ in.; demy 16mo, $4\frac{3}{8}$ by $5\frac{5}{8}$ in.; demy 32mo, $2\frac{13}{16}$ by $4\frac{3}{8}$ in. Therefore in order to arrive at any ordinary subdivision size it is necessary first to memorize the standard size, and secondly to

keep in the mind's eye the above diagram in order to know just how to divide the sheet.

In order to obtain folio, divide the long dimension by 2, thus 1 fold produces 4 pages; for 4to, divide both dimensions by 2, thus 2 folds produce 8 pages; for 8vo, divide the long dimension by 4, and the short by 2, thus 3 folds produce 16 pages; for 16mo, divide both dimensions by 4, thus 4 folds produce 32 pages; for 32mo, divide the long dimension by 8, and the short by 4, thus 5 folds produce 64 pages.

When pages are imposed for the regular subdivision sizes it should be obvious from Fig. 1 that a 16-page forme would be arranged as four rows of four; a 32-page forme would be laid down as four rows of eight, and so on.

Long Subdivisions. In order to obtain long 4to, divide the long dimension by 4; for long 8vo, divide the long dimension by 2, and the short by 4; for long 16mo, divide the long dimension by 8, and the short by 2 (Fig. 2).

While the folds required for the above subdivisions are the same in number as for the ordinary subdivisions it will be noted that the pages would require a different imposition scheme. For example, 16 pages of long 16mo would be arranged as two rows of eight instead of four rows of four.

Irregular Subdivisions. To obtain 6to,

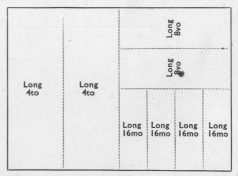

Fig. 2. *Some long subdivisions of a sheet.*

divide the long dimension by 3, and the short by 2; for long 6to, divide the long dimension by 2, and the short by 3; for ordinary 12mo, divide the long dimension by 3, and the short by 4; for square 12mo, divide the long dimension by 4, and the short by 3; for long 12mo, divide the long dimension by 6, and the short by 2; for 24mo, divide the long dimension by 6, and the short by 4; for long 24mo, divide the long dimension by 4, and the short by 6 (Fig. 3).

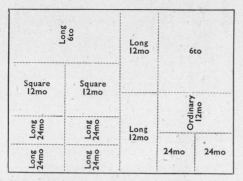

Fig. 3. *Various irregular subdivisions of a sheet, which are fully explained above.*

Folding Printed Sheets

Machines are available to fold large and small sheets and for parallel or right-angle folding. The scheme of imposition is nearly always dictated by the folding department, and the compositor arranges the pages therefore to suit the requirements of a particular folding machine. In some offices it is the practice to have the various schemes printed on cards and numbered. Thus the only information necessary in the composing department is the scheme number. The compositor—or stone-hand, as the imposition craftsman is termed—has thus only to look up the card indicated and the imposition scheme is to hand.

There are many different ways of arranging pages for printing, and it should be clearly understood that while the stone-hand can impose the pages

quite easily in almost any position, and the machine-man can print the sheets with the pages in any kind of sequence, an incorrect scheme may mean hours of extra time to deal with the sheets in the folding department.

If the sheets are to be folded by hand, the folding department is again in the best position to decide the scheme of imposition. Possibly there is but one scheme of imposition, meaning one operation by the stone-hand, but there may be thousands of sheets to be folded individually. Planning for imposition and subsequent printing and folding, must therefore be done with great care. If there are other problems, such as colour work requiring close register in printing, the machine-man should be consulted before deciding the scheme. When illustrations are required to "bleed" off the page, a larger size of paper is generally required for printing the forme.

There are many alternative schemes for all purposes and where the work of the departments is co-ordinated and the respective overseers talk over their problems it is nearly always possible to evolve a plan to suit all parties.

Before proceeding to deal with the schemes of imposition it may be well to have a clear understanding of the marginal terms used in imposition.

Heads. The space between pages which are placed head to head. In addition to the white space necessary to produce the planned head margin on the finished work, this includes $1\frac{1}{2}$ ems (18 points) for the head trim of $\frac{1}{8}$ in. While it is usual practice to trim $\frac{1}{8}$ in. at the head, the amount can be varied if circumstances make this necessary. For example, if the book has been planned for a 4-em head margin, $9\frac{1}{2}$ ems would be required in the heads—4 ems for each page, plus the trim $\frac{1}{8}$ in. or $\frac{3}{4}$ em per page $= 9\frac{1}{2}$ ems.

Backs. The space between the sides of mated or companion pages, which becomes, when folded, the back of the book. For example, if the single back margin is to be 3 ems, at least 6 ems would have to be placed in the backs in the forme.

Tails. The space between pages placed foot to foot including the trim at the foot of the job. If the foot margin on the finished book is to be 6 ems and a $\frac{1}{4}$-in.

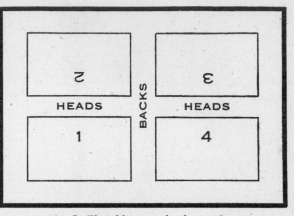

Fig. 5. *The oblong, or landscape four.*

trim has been allowed, 15 ems should separate the pages.

Gutters. The space between the *sides* of two pairs of mated pages including the trim on the fore-edge or front of the book. Assuming 5 ems to be the intended margin and a $\frac{1}{4}$-in. trim has been allowed, 13 ems would be required in the gutters.

Fore-edges. These margins do not

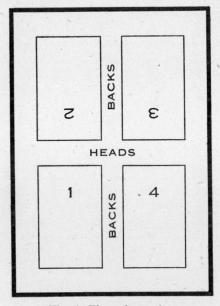

Fig. 4. *The ordinary four.*

take form until the sheet is printed, and they are the spaces between the sides of the pages and the edges of the paper. If the back and gutter margins have been allocated correctly, each fore-edge margin will be exactly half the gutter margin. It is essential, therefore, that the print be centred on the paper.

Four-page Schemes. The learner cannot do better for a start than analyse the scheme of imposition for the ordinary four-page job in Fig. 4.

It will be noted that:—

1. Page 1 is in the left lower corner with the head away from the stone-hand.

2. The last page (4) is on the right of page 1.

3. The two centre pages (2 and 3) are head to head with the first and last pages.

4. Each pair of folios added together totals one more than the number of pages in the forme ($1+4=5$; $2+3=5$).

If the above four items are memorized all the *ordinary* schemes of imposition will be found comparatively simple, because the same rules apply. Take, for example, Fig. 5, the oblong or landscape four.

The above-mentioned four rules still apply, but there is an important difference in the method of perfecting or

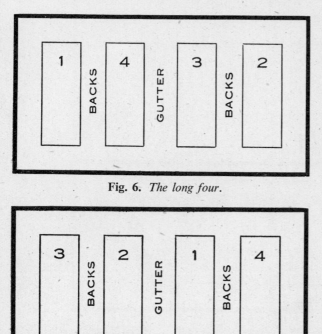

Fig. 6. *The long four.*

Fig. 7. *The long four (imposed from the centre).*

imposed in one forme and printed on one side of the paper. The paper is then turned and printed again from the same forme; thus each perfected sheet gives *two* complete copies of the pages in the forme when the sheet is cut through the centre. In the case of the ordinary and oblong fours, the perfected sheet would be cut across the heads before folding. The long fours (Figs. 6 and 7) would be cut through the gutters.

Sheet Work. A number of pages imposed as two formes, termed *inner* and *outer.* The outer forme, in which are the first and last pages of the sheet, is printed on one side of the stock. The forme is then lifted and the inner forme takes its place and is utilized to back up the sheets already printed on one side by the outer forme, thus producing one complete copy of the sheet.

To summarize: *half-sheet work* means *one* forme which prints *both* sides of stock and produces *two* copies per sheet. *Sheet work* means *two* formes, one for *each* side of the stock and produces *one* copy per sheet.

So far as the four-page schemes are concerned, therefore, it is only necessary to remember that if the job is to be worked as sheet work, pages 1 and 4 will be the outer forme and pages 2 and 3 the inner forme. In this connection it may be as well to remember that when imposing pages 1 and 4 it is the usual practice, when dealing with a single row of pages, to have the pages with the heads towards the stone-hand. Page 1, therefore, will be at the right of page 4 with the head nearest to the worker.

backing-up. If the sheet was turned as for the ordinary four, page 4 would back page 1. In order that page 2 may back page 1, therefore, the sheet must be turned, or tumbled, as it is termed, in its short direction. Thus the landscape four is known as a tumbler scheme—in other words, a scheme which requires both long edges of the sheet being fed to the grippers.

If the pages are narrow, and offcuts of paper are being made use of, or if it is necessary for some reason to have certain pages on the outside, the alternatives shown in Figs. 6 and 7 may be utilized.

All the four-page schemes reproduced are, of course, to be printed half-sheet work, and it may be advisable at this stage to define briefly two terms which seem to cause confusion to learners.

Half-sheet Work. A number of pages

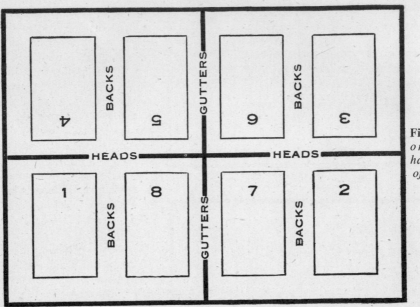

Fig. 8. *The ordinary half-sheet of eights.*

Eight-page Schemes. For a moment, refer back to the four rules given at the commencement of the four-page schemes. Note that page 1 is again in the left lower corner with the head away from the worker, the last page (8) is on its right, the two middle pages (4 and 5) are head to head with the first and last pages (1 and 8); and each pair of folios totals one more than the number of pages in the forme $(1+8=9; 7+2=9; 4+5=9; 6+3=9)$. The gripper edge would normally be at the foot of pages 1, 8, 7 and 2.

If required to be worked as sheet work (sheets of fours) the pages would be arranged as in Fig. 8, but in two chases. The left-hand four pages would be the outer forme, and the right-hand section the inner forme. The gripper edge of the former will be at the sides of pages 1 and 4; for the inner forme at the sides of pages 2 and 3.

Alternative Eight-page Schemes. Probably the best way to memorize the alternative eight-page schemes is to make a careful study of Fig. 9, noting particularly the fact that alternative schemes can be arranged by bringing together the two Bs, the two As, and the two Cs. The two latter schemes may be useful when working two eight-page jobs together, in which case the sheet would, of course, be doubled and the gripper edge at the left of pages 1, 4, 3, 2.

The Oblong or *Landscape Eight* (Fig. 10) is a scheme which the learner often finds difficult to memorize. For some reason or other the tendency is to place page 3 at the top right corner. But by remembering the rule that each pair of folios totals one more than the pages in the forme this mistake will be avoided.

Another rule which may prove useful at this stage is as follows: the second quarter of a scheme (pages 3 and 4) comes head to head with the first quarter (1 and 2).

There is always the danger that the attempt to memorize too many rules will defeat its object; but concentration on the four mentioned will amply repay the effort involved.

The gripper edge will normally be at

the sides of pages 1, 4, 3 and 2; the cut after perfecting will be across the tails between pages 3 and 4. The folding consists of two right-angle folds commencing with the short dimension.

Sixteen-page Schemes. It is only necessary to memorize the *first quarter* of any ordinary scheme. For example, in the ordinary half-sheet of sixteens (Fig. 11) we have the first quarter of the scheme—pages 1, 2, 3 and 4—in the four corners. If the rule regarding the second quarter is memorized there is no difficulty in placing page 5 at the head of page 4, page 6 at the head of page 3, page 7 at the head of page 2, and page 8 at the head of page 1. The rule is repeated for the sake of emphasis—*the second quarter of the scheme is placed head to head with the first quarter, so the last folio of the second quarter comes over page* 1.

Half the scheme is now completed and to finish is quite simple. All that is necessary in order to fill in the second half of the scheme, is to trace the pages backwards, filling in the folios at the same time. For example, page 9 at the side of page 8, 10 at the side of 7, and

so on, until folio 16 at the side of 1 is reached. Thus each pair of folios will total 17—a useful means of checking.

If required to be worked as sheet work, the lower half would be the outer forme, while the top half would be the inner forme. The gripper edge for the outer forme would be at the foot of pages 1, 16, 13, 4; for the inner forme at the foot of pages 3, 14, 15, 2. If several formes are to be printed and signatures are necessary, they would be placed at the foot of the first page of each section, B at the foot of page 1, C at the foot of page 17, and so on; while the subsidiary signatures B2, C2, etc., would be placed at the foot of pages 3 and 19 of the inner formes. The subsidiary signatures on the inner formes serve to designate the formes and make for easy identification; they also indicate the gripper edge and thereby help in placing the formes correctly on the bed of press, because the subsidiary signatures (B2, C2, etc.) occupy the same position on the machine bed as the main signatures. The main signatures are for use in gathering and collating the sections in the binding department.

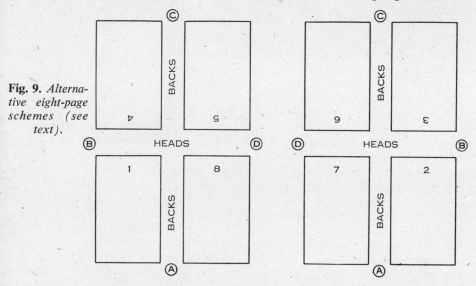

Fig. 9. *Alternative eight-page schemes (see text).*

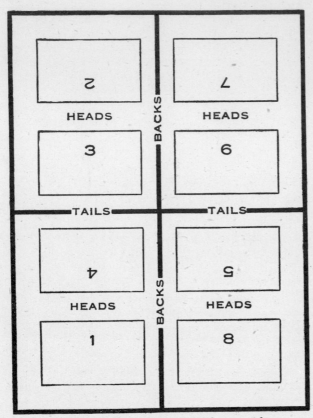

Fig. 10. *The oblong, or landscape eight.*

It must be understood, however, that it is unwise to deviate from the normal schemes unless some folding difficulty can be overcome by so doing. In nearly all cases, the binding department should have the final word.

Fig. 13 is one of the schemes used for the Cleveland folding machine, and is easily memorized from the ordinary sixteen. The only difference is the transposition of the lower eight pages to the top as demonstrated in Fig. 12 (by bringing together the four As).

It will be noted that the folds for the two schemes are identical, but in the Cleveland sixteen the lowest folios are brought near the centre and consequently near the cut. This means that if the perfected sheets are cut correctly there will be identical margins at the foot of page 1 on both sections—and as this side is the lay for the folding machine, it will now be realized why it becomes necessary to adopt a change in the imposition scheme.

In the ordinary sixteen, there is liable to be a variation in the margin from page 1 on one side of the sheet unless the paper is absolutely square in its broad dimension. For example, assuming the ordinary half-sheet of sixteens is on the machine, and the side-lay for printing the first side is at the foot of page 1, there would be a regular and accurate margin from page 1. But in backing up, the same edge of the sheet is fed to the side lay, which means that the lay must be at the foot of page 2.

The gripper edge will normally be at the side of pages 1, 8, 7 and 2; the cut across the tails. The folding will be three right-angle folds—first, pages 3 to 2; second, 5 to 4; third, 9 to 8.

Alternative Sixteen-page Schemes. Fig. 12, with its accompanying letters, A, B, C, D, demonstrates how three alternative schemes can be obtained. No. 1 by transposing the lower eight pages to the top (bringing together the four As) which gives a scheme suitable for folding on the Cleveland folding machine; a second alternative is arrived at by transposing the left-hand eight pages to the right (bringing together the four Bs); and the third is a combination of the previous two schemes (bringing together four As and four Bs).

Thus if there is any variation in the length of sheet, that variation will show itself at the foot of page 1 in the second printing.

The Oblong or *Landscape Sixteen* (Fig. 14). Here again it is only necessary to memorize the first quarter of the scheme if the preceding simple rules have been learnt. Similar alternatives can be arranged as demonstrated in Fig. 12, but it must be remembered that landscape-shaped pages are being dealt with, and the page in the left lower corner is placed with the head away from the stone-hand.

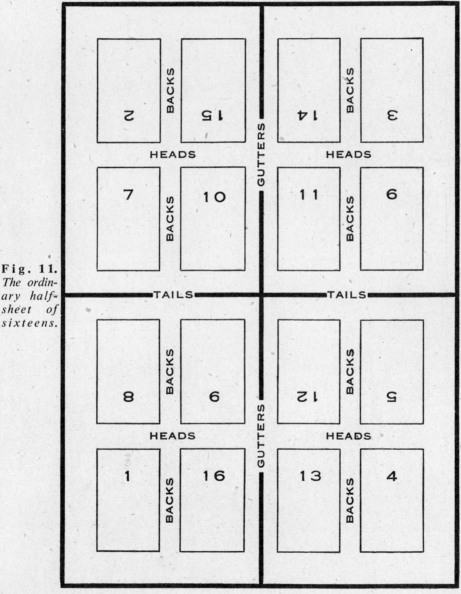

Fig. 11. *The ordinary half-sheet of sixteens.*

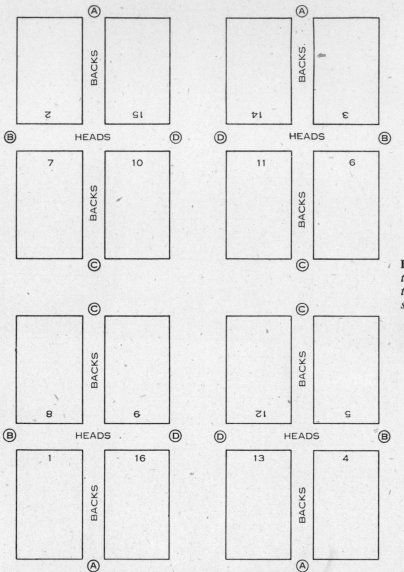

Fig. 12. *Alternative sixteen page schemes (see text).*

The cut is down the centre; gripper edge at the foot of pages 1, 16, 15, 2.

Twelve-page Schemes are not very popular in the composing, machine, or folding departments. For ordinary 12mo (Fig. 15) the pages are arranged in three rows of four.

It should be obvious, even to the learner, that this scheme cannot be backed up in the usual way. In order to avoid the middle four pages backing themselves, the sheet must be turned in its short direction, or as it is often termed—work and tumble. This means that both long edges of the sheet must be fed to the grippers. In order to ensure perfect back-up register, therefore, the stock must be squared and trimmed

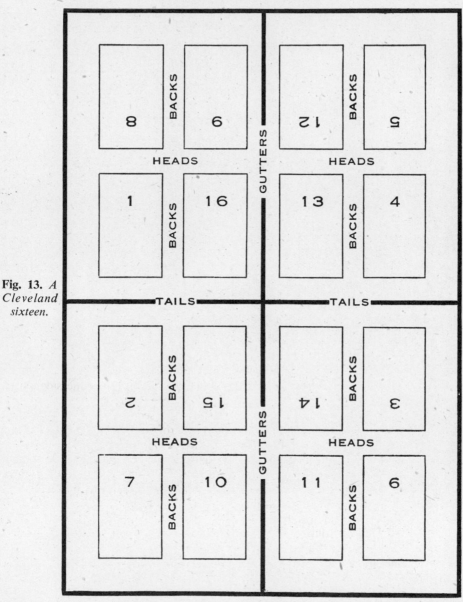

Fig. 13. *A Cleveland sixteen.*

perfectly uniform before printing.

For the scheme in Fig. 15 the side-lay on the machine should be at the sides of pages 3, 10, 9 and 4. It is here that many machine minders—even after long experience—make a blunder. They have become accustomed to centring the print on the paper, which is the normal procedure; but here we have heads at the side-lay and feet at the opposite side of the sheet. Moreover, the first fold (after the sheets have been cut down the middle) is two-thirds down the sheet.

To assist the folders the stone-hand should insert a piece of fine rule between pages 8 and 11 (as indicated in Fig. 15).

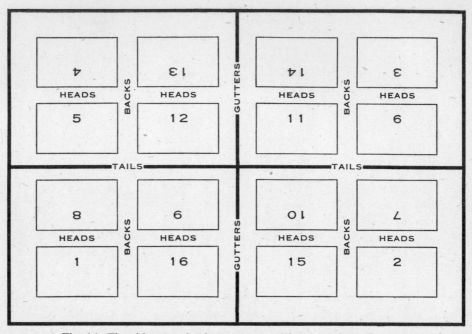

Fig. 14. *The oblong, or landscape sixteen. The cut is down the centre.*

The machine minder, therefore, should make his side-lay just a little (say $1\frac{1}{2}$ points) less than the distance from the head of page 8 to the folding mark. The reason for this is that page 9 will fold in to the rule, and the next fold is to page 11, thus the heads of pages 8 and 11 outset the head margin of page 9 and thereby require just a little extra space. If the stone-hand has made his margins correctly and the paper has been cut accurately, the second fold could be to paper.

The scheme known as "twelve pages with offcut" is easier to understand if it is realized that it folds as an eight and four—the eight being inset into the four.

To the learner who practises the law of association in order to memorize the various schemes, it will be found quite easy to remember. The scheme is arranged as an ordinary eight-page (starting with folio 3) and underneath is the outside four (folios 1, 12, 11 and 2). The sheets are printed one side; tumbled and perfected; cut firstly down the centre and secondly between pages 1 and 3; folded as two sections; and insetted for stitching. The side-lay is usually at the foot of pages 5, 8, 7 and 6. Certain text-books reproduce a scheme which produces the four-page section as pages 5, 6, 7 and 8. This should be avoided, as the binders normally prefer the eight-page as the inner section.

Fig. 16 is the scheme for twelve pages, long 12mo—two out of the short dimension, and six out of the long. This scheme is a tumbler, the reason being that it could not be folded to give one combined fold in the back if worked as an ordinary work and turn. The sheets will be cut across the heads before folding. The side-lay should be at the sides of pages 9 and 10 and of such dimension as to fold in correctly to the folding mark half-way between pages 8 and 11. Thus the job requires three parallel folds: (1) page 9 to 8; (2) page 3 to 2; and (3) page 7 to 6.

Imposition Schemes for Folders are very easy to memorize. They are normally arranged in two rows and the folios start at the left lower corner and are arranged in numerical order until the last folio comes at the side of page 1. They are usually tumblers and, of course, are not trimmed or stitched after folding. The job opens out so that page 1 is read; turn the page and read on for page 2; then unfold the sheet so that pages 2, 3, 4, 5, 6 and 7 are at view; turn the sheet for pages 8, 9, 10, 11 and 12. There are three parallel folds; or the fold may be in the form of a roll fold.

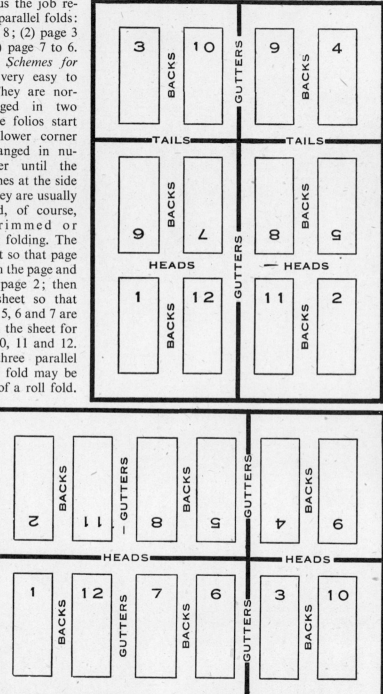

Fig. 15. *(Top) Twelve pages to fold without offcut.*

Fig. 16. *(Right) Twelve pages, long 12mo.*

CHAPTER SIX

PROOFS AND PROOFING

CORRECT METHODS OF PROOFING. PROOF ROLLERS. HAND PRESSES. USE OF TYMPAN AND FRISKET. MODERN DEVELOPMENTS. COMPOSITORS' PRESS. SELF-INKING GALLEY PRESSES. ELECTRIC PROOF PRESSES. SPEEDY PRESS.

THE taking of proofs is an important operation in any composing room; so much so, that in some large printing offices specialist pressmen are employed who are responsible for producing all the proofs.

In the average composing department, however, proofs are taken by the compositors and apprentices as part of the routine work.

The first proof is taken for the reader, who carefully checks the proof from the copy and marks the necessary corrections. In order to facilitate the work of the reader the proof should have the maximum legibility with the minimum of pressure. Too much pressure does not give a true reproduction of the type face. The right amount of ink also must be used; too much will make the proof dirty to handle and will also make more difficult the work of detecting minor errors and battered type which may escape notice until the job is on machine, when corrections become much more expensive.

It is imperative, too, that the type matter be at right-angles to the galley before being tied or quoined up. When type is off its feet the proof shows only one side of the type characters. Such proofs should not be tolerated in any printing office, as they are the result of careless and slipshod workmanship.

For small jobbing work the usual manner of inking is by means of a small hand roller. This consists usually of an iron frame with spindle fitted into a wooden core which is covered with composition, consisting of a mixture of gelatine, glycerine and sugar-house syrup, to a thickness of about $\frac{1}{2}$ in. At the top of the frame is a wooden handle—on larger rollers sometimes two. The roller is used first to distribute the ink on a steel slab and secondly to ink the printing face of the type.

Proof Rolling

The rolling should be done carefully from head to foot or angular fashion, but not sideways. The latter method will cause the type matter to get off its feet. After use, the roller should be hung near at hand. Normally a hook is provided for this purpose beneath the ink slab. Observance of this practice will give the roller a longer working life and prevent flats or distortion.

Ink should not be allowed to dry on the roller. When this happens consistently, the surface accumulates a scaly coating of dried ink and it becomes extremely difficult to obtain a good proof. Inks are now available which will dry on the paper, yet remain moist on the roller for a considerable time. Some roller frames are so made that, when replaced on the slab, the surface of the roller does not rest on it. Near the ink slab and in a convenient position should be placed a fixture for the solvent can, brush, and rag, for cleaning the type immediately after the proof has been taken. Some composing departments have special receptacles for proofing paper of various sizes. These help to prevent the sheets from getting mixed up and being blown about the room (Fig. 1).

So much for the preliminaries to proof pulling. As regards the proofing presses, they are many and varied. The following are some of the most popular types together with their particular advantages:—

The *Hand Press*. While the flat-bed cylinder and rotary presses have superseded the old hand press for producing the bulk of printed matter, the hand press is still retained in many composing departments for proofing purposes. In order to obtain good proofs on a hand press the following points should be observed: the matter for proofing should be placed in the middle of the bed to ensure even pressure. For very small jobs or open rule formes place type-high (·918 in.) bearers at each side to prevent undue pressure and consequent damage both to type face and tympan of press. Roll the forme and place the paper in position on the forme without slurring movement. Bring down the tympan and run the bed under the platen by means of the winding handle. This operation should be done steadily and without jerking the bed, otherwise a slurred proof will result.

Next, pull over the impression handle. This causes the platen to descend and to exert pressure on the tympan (the frame on which the paper is placed),

PROOFING ON THE ALBION HAND PRESS

Fig. 1. *Note that rolling is done angular fashion and the page is centred on the bed. Receptacles are placed conveniently for paper, solvent, brush and rags.*

paper and forme, thereby producing an impression of the inked printing surface. The impression handle is then allowed to return, thereby releasing the pressure; the bed is then wound from under the platen, the tympan raised and the printed sheet lifted from the forme.

Although this may seem a lengthy procedure, it is possible to produce proofs fairly speedily on this type of press. To summarize, it may be said that hand presses, of which the Albion (Fig. 1) and Columbian are typical examples, are satisfactory for small numbers of proofs so long as the impression is accurately adjusted and the tympan is kept in good condition.

A frisket (thin iron frame) should be available for fixing on the tympan, but used only for a short run, say of a two-colour window bill or similar work. The frisket serves to hold the sheet to the tympan, to which it is positioned by means of pins and to lift the sheet from the forme after printing. The frisket also prevents the chase and furniture from marking the sheet.

The *Compositors' Press* is a very handy little press which takes up a minimum of space and can be used for the smaller classes of work, thereby keeping the larger presses free for the work for which they are best suited. The compositors' press can be adjusted for type or galley without the use of a bed-plate. The impression roller is in eccentric bushings which are adjusted very speedily for the particular requirement. The press has a bed measurement of $32\frac{3}{4}$ by $16\frac{1}{2}$ in., the printing surface is 26 by $16\frac{1}{2}$ in.

Self-inking Galley Presses. The modern composing department dealing with many galleys of mechanically composed type matter requires at least one self-

VANDERCOOK PROOF PRESS

Fig. 2. *The old type of proof press is being superseded by the self-inking galley press, such as the above, which is hand operated. The inking carriage is moved quickly from one end of the press to the other. Note the compact arrangement of the inking rollers.*

inking galley press. The old types of galley press with lever and platen pressure or with blanket-covered cylinder and hand rolling, have been superseded by the up-to-date Vandercook (Fig. 2) or Pullman type of self-inking presses.

These presses consist of a bed and two inking slabs—one at each end of the press—an impression cylinder and an inking carriage mounted on an iron stand. There are two sets of racks at each side of the bed; the outer racks are for the impression cylinder and the inner racks for the inking carriage.

A proof is taken by placing a column galley of type on the press; the type is inked by quickly moving the inking carriage, which has

ELECTRIC PROOF PRESS
Fig. 3. *Used chiefly for galley proofs of mechanical composition. Forty proofs a minute can be obtained on the latest models.*

two rollers, from one end of the press to the other. A sheet is laid, the cylinder moved to the opposite end, and the proof taken off by hand. For further proofs repeat the operation, but inking carriage and cylinder are moved in the reverse direction.

Electric Proof Presses (Fig. 3) are now coming into use and these are capable of proofing up to forty proofs a minute, according to the skill of the operator. They are therefore very useful for

news and periodical and similar classes of rush work.

The bed is mounted at a convenient height and is stationary. A touch of a lever at the front of the press starts the motor which operates the rollers and impression cylinder in an endless belt movement; over the type matter on the bed, around, and under the bed completes the cycle. Thus the sheet is laid on the forme, the impression cylinder passes over, the sheet is taken off, the

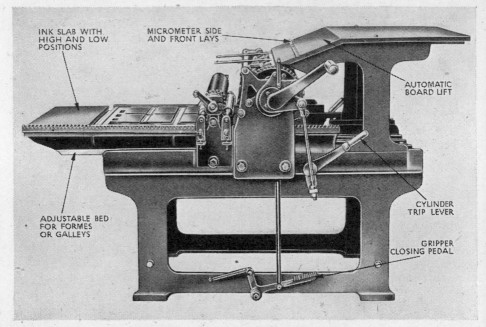

INK SLAB WITH HIGH AND LOW POSITIONS

MICROMETER SIDE AND FRONT LAYS

AUTOMATIC BOARD LIFT

CYLINDER TRIP LEVER

ADJUSTABLE BED FOR FORMES OR GALLEYS

GRIPPER CLOSING PEDAL

VERAX SELF-INKING PROOF PRESS

Fig. 4. The Verax is a modern type of press, suitable for proofing type or blocks with or without a galley. This press is made in two sizes, demy and royal, and can be used for colour work, as very accurate register is obtained in proofing on this press.

rollers pass over, and so the operations proceed.

The *Verax Self-inking Proof Press* (Fig. 4) is a very satisfactory type of press for proofing type or blocks either with or without a galley. The press is on the same principle as the flat-bed cylinder machine: the bed travels left and right, while the cylinder rotates in fixed bearings. The machine is fitted with two large inking rollers surmounted by a steel reciprocating drum. There is also an ink slab providing ample ink distribution for a number of proofs. The rollers and slab can be quickly altered to alternative positions if not required. Sheets are fed in to lays at the top of the cylinder and the grippers are closed by means of the pedal at the foot of the machine. Both side and front lays have micrometer adjustments. This is a great asset when proofing work in two or more colours, when accurate register is essential.

The *Speedy Press* is an ideal press for proofing large formes or for printing short runs. The bed is adjustable as regards height, so that galleys of matter may be proofed as well as ordinary formes. The cylinder travels along the bed to the left for the printing movement and is raised for the return movement. The bed is stationary. The ink slab can be lowered to facilitate the placing and removal of formes. Front and side lays are provided for fine register while for an odd proof the sheet may be laid on the forme. The inking system is ample and simple to operate.

The reader should refer also to Chapter 9, where the subject of proofs and proofing presses is further described and illustrated in connection with letterpress machine work.

CHAPTER SEVEN

COMMERCIAL PRINTING

ORGANIZATION OF ADVERTISING AGENCIES. TRAINING OF LAYOUT MEN. TYPE FACES: CLASSIFICATION AND SPECIMENS. BORDERS AND ORNAMENTS. PRINCIPLES OF DESIGN. TYPOGRAPHICAL HARMONY. TOOLS AND EQUIPMENT. IMPORTANCE OF LAYOUT IN COMPOSING. PREPARING THE LAYOUT. USEFUL RULES. LETTERPRESS POSTERS.

AT the present time there is a growing tendency towards specialization in the printing industry. Newspapers, periodicals, books and office stationery have become to a large extent the products of the specialist firms.

Nevertheless, there is still a wide variety of work available to the general or jobbing printer, and in certain respects he holds one distinct advantage over the news and periodical specialists: he can deal directly with his client. Practically all the big advertisers now deal directly with the advertising agencies who in turn direct the advertising campaigns in their entirety.

Advertising Agencies

The organization of a typical advertising agency is as follows: directors; executive; media; market investigation and planning; statistics; space buying; accounts; copy-writers; creative group; artists and photographers; production; typography; printing; vouchers and dispatch.

Most of the display advertisements in newspapers and periodicals are planned by advertising agencies. The normal method employed in a national Press campaign is for the agency to submit to the client a complete scheme embodying designs, layouts, copy and rates, together with a schedule of press dates for the suggested media in which the advertisements will appear during their yearly or half-yearly bookings.

When the scheme has been finally accepted the first settings are put in hand, this work usually being done by a trade house. Complete proofs of the advertisements are next submitted and upon being passed, moulds or stereos are prepared and dispatched to the various newspaper offices. Thus the same advertisement, duplicated from the original setting, often appears in numerous papers and periodicals.

So far as periodicals are concerned, it is customary also for the agency to write the copy and produce the layouts, the actual setting being done in the composing room of the periodical in which the advertisement is to appear.

By reason of the high standard both in design and typography set by many of our leading advertising agencies, it has become apparent to many general commercial printers concerned with the production of advertisements, folders, stationery, forms, menus, catalogues, booklets and the like, that to justify any claim to be recognized as creative printers, they, too, must have their own layout departments.

Layout Department

Fortunately, there are some compositors—and machine-men, too, for that matter—with a definite flair for design and layout. Progressive employers see to it that such men (and apprentices) are given every encouragement to undertake additional training at technical and art schools. These young men often develop into competent layout men, their practical knowledge of the printing trade serving them in good stead.

Thus it is that nowadays every progressive printing establishment has its own layout department—or, at least craftsmen who are capable of producing finished layout designs for the client and "marked-up" layouts for the compositor. The advantages from this procedure are many. Full use can be made of the type faces and decorative material available in a particular office, and, in addition, it is often the layout—the "blue print" of the printed work—designed by a man who understands the art of sales-producing schemes which result in a satisfied client and a repetition of orders for the printer.

Classification of Type Faces

One of the first considerations in the production of a layout is the selection of a suitable type face or faces. There are no hard and fast rules in this matter of selection, but some knowledge of type designs and their development is essential.

The following notes and a broad classification of some of the present-day type faces will help to simplify matters somewhat for the beginner. It is some consolation for the learner to know that there are so many type faces available today that even the typographical expert will not attempt to name every type face at first sight.

Romans and their Italics

Roman capitals and lower case have been used in printing since about 1465. Small capitals and italic were first made in type about 1500. At first only the italic lower case letters were made and were used with roman capitals. In Venice about 1470, Nicolas Jenson, a Frenchman, improved the existing romans, and derivatives of his types,

known as Venetians, are still in use. Two examples are:—

Cloister Old Style *with its Italic* Linotype Venezia *with its Italic*

In the eighteenth century, Giambattista Bodoni, an Italian printer, produced a different style of roman. Up to that time all roman types were known as old style, the lower-case letters being modelled after the writing of that day. Bodoni changed the sloping, bracketed serifs, the oval terminators, and oblique emphasis of the strokes and gave them fine serifs with little or nothing in the way of brackets, well-rounded terminators, and vertical emphasis. This resulted in a style more precise and formal than the old style and became known—and is still known—as modern. The following is a modern roman:—

Bodoni and *Bodoni Italic*

During the nineteenth century, English, Scottish and American typefounders slightly altered the above Bodoni, giving the straight serifs a slight bracket. One of these transitional faces is

Linotype Scotch Roman *with its Italic*

About the year 1726, William Caslon, the famous British typefounder, cut the punches for his pica (12 point) Caslon Old Face. Other sizes quickly followed and became very popular. Although the moderns caused its temporary eclipse, Caslon was soon revived, and is today popular in Britain and in America. Caslon Old Face is a suitable type for practically all classes of work, but is at its best when printed on an antique laid or antique wove paper.

Caslon Old Face *with its Italic*

The following are a few of the many romans available on the mechanical composing machines, and suitable for bookwork, periodicals, folders, and similar work. In the larger sizes they are also used for display work. The size of the following specimens is 10 point.

BASKERVILLE *(Monotype)*

NOTHING, perhaps, astonishes one more upon closely examining many of these earliest printed works than the remarkable or, one might almost say, *wonderful regularity* of the type in body, height,

PLANTIN *(Monotype)*

NOTHING, perhaps, astonishes one more upon closely examining many of these earliest printed works than the remarkable or, one might almost say, *wonderful regularity* of the type in body, height,

GARAMOND *(Monotype)*

NOTHING, perhaps, astonishes one more upon closely examining many of these earliest printed works than the remarkable or, one might almost say, *wonderful regularity* of the type in body, height,

ALDINE BEMBO *(Monotype)*

NOTHING, perhaps, astonishes one more upon closely examining many of these earliest printed works than the remarkable or, one might almost say, *wonderful regularity* of the type in body, height, and line, and if

PERPETUA *(Monotype)*

NOTHING, perhaps, astonishes one more upon closely examining many of these earliest printed works than the remarkable or, one might almost say, *wonderful regularity* of the type in body, height, and line, and if anything

GOUDY OLD STYLE *(Monotype)*

NOTHING, perhaps, astonishes one more upon closely examining many of these earliest printed works than the remarkable or, one might almost say, *wonderful regularity* of the type in

ESTIENNE *(Linotype)*

NOTHING, perhaps, astonishes one more upon closely examining many of these earliest printed works than the remarkable or, one might almost say, *wonderful regularity* of the type in body, height, and line, and if any

GRANJON *(Linotype)*

NOTHING, perhaps, astonishes one more upon closely examining many of these earliest printed works than the remarkable or, one might almost say, *wonderful regularity* of the type in body, height, and line

BOOKPRINT *(Linotype)*

NOTHING, perhaps, astonishes one more upon closely examining many of these earliest printed works than the remarkable or, one might almost say, *wonderful regularity* of the type in body, height,

GEORGIAN *(Linotype)*

NOTHING, perhaps, astonishes one more upon closely examining many of these earliest printed works than the remarkable or, one might almost say, *wonderful regularity* of the type in body, height,

KENNTONIAN *(Intertype)*

NOTHING, perhaps, astonishes one more upon closely examining many of these earliest printed works than the remarkable or, one might almost say, *wonderful regularity* of the type in body, height,

EGMONT *(Intertype)*

NOTHING, perhaps, astonishes one more upon closely examining many of these earliest printed works than the remarkable or, one might almost say, *wonderful regularity* of the type in body, height,

BOOKFACE *(Intertype)*

NOTHING, perhaps, astonishes one more upon closely examining many of these earliest printed works than the remarkable or, one might almost say, *wonderful regularity* of the type in body, height,

Sans Serifs and their Italics

As the name implies, sans serif types have no serifs, and the recent designs have enjoyed an enormous popularity in display work. Sans serif types are about a hundred years old, and were probably first cut on wood for posters. The early sans serifs were monotonous and lacked proportion. The modern versions, while retaining the two characteristics— uniformity in thickness of strokes and absence of serifs—have been made much more attractive by varying the configuration and widths of the letters.

The following is a selection of contemporary sans serifs:—

Gill Medium Sans Serif

Gill Medium Sans Serif Italic
Monotype

Metromedium

Metromedium Italic
Linotype

Vogue Light and **Vogue Bold**
Intertype

Tempo Medium

Tempo Medium Italic
Ludlow

Cable Bold

Erbar Medium

Erbar Medium Italic
Soldans, Ltd.

Egyptians

Like the sans serifs the present-day Egyptians are a re-designed version of types which appeared over a hundred years ago. The main characteristics are the slab-shaped serifs, and the uniform thickness of the strokes. They have attained an appreciable amount of popularity in advertising and general display work. The following is a representative selection of modern Egyptian:—

Rockwell Medium
Monotype

Memphis Medium
Linotype

Cairo Light
Intertype

Karnak Intermediate
Ludlow

Beton Bold
Soldans, Ltd.

Scripts

Script types are more or less imitations of different styles of handwriting.

Because of the slope of the letters, the long flourishing ascenders and descenders, and the necessity for joining up the letters to imitate handwriting, the formal scripts are usually cast on special bodies.

Special spaces are also required and are cast with bodies similar to the type. There are also suitably shaped quads for the start and finish of each line. Script types require careful handling so as to avoid damaging the kerns. They still find uses in certain classes of work such as law printing and receipt forms, but have been largely superseded by the modern scripts, which are much in demand by certain advertisers. When used sparingly, say for the main lines in advertisements, letter-headings, menus and booklets, and with a suitable roman, they are very effective and often give a sparkle and liveliness to a typographical display. Many of the modern scripts are cast on bodies which are similar to ordinary types.

The following is a selection of formal and modern scripts:—

Palace   *Society*
Stephenson, Blake & Co., Ltd.

Bernhard Cursive, Bold
Soldans, Ltd.

Mandate   **Hauser**
Ludlow   Ludlow

Mayfair Cursive   *Coronet*
Ludlow   Ludlow

Temple   *Mercury*
Monotype   Stevens, Shanks & Sons, Ltd.

Samson   *Trafton*
Soldans, Ltd.   Soldans, Ltd.

Allegro   *Ariston*
Soldans, Ltd.   Continental

Gillies Gothic   *Legend*
Soldans, Ltd.   Soldans, Ltd.

BODONI BOLD abcd
Monotype

ELEGANT INLINE C
Caslon

ULTRA BODONI
Monotype

CORVINUS LIGHT abcdef
Soldans, Ltd.

GILL SANS Bold ab
Monotype

CORVINUS MEDIUMab
Soldans, Ltd.

ROCKWELL abcde
Monotype

CORVINUS BOLD bcd
Soldans, Ltd.

TIMES ROMAN ab
Linotype and Monotype

ERBAR BOLD abcdef
Soldans, Ltd.

TIMES BOLD abcde
Linotype and Monotype

NEULAND 34567
Soldans, Ltd.

LOCARNO abcdefghijkl
Soldans, Ltd.

BETON BOLD abcde
Soldans, Ltd.

BERNHARD BOLD ab
Soldans, Ltd.

CAMPANILE abcdefghijklmnopqrs
Ludlow

TEMPO INLINE AB
Ludlow

PLAYBILL abcdefghijklmn
Stephenson, Blake & Co., Ltd.

GOTHIC CONDENSED abcdefghij
Ludlow

SLIM BLACK ABCDEFGHIJKL
Soldans, Ltd.

KARNAK OBELISK abcdefghijklmno
Ludlow

METROPOLIS ab
Caslon

NICOLAS JENSON B.
Ludlow

PRISMA 123457
Soldans, Ltd.

STELLAR abcdefghijklmnopq
Ludlow

LYDIAN abcdefghijklm
American Type Founders Co.

EDEN LIGHT abcdefghijk
Ludlow

CARTOON LIGHT A
Soldans, Ltd.

OLD FACE OPEN
Stephenson, Blake & Co., Ltd.

DISPLAY TYPE FACES

There are hundreds of type faces available for commercial printing. The above is a representative selection of display faces in general use at the present time, but fashions in typography are constantly changing, and new type faces are always being designed.

Ludlow Borders

Milled Rules

Continuous Borders (Monotype)

Rules

18th Century Borders (S. B. & Co.)

Monotype Borders

ORNAMENTS AND BORDERS

The above selection gives some indication of the wide range of ornamental material available to the typographical designer. By means of a combination of various borders a great variety of artistic effects may be readily obtained.

Gothic Type Faces

Gothic (Old English), or Text, as it is often termed, has been used since the earliest days of printing from movable types. It was copied from the calligraphy of early manuscripts.

Nowadays, Gothic type is still considered suitable for occasional display lines when the work is of an ecclesiastical nature, or when suggested by harmony of period or subject. Legal printing of certain kinds also calls for occasional words or lines in Gothic type. The following is a selection of Gothics:—

Tudor Black   **Abbey Text**
Stephenson, Blake & Co., Ltd.

Ancient Black   **Saxon Black**
Stephenson, Blake & Co., Ltd.

Washington Text   **Festival Text**
Stephenson, Blake & Co., Ltd.

Cloister Black   **Ye Carton Black**
C. W. Shortt & Co., Ltd.   Stevens, Shanks & Sons, Ltd.

Minster Black   **Old English**
Stevens, Shanks & Sons, Ltd.

While it would be misleading to claim that a knowledge or study of general principles will ensure success as a typographical designer, there is no doubt that they are a valuable aid to the full understanding of these principles.

Principles of Design

Good design, whether it be in printing or building or clothing, depends upon the knowledge and application of certain general principles, such as proportion, balance, harmony, contrast, and fitness for purpose.

It is necessary also for the layout man to be expert in copying the numerous type faces. This is not so very important if the layout is for the compositor, because all he requires for his work is the general plan, indicating type sizes and faces and allocations of white space; but when the layout is for the client, markings showing type sizes and other particulars are not necessary. The sketch should be a clear indication of the appearance of the finished job.

The student who would master the art of letter design will find much useful information and the ideal introduction to the subject in Edward Johnston's *Writing and Illuminating and Lettering*, which is in most reference libraries.

Proportion. As applied to typographical design, proportion may be defined as the relation of width to length, or area to area. Good proportion is important at the start in planning the shape of the page. For economic reasons it is customary to work to definite subdivisions of paper for many classes of work. It will be found that some of the subdivisions are more pleasing to the eye than others. Those sizes which have a ratio of approximately three to five (as regards width and length) will generally prove to be the most attractive. A size such as crown square 12mo would be unattractive. There is no proportion where the dimensions are equal. Good proportion can be defined as a pleasing inequality in the parts of a whole.

Even if the shape of the page or section of a page has been pre-determined, the margins can still be allocated according to the rules of good proportion. If a border is used, therefore, allocate the white space inside and outside the border with discrimination. Do not have uniform margins. Whether the greater margin goes inside or outside the border depends on the job; but in the majority of cases it is placed outside. Correct proportions for bookwork margins are illustrated in Chapter 4.

The placing of the main display features; deciding the sizes of types, groups, panels or other parts of the page; allocating the white space: all these affect the proportion of the general design.

It is advisable, therefore, to avoid

equal masses, margins or groupings, and to cultivate, by study, a critical eye so as to appreciate the differences from mechanically considered ratios.

The average learner finds that the correct balance between type matter and white space is a most elusive subject to master and he is often exasperated when his first proofs are marked with apparently unimportant transpositions of spacing—sometimes involving very small changes. But these alterations of a point or so often make all the difference between a first-class or second-class result.

Vertical balance, or balance from top to bottom, may be determined mathematically. This method is not necessary or desirable to the trained craftsman, but is an interesting approach to the subject for those who are eager to train the eye.

The tone value of the printed matter must be taken into consideration, as darker tones have normally a greater attraction than the lighter tones, and are, therefore, for purposes of balance, heavier (Figs. 1 and 2).

Typographical Harmony

Harmony is achieved when types, initials, decorative elements, borders, illustrations, and all the other elements in the design, including the stock on which the job is printed, combine to form a harmonious whole (Figs. 3 and 4).

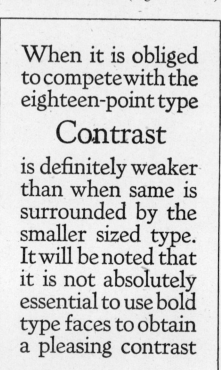

Gulliver among the Lilliputians was a colossus; in Brobdingnag he was equally noticeable as a dwarf. It is by comparison that objects assume size or smallness, that they are distinguishable from their surroundings. The knowledge of this fact is the key to arresting and stimulating display. Twenty-four-point type by

Contrast

with eight-point has far more effect than it has when it is surrounded by the eighteen-point. A comparison of these two settings should convince anyone that display does not depend on mere grossness, but upon contrast in type sizes. A further contrast is gained between type and its surrounding white space. The greater the white space in a job, the greater is the opportunity for getting contrast. A vital principle of type display, and probably the one most abused, is Contrast. When employed, great skill and judgment are necessary; attain harmony first, and then proceed to be elegantly bold, not blustering.

When it is obliged to compete with the eighteen-point type

Contrast

is definitely weaker than when same is surrounded by the smaller sized type. It will be noted that it is not absolutely essential to use bold type faces to obtain a pleasing contrast

CONTRAST IN TYPOGRAPHY

Fig. 1. *It is by judicious variations in size, as well as in the character of type face, that contrast in typography is most effectively obtained, as shown in the above examples.*

TONE VARIATION IN DISPLAY WORK

Fig. 2. *A wide range of effect can be produced by the use of tone variation. The light tone is an effective contrast to the bold tone, which is often preferred for commercial work.*

Type combinations which produce disagreeable contrasts should always be avoided. For example, types such as Bodoni, with their precise mechanical appearance, should not be used in conjunction with old-face types such as Caslon.

Condensed type faces look best on narrow pages, while extended type faces require a wider page; types of normal width harmonize as regards shape harmony on any well-proportioned page. While this does not necessarily mean that a narrow page *must* have a narrow-set type or that a landscape-shaped job *must* have an extended type, it does suggest that the shape of a page assists in the selection of the shape of the type.

With regard to initial letters it is a safe rule to use a larger size of the same series as used in the text matter. If an ornamental initial is preferred, the actual letter inside the decoration should harmonize with the text. The alignment of initial letters with text matter, both vertically and horizontally, should ignore the serifs; and it is important that the foot of the initial letter should align exactly with the lowest line of the text which it covers. The initial M in the word Menu in Fig. 4 partly demonstrates this particular point.

It is largely a matter of opinion as to which produces the more effective appearance—tone harmony or contrast in tones. Those with æsthetic tastes usually

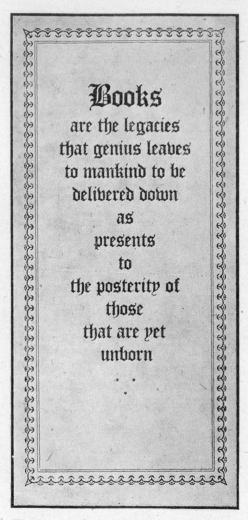

𝕭ooks
are the legacies
that genius leaves
to mankind to be
delivered down
as
presents
to
the posterity of
those
that are yet
unborn

Fig. 3. *A good example of typographical harmony. In the original, printed on toned paper, the inner plain border was worked in red.*

prefer that all the elements in the design shall blend into an even tone. The average advertiser, however, is generally in favour of contrast.

Guiding Principles

Here are a few guides which should help the would-be typographer to attain good results.

While the shape harmony of borders and initials is important, the tone value should also be taken into consideration. Too often is the border or initial allowed to distract the eye from the main message; they should blend with or be a subordinate part of the composition. It is on this point that some clever artist-designers, successful in other respects, fail to achieve the best results. They allow their artistic expression full scope and put all their skill and individuality into the design of borders and ornamentation, but they treat the type matter as more or less of secondary importance.

Underlining of words or lines does not always succeed in giving the desired emphasis, but if underlining is used the rules should be of the same weight as the main strokes of the letters they are to be placed beneath.

Symmetry and Asymmetry

When a design is so arranged that, when folded down the centre, both halves are equal in shape, then it is symmetrical with respect to the dividing line.

When a design is so arranged that all the lines are either full out or centred in the measure, then that design is symmetrical with respect to its vertical axis. This is often a popular arrangement for many classes of work and is usually termed the centred style (Fig. 3).

There is one danger, however, especially to the learner, and that is the tendency to force wording into a design symmetrical with respect to its horizontal axis. The result is invariably very unsatisfactory.

Asymmetry simply means a lack of symmetry, and is obtained by placing the type groups *irregularly* with regard to the vertical axis. The resultant designs are often more interesting; and, if executed with skill, there is a liveliness and movement which is frequently absent in symmetrical display (Fig. 4).

The following items may be considered as the minimum of equipment for the layout man in a medium-sized printing establishment: a desk or table about 5 ft. by 3 ft. and an adjustable sloping drawing-board with T-square long enough to extend beyond the board; a 60 deg. 12-in. celluloid set-square; a steel type-rule; one pair of needle-point dividers; a boxwood rule with bevelled edges; a magnifying glass and a reducing glass. In addition to type books, it is necessary to have a box-file of type specimen sheets and proofs of all borders and decorative material. The jobbing and display type specimens should show the complete alphabet, with figures in roman and italic, and a line or so of words in caps, small caps and lower case; the text or body faces should consist of at least a dozen or so lines of each face and size.

The layout man's equipment must also include a selection of coloured pencils and crayons, and ordinary pencils of varying degrees of hardness; poster colours; tubes of process white and Indian drawing inks; lettering pens; indiarubber and ink-eraser; scissors. A rubber solution (made by P. B. Cow & Co., Ltd.) is universally used by typographers and artists as an adhesive, because any paper so treated will never cockle.

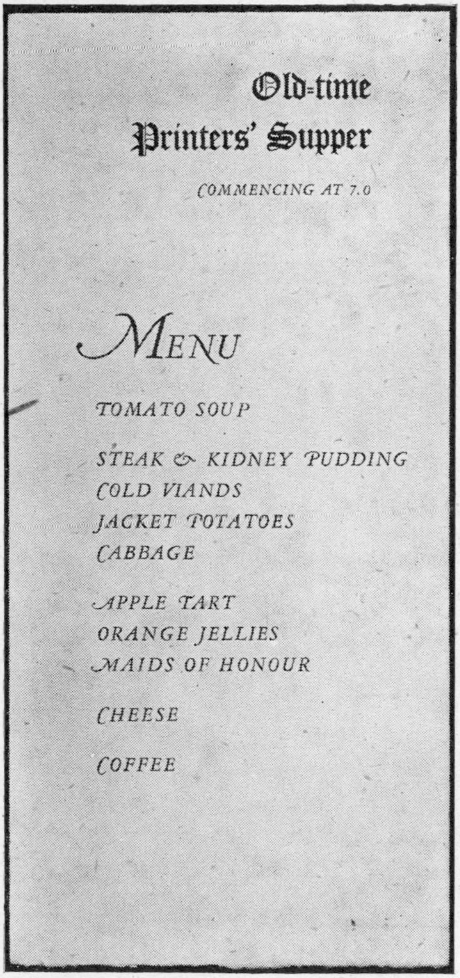

In addition to the above, samples of paper and cover stocks will be required to suit the various classes of work. Thin bank or other semi-transparent paper will enable tracings to be made, and graph paper may prove useful for catalogue work in cases where many small blocks have to be incorporated. When the layout is for the client, however, the layout is invariably done on a light-weight cartridge paper, because in many cases the actual stock will not "take" a pen or a brush. A sample of the actual stock, however, is submitted, together

Old-time Printers' Supper

COMMENCING AT 7.0

Menu

TOMATO SOUP

STEAK & KIDNEY PUDDING
COLD VIANDS
JACKET POTATOES
CABBAGE

APPLE TART
ORANGE JELLIES
MAIDS OF HONOUR

CHEESE

COFFEE

Fig. 4. *A pleasing contrast of type faces. The words set in Gothic type were printed in red in the original menu.*

with the layout and estimate of the cost of the completed job.

A small hand guillotine is a useful addition to the layout man's equipment.

An accurately sketched layout avoids any uncertainty as regards result. The finished work is visualized from the start, and any alterations by clients or others can be arranged before actual composition begins. As all the type faces and sizes are indicated, considerable

LONDON COUNTY COUNCIL
LONDON SCHOOL OF PRINTING AND KINDRED TRADES
61 Stamford Street, Blackfriars, London, S.E.1

ANNUAL EXHIBITION 1945

including examples of

Hand and Machine Composition, Layout and Design
Lettering, Letterpress, Lithographic and Photogravure
Printing, Photo-Lithography, Bookbinding, Marbling
Ruling, Electrotyping and Stereotyping. Also exhibits
demonstrating the applications of Science to printing

Monday, 2nd July, to Saturday, 7th July, 1945

9 a.m. to 5 p.m. daily; Saturday 9 to 12

All interested in printing are invited to attend   ELLIS THIRKETTLE, *Principal*

AN EFFECTIVE INVITATION CARD

Fig. 5. *The above invitation card, in which the main heading and border in the original were printed in red, is an example of economy in type faces and of effective spacing.*

saving of time in setting is effected. If borders or ornaments are required these are indicated together with their dimensions. In the case of a rush job, the layout copy may be cut up, and two or more compositors may work on the same job and still produce the work as originally planned.

Another important point: a displayed layout can be given to compositors who have little or no creative ability. In other words, compositors who may be very efficient craftsmen so far as intricate tabular work, make-up and imposition are concerned can be given high-class display work without danger of lowering the standard of design.

To summarize, the layout reduces the risk of extensive alterations after the first setting has been made, and thereby avoids the extra charges likely to be incurred for corrections (Fig. 7).

Preparing the Layout

The following rules in connection with layouts based on long experience will be of assistance to the beginner.

1. Study the copy. Determine features which are to be the principal and subordinate.

2. Sketch a few very rough layouts (or visuals), showing different ideas for general treatment. These need not be actual size—although some typographers prefer this—and, for an ordinary advertisement, need only take about five minutes.

3. Decide which sketch is most effective for the job, then draw the layout to actual size, and on suitable stock.

Graph paper may be preferable if the layout is for the typesetting machine operator.

4. Sketch in the main display lines, using very fine guide lines in order to keep the lettering neat and straight. Keep roman upright and italics and scripts at the correct slant. If the layout is done in the composing department the main display lines may be set up, and a proof taken and stuck up in position.

5. If using plain rule borders, draw these in; but if using ornamental border, it is advisable to paste on a section from a proof. Actual dimensions of borders must be shown.

6. Indicate the space to be occupied by the body or text matter by cutting up and pasting down a proof of the size and face of type selected; or by means of short wavy lines to represent words; or by other methods which vary according to the custom of the house.

7. The copy for the body matter should not be written on the layout, but is typed on separate sheets headed COPY, and lettered or numbered to coincide with letters or numbers on the layout.

8. Ring round all instructions on the working layout to prevent them from being taken for copy.

In dealing with catalogues, folders and brochures, it is always advisable to

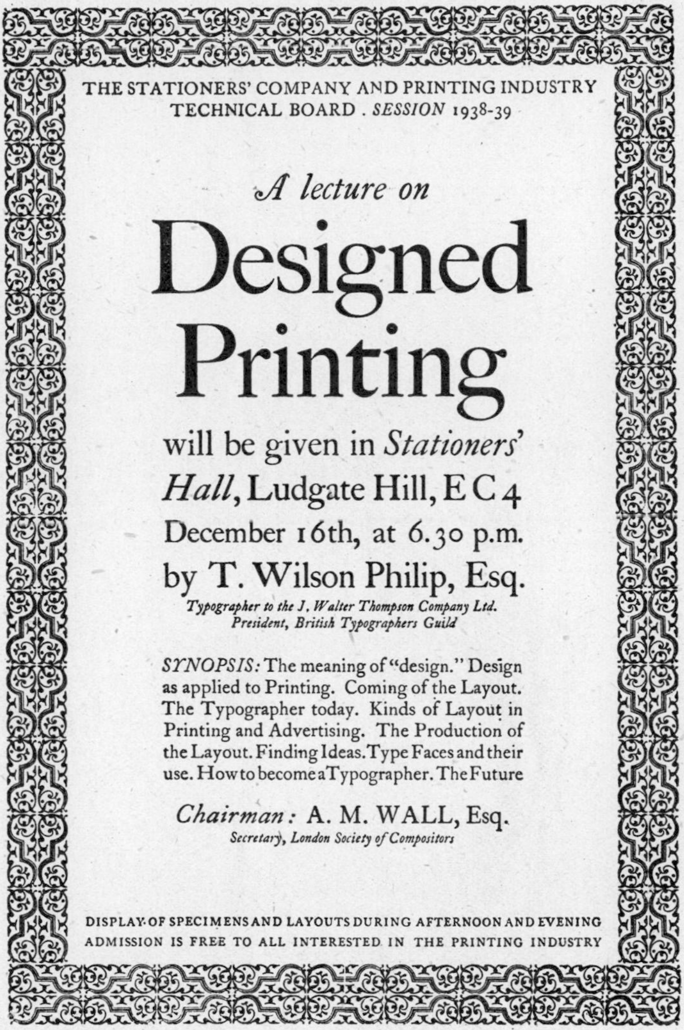

THE STATIONERS' COMPANY AND PRINTING INDUSTRY
TECHNICAL BOARD . *SESSION* 1938-39

A lecture on

Designed Printing

will be given in *Stationers' Hall*, Ludgate Hill, E C 4
December 16th, at 6.30 p.m.
by T. Wilson Philip, Esq.

Typographer to the J. Walter Thompson Company Ltd.
President, British Typographers Guild

SYNOPSIS: The meaning of "design." Design as applied to Printing. Coming of the Layout. The Typographer today. Kinds of Layout in Printing and Advertising. The Production of the Layout. Finding Ideas. Type Faces and their use. How to become a Typographer. The Future

Chairman: A. M. WALL, Esq.
Secretary, London Society of Compositors

DISPLAY OF SPECIMENS AND LAYOUTS DURING AFTERNOON AND EVENING
ADMISSION IS FREE TO ALL INTERESTED IN THE PRINTING INDUSTRY

Fig. 6. *Set in Caslon Old Face, with an appropriate border, this handbill is an admirable example of Designed Printing. The measurements of the border in the original were* $5\frac{1}{2} \times 8\frac{1}{2}$ *in.*

LAYOUT FOR SET OF STATIONERY
Fig. 7. *Showing a series of rough layout sketches for
letter-heading, statement, receipt form, post-card and business card.*

make up a dummy. The procedure is briefly as follows:—

1. Stitch or sew the required number of sections together with the cover, and trim to the size required. Use the stock which is intended for the printing of the job.
2. Design the cover, using the colours intended for printing.
3. Sketch the layout showing margins for at least one pair of facing pages.
4. Indicate the positions of illustrations and advertisements and the style of make-up.
5. If there are numerous illustrations, it may be advisable to make a complete layout for each page.

The dummy is indispensable to the compositor and stone-hand for measures, type faces and sizes, for make-up, and for making margins in the formes. It is also useful to the machine-man, as a colour guide for the cover design; to the binding department as showing the method of sewing and stitching; and (very important) to the cutter, who thus has a guide as to the margins required on the finished work.

Letterpress Posters

Letterpress posters are an effective and popular means of conveying messages to the general public. Prominent amongst the regular clients for this class of work are theatres, cinemas and auctioneers. But a glance over the hoardings will show that many others use this means of advertising—including printers themselves.

The jobbing printer has a section of the composing room specially planned and equipped for the production of posters. Heavy founts of metal types, say from 48 to 72 point are required. The ordinary cases are not suitable because of their limited capacity and the inconvenience and damage in setting and distribution. Special cases are used in which the letters are kept upright and in lines divided by movable strips of wood which slot into grooves at the sides. Similar cases and shelves are used also for the founts of wood letter, which vary in size from approximately 6 line (or 72 point) to 75 line (nearly 13 in.).

The material for spacing and justifying the lines is kept in handy receptacles. Ample space is required, too, as regards imposing surfaces because posters are usually of double crown size or multiples thereof, the poster being produced in sections termed sheets. Thus an eight-sheet double crown poster would consist of eight formes each of double crown size or four formes of quad crown.

The left-hand sections are printed with a margin of about 4 ems at the right to allow the overlap of the right-hand section. Likewise allowance must be made for the lower sections to overlap the upper sheets. Occasionally large wooden letters must be cut through vertically so that the parts may print on separate sheets and appear as one when pasted up.

The planning of posters so far as sketches or layout is concerned is nearly always done by the compositor responsible for the setting. He sketches a few miniature visuals, decides on the general layout, then proceeds to assemble the main display lines either in long wooden composing sticks, or direct on to the imposing surface.

When large numbers of posters are dealt with it is advisable to have a separate poster room complete with full series of poster types, imposing surfaces, forme racks, and a cylinder proofing press for proofing and short runs. Some well-organized printing houses go still further and have a large letterpress machine installed in the poster room, thus saving transport of formes from one part of the works to another.

CHAPTER EIGHT

THE READING DEPARTMENT

AIDS TO GOOD READING. QUALIFICATIONS OF THE READER. CORRECTION MARKS EXPLAINED. REVISES AND PRESS PROOFS. REFERENCE LITERATURE. PUNCTUATION: RULES AND EXAMPLES. USE OF THE HYPHEN. COMPOUND WORDS.

IN an up-to-date printing office equal care is given to the planning of the reading department as to the other departments. It should be situated in close proximity to the composing room, but isolated enough to be free from the noises caused by the locking-up and planing down of formes or the running of mechanical composing machines.

The reader should be provided with a desk large enough to accommodate the full sheets which he will be called upon to read and revise. Reading entails a great strain on the eyes, therefore the lighting should be of the best. In short, the conditions should be such that the reader can concentrate his attention on his work without physical discomfort or irritation. This last word brings to mind an additional point: no one should be allowed to interrupt a reader unnecessarily. Many mistakes occur in print simply because the reader has been rushed or interrupted during the course of his exacting duties.

The reader must also be provided with a capable assistant to read the copy while he checks the proof and makes the appropriate marks. It is the practice in some offices for the composing apprentices to serve six months or so as reading boys. The boys thereby gain first-hand experience in spelling, punctuation and the style of the house.

Generally speaking, the reader is responsible for ensuring that the finished job corresponds with the original copy, and also for seeing that the style of the house has been followed. He must mark all errors of spelling, grammar, and typographical slips. In addition, he must check illustrations, impositions, imprints and, if necessary, call attention to anything which may possibly be of a libellous nature.

The qualifications for a good reader may be summarized as follows: he must be a man of proved ability as regards English, spelling, grammatical construction, punctuation, word division, and, in addition, have unlimited patience and a capacity for thoroughness in all he does.

The Association of Correctors of the Press and the Provincial Guild of Printers' Readers have instituted entrance examinations with a view to encouraging aspirants to the reading desk to study the necessary subjects.

Reader's Correction Marks

The reader marks his corrections on the rough (or reader's) proof, usually in red ink. The correction marks, written in the margin, are placed in horizontal alignment with the lines to which they refer, and in the right or left margin, according to the position of the corrections from the centre of the text. When there are two or more corrections in one line, the marginal marks should be placed so that they read from left to right, and each correction is separated by a diagonal stroke. The full point, colon, and leader (..) are encircled in order to distinguish them from the comma, semi-colon and ellipsis respectively. When letters or words are to be altered, these are struck through on the proof and the letters or words to be substituted are written in the margin, followed in each case by a diagonal stroke. For ordinary run-on matter it is not advisable to link up the marginal mark to the text mark.

A list of symbols used by readers for proof marking, together with their meanings, and also the corresponding marks in the text is shown on pages 92 and 93; and a page marked for correction by the reader is given on page 94. The same page, with the reader's corrections carried out, is shown on page 95.

The reader always signs and dates the marked proof. If the words *Show revise* are added it means that a further proof must be submitted to him after the corrections have been made, so that he may revise the work.

The word *Press* means that the sheet or job is ready to print off. *Clean proof* indicates that a clean proof is required. If more than one, the number is stated.

Generally speaking, only matter actually to be printed should be written on the proof. If comments or general instructions are written on the proof they should be encircled and headed by the words *To printer* (underlined).

Reference Literature. The following books should be available for reference in all reading departments: *The Concise Oxford Dictionary*, edited by H. W. and F. G. Fowler; *A Dictionary of Modern English Usage*, by H. W. Fowler; *The King's English*, by H. W. and F. G. Fowler; *Authors' and Printers' Dictionary*, by F. Howard Collins; *Rules for Compositors and Readers at the University Press, Oxford*, by Horace Hart, M.A.

In addition to the above, reference books should be available dealing with the specialized and technical matter relating to the special classes of work undertaken by a particular firm.

Readers find it advantageous to keep a book in which to note in alphabetical arrangement all items which they consider may be of assistance to them in their work, and most readers acquire in course of time quite a valuable collection of reference books.

Many readers have a useful working knowledge of modern languages, and some readers can even check the work of scholars in the classical languages.

Tributes to the reader for his invaluable assistance have frequently been paid by authors, including many whose names are household words.

Punctuation

Punctuation may be defined as the art of making a written or printed passage more intelligible to the reader. There is a tendency with many writers to over-punctuate. Then again, there are others who are either in too much of a hurry to include the points of punctuation, or feel it desirable to rely on the skill of the compositor and the printer's reader.

The compositor, of course, follows copy for punctuation when the copy has first passed through the reader's hands, or when the author has so instructed. Some authors are very particular in this.

The following brief notes on punctuation are included primarily for the guidance of young compositors.

The *full point* (or *period*) is used to mark the end of a sentence and to denote an abbreviated word. Some offices omit the full point after such contractions as *Mr* and *Dr* (for doctor). The style of the house must be observed, however, in this connection. The full point should not be used after roman numerals or symbols, e.g. MCMXLV, 4to, 3rd, except at the end of a sentence. Full points should not be used at the ends of display lines, neither should they appear on titles, half-titles, or headings in books.

Marginal mark	Meaning	Corresponding marks in the text
ℛ	Delete (take out)	Strike through words or letters to be taken out
ℛ̰	Delete and close up	Strike through and place ⊃ above and below words or letters to be taken out
#λ	Insert space	Caret mark ⋏ in required position
·stet	Leave as printed	Dots under letters or words which are to remain
caps	Change to capital letters	Three lines under letters or words to be altered
s.c.	Change to small capitals	Two lines under letters or words to be altered
caps & s.c.	Use capital letters for initial letters and small capitals for remainder of words	Three lines under initial letters and two lines under remainder of the words
l.c.	Change to lower case	Encircle letters to be changed
bold or clar	Change to bold type	Wavy line under letters or words to be altered
ital.	Change to italics	Line under letters or words affected
rom.	Change to roman type	Encircle words to be altered
w.f.	Wrong fount—replace by letter of correct fount	Encircle letter to be altered
ꝺ	Inverted type	Encircle letter to be altered
×	Broken letter—replace by undamaged character	Encircle letter to be altered
eq #	Make spacing equal	∟ between words
less #	Reduce space	∟ between words
trs.	Transpose the order of letters or words	∟⎴ between letters or words (numbering when necessary)
□λ	Indent one em	
‖	Correct the vertical alignment	As marginal mark
＝	Straighten lines	As marginal mark, drawn through lines to be straightened

Marginal mark	*Meaning*	*Corresponding marks in the text*
⊥	Push down space	Encircle space affected
n.p.	Begin a new paragraph	[before first word of new paragraph
run on	No fresh paragraph here	Connecting line between paragraphs
spell out	The abbreviation or figure to be spelt out in full	Encircle words or figures to be altered
out – see copy	Insert omitted portion of copy	Caret mark ⋏ in required position
⊙/	Insert full point	" "
,/	Insert comma	" "
(:)/	Insert colon	" "
;/	Insert semicolon	" "
-/	Insert hyphen	" "
?/	Insert interrogation mark	" "
em/	Insert one-em rule	" "
en/	Insert one-en rule	" "
!/	Insert exclamation mark	" "
ʼ/	Insert apostrophe	" "
²/	Insert superior figure	" "
₂/	Insert inferior figure	" "
“/ ”/	Insert quotation marks	" "
(...)/	Insert a three-dot leader	" "
(/)/	Insert a shilling stroke	" "
(?)	Refer to appropriate authority	Encircle words, etc., affected
(/)	Insert parentheses	Caret marks in required positions
[/]	Insert brackets	" "
fi	Use ligature (fi) instead of separate letters	⌒ enclosing letters concerned
æ	Use diphthong (æ) instead of separate letters	" "

caps/   LIKE MOST authors, I am so greatly indebted to the   *b/ #/*

          printer and his reader for their work and help in the   *l*

l.c.   production of my Books, that I cannot point out their

          weaknesses without some stings of remorse for my   *x*

          ingratitude. Besides, an author is not a fair judge of

w.f.   a printer, because the author himself spoils the printers   *y*

⊙/   work/ This arises from the fact that the main difference   *e/ r/*

          between a well-printed page and an ill printed one

n/   lies in the evenness of the block of colour presented by

⊙ #   *I/*   the letterpress if the justification is made solely to

          comply/with/some/office/rule/against/dividing/words   *eq.#*

          at the end of a line, or if the spaces between the sen-

t/   ences are made as long as possible, or if the page is

⊙   is leaded, and the type kept small, so as to make the

‖   ‖white the [feature] chief instead of the black, then no   *trs.*

          ingenuity of ornament, of gilt edging, or silky surface   *r/*

ff/   in one fashion, or affectation of Caslon's type and

    r/   deckle-edged handmade paper in another, will make

          the book look well. Not only will there be the transy-

v/   erse bars of white made by the leads, but rivers of

          white will trickle up and down between the words   *stet*

   n/   like raindrops on a window pane and the block of

etter/   l/press will be grey here and whitey-brown there and   *;/*

  ‖   m‖ildewy in the other places, instead of a rich, even

⊙/   colour all over/ Now I think it cannot be denied he   *out- see*

          has actually gone out of his way to introduce leads   *copy*

run on   and spacings wherever he can.   *#/*

          And even the most cultivated authors encourage   *trs*

⊙/   him in this/for instance, Ruskins books, as printed

  ;/   under his own supervision are instructive examples of

rom.   (everything) a book should not be. In the books of a   *ital./*

          great artist-printer like William Morris/ you find that   *;/*

          not only did he discard leading and make it an invariable   *w.f.*

THE READER'S PROOF

*A page of type matter, showing all the mistakes made in the
original setting. The reader's correction marks are shown
exactly as these would be written on the proofs. The method of
marking is that approved in the latest official recommendations.*

LIKE MOST AUTHORS, I am so greatly indebted to the printer and his reader for their work and help in the production of my books, that I cannot point out their weaknesses without some stings of remorse for my ingratitude. Besides, an author is not a fair judge of a printer, because the author himself spoils the printer's work. This arises from the fact that the main difference between a well-printed page and an ill-printed one lies in the evenness of the block of colour presented by the letterpress. If the justification is made solely to comply with some office rule against dividing words at the end of a line, or if the spaces between the sentences are made as long as possible, or if the page is leaded, and the type kept small, so as to make the white the chief feature instead of the black, then no ingenuity of ornament, or gilt edging, or silky surface in one fashion, or affectation of Caslon type and deckle-edged hand-made paper in another, will make the book look well. Not only will there be the transverse bars of white made by the leads, but rivers of white will trickle up and down between the words like raindrops on a window pane; and the block of letterpress will be grey here and whitey-brown there and mildewy in the other places, instead of a rich, even colour all over. Now I think it cannot be denied that many fashionable books show that the printer has not only not known this first canon of his art, but that he has actually gone out of his way to introduce leads and spacings wherever he can. And even the most cultivated authors encourage him in this: for instance, Ruskin's books, as printed under his own supervision, are instructive examples of everything a book should *not* be. In the books of a great artist-printer like William Morris, you find that not only did he discard leading and make it an invariable rule to set his type

THE CORRECTED PROOF

The same page of type matter as that on the opposite page, but with all the compositor's errors corrected. Uniformity in style of marking is of great importance, both in saving time and in obtaining accuracy when carrying out corrections.

The *comma* is used to indicate a pause either of sense or of sound. It should be used with discrimination, however, bearing in mind that in general there is a tendency to over-use. The *Authors' and Printers' Dictionary* gives this advice: In cases of doubt, *omit*. Words such as *however* and *moreover* are usually preceded and followed by commas. A comma is used before and between titles, such as E. B. Temple, M.A., B.Sc.; to separate repeated words or lists of words; and after every third figure from the right in statistics.

The *semicolon* marks a pause longer than a comma, and is used when a sentence consists of two or more independent clauses; to separate short phrases when several run in succession; and to mark important divisions of a sentence.

The *colon* is used to mark an abrupt pause before a further but connected statement. Some writers find it useful to introduce or sum up a list of clauses separated by semicolons. The colon is also used to introduce quotations, and passages of direct speech.

The *dash*—or em rule as it is termed in printing—is used to indicate a sudden change of thought; where a sentence is parenthetical; and to signify faltering or stammering speech. The dash is sometimes preferred in place of parentheses. The single dash is sometimes used after a colon when used to introduce a list of objects. Use the en rule to join two dates, as 1946–47.

The *2-em dash* is used where a

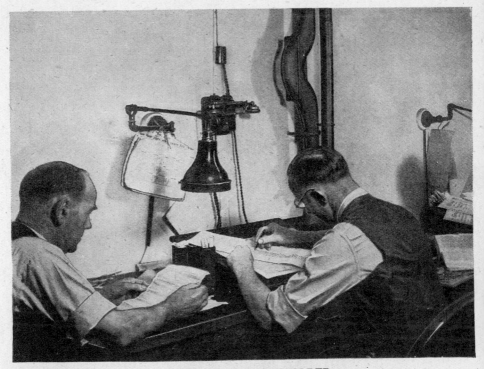

READER AND COPY-HOLDER

Note the pneumatic copy conveyor and the adjustable shaded light giving direct light without glare. Apprentice compositors are often employed as copy-holders as part of their training, so as to familiarize them with the style of the house.

sentence is unfin-
ished or interrupted,
or to denote the
omission of a word,
such as a swear
word, which might
offend the suscepti-
bilities of a reader.

The *apostrophe* is
used to indicate the
omission of some
letter or letters, e.g.
it's for *it is*; *can't*
for *cannot*; *tho'* for
though; but no
apostrophe is
needed when the
word retains only
the first and last
letters, e.g. Mr., Dr.
The apostrophe is
also used to mark
the possessive case.
For singular and
plural nouns that
do not end in s, the
possessive is formed
by adding 's, e.g.
Albert's keys; wo-
men's hats; for
plural nouns ending
in s, the apostrophe
is placed after the s,

COPY CONVEYOR FOR READING DEPARTMENT
*Used to convey copy and proofs to reading department. Proofs
are placed in holder A and collected by the travelling fitment B.
Proofs from readers are deposited in the basket C.*

e.g. boys' club. For singular nouns ending in s, add 's, e.g. St. James's Park;
but when the final s would be silent in
speech it is generally omitted, e.g. for
conscience' sake. An apostrophe followed by s forms the plurals of figures
and letters, e.g. 2's, 3's, and 4's; a's, b's,
and c's. The apostrophe is also used in
Irish names, such as O'Donoghue
and O'Connor.

No apostrophe is used in pronouns
such as hers, his, ours, yours, or theirs.

Parentheses () and *brackets* [] are used
to enclose some afterthought, interpola-
tion or explanation. The former are also
used to enclose reference figures or
letters, e.g. (1), (*a*). The *Authors' and
Printers' Dictionary* states: No stop is
needed before or after a mere statement
in parentheses which might be omitted
without altering the meaning of the sentence. When only part of a sentence is
within the parentheses, the point to be
outside, but when the full sentence is
parenthetical it should be inside.

Brackets denote that the intrusion is
more marked. Where brackets and parentheses are used in the same sentence,
the latter enclose the subordinate item.

Quotation marks are used to indicate

the quotation of something spoken or written, e.g. "Many quotation marks," he said, "are unnecessary." Or, according to one authority: "The apostrophes at the end of the quotation should come *after* all punctuation marks." Many printing houses have their own rules with regard to the placing of punctuation points before or after the end quotes; also with regard to single or double quotes for direct speech.

The *exclamation mark* is used after exclamatory words or sentences, e.g. Alas! Oh! Halt! O soft embalmer of the still midnight! A capital letter is required after the exclamation mark only when it ends a sentence.

The *interrogation* or *question mark* is used at the end of a direct question, e.g. What is it? How is it defined? No question mark is required at the end of an indirect question, e.g. I was asked how it could be defined.

The *hyphen* is used to avoid ambiguity in words which have the same spellings but different meanings, e.g. re-fuse, refuse; re-mark, remark; re-lay, relay; re-sign, resign; re-sort, resort; re-coil, recoil; re-mount, remount; re-strain, restrain; re-dress, redress.

The hyphen is used between the vowels in such words as co-operation; re-enforce; pre-arrange; pre-existing; pre-ordain; *but* reunion; prepossess; etc. Thus the hyphen assists pronunciation.

Rules for Compositors and Readers at the University Press, Oxford, gives the following helpful rules on the subject of hyphened and non-hyphened words:—

The hyphen need not, as a rule, be used to join an adverb to the adjective which it qualifies, as in: a beautifully furnished house; a well calculated scheme.

When the word might not at once be recognized as an adverb, use the hyphen, as: a well-known statesman; an ill-built house; a new-found country.

When an adverb qualifies a predicate, the hyphen should *not* be used, as: this fact is well known.

Where either (1) a noun and adjective or participle, or (2) an adjective and a noun, in combination, are used as a compound adjective, the hyphen *should* be used: a poverty-stricken family; a blood-red hand.

A compound noun which has but *one accent*, and from familiar use has become one word, requires no hyphen. Examples: blackbird; byname; byword; hairbrush; hairdresser; handbook; handkerchief; mantelpiece; nowadays; schoolboy; schoolgirl; seaport; teapot; torchlight; upstairs; watchcase.

Many words in common use, originally printed as two words or hyphenated, are now used without the hyphen. Examples: aircraft; anybody; cornfield; everyday (used as adj.); eyewitness; goodwill; horseshoe; milestone.

Compound words of *more than one accent*, as: cherry-pie; gravel-walk; will-o'-the-wisp; require hyphens.

Half an inch, half a dozen, etc., require no hyphens. Print the following also without hyphens: any one; every one; no one; post office; some one; two and six.

The hyphen is used also at the end of a line to indicate that part of a word has been carried over to the next line. Too frequent word division is not advisable, but division is definitely preferable to bad spacing.

A word is usually divided in type setting in accordance with its phonetic syllables. Whenever possible, the part of the word at the end of the line should suggest the remainder, e.g. happi-ness, not hap-piness. When two or three consonants come together the words are still divided between syllables, e.g. num-ber, frus-trate. Certain prefixes and suffixes may be separated, e.g. dis-obey; trans-action; avail-able; resist-ance.

CHAPTER NINE

PRESSES, PLATENS AND WHARFEDALES

DEVELOPMENT OF THE HAND PRESS. ALBION AND COLUMBIAN PRESSES. CYLINDRICAL PRESS PRINCIPLES. CYLINDER AND ROTARY PROOF PRESSES. PLATEN MACHINES: LIGHT AND HEAVY. MAKING-READY ON PLATENS. WHARFEDALE STOP-CYLINDER MACHINES. MECHANICAL ADJUSTMENTS. TWO-COLOUR WHARFEDALES.

THE work of a letterpress machine printer is a strange mixture of art and science, for the machine-man is as much artist as artisan. In most of his work he is governed more by feeling than by exact rules of working, for no two jobs are alike and every man's methods vary. The introduction of the printing machine took the labour out of the work, but did not simplify it in any way, rather making it infinitely more complex. Even the modern precision-made machine is as a brush is to the painter, or the piano to the pianist, needing the skilful hands, the imaginative mind and the tasteful feeling of a printer who will express his ideas through his machine. If it is difficult work to perform, it is also equally difficult to teach, but we cannot go far wrong if we stress the importance of the technique of the art, and the need for care and attention in little things, for therein probably lies one of the main secrets of the expert machine minder.

Hand Presses

The Joiner's Press. The original hand printing press of 1440 followed the methods and lines of the still older presses used at that time for making wine and for pressing linen. The pressure was applied by means of the simple screw turning on to a flat plate or platen. For a long time, printing presses con-

tinued to be made entirely of wood, and thus became known as the Joiner's press.

Crude though these machines were, the degree of skill attained by the craftsmen who worked them was remarkable. Particularly so in regard to register work; and many of the earliest specimens of their work show a standard of accuracy in close register work equal to anything produced today on our modern precision-made machines.

The All-iron Press. No outstanding improvement in the mechanical principle of the hand press took place for nearly two hundred years. There were, however, modifications and improvements from time to time in the methods and materials of their construction, chiefly in the matter of substituting metal for wood in certain parts to attain greater strength. Thus a metal screw had replaced the wooden screw in 1550, and there are still presses in existence which combine wood, brass and iron in their construction. One such press can be seen at Aston Hall, Birmingham.

A great improvement in the hand press was effected in 1620, with the introduction of the Blaew press which featured a suspended platen and the first travelling carriage. Not until 1800 do we get the first all-iron press introduced by Earl Stanhope. Though the Stanhope still employed the screw principle for impression, it combined an ingenious system of leverage in conjunction with the screw, which is a present-day principle of engineering used for applying pressure. On the Stanhope press, two men could produce two hundred impressions an hour, and this press was quickly taken up by *The Times* and other printers who were anxious to "keep up with *The Times*."

The Inclined Plane. The need for still greater power in the impression, necessitated by the woodcut illustrations popular at the time, was responsible for several important improvements on the Stanhope screw method for applying the pressure. Greater power was obtained by use of the inclined plane.

Thus in the Cogger press, power was acquired by a multiple cross-arm lever drawing about one-quarter round a collar into which two iron studs were fitted. These studs moved up inclined planes of unequal degree of inclination giving the platen a fast downward movement towards the point of pressure, then a slower movement with greater power and dwell for the impression.

The Toggle Press. The well-known Albion press of 1823 employed the toggle-jointed lever principle for obtaining its great pressure. A toggle joint is an elbow or knee-shaped joint. When the two parts of a toggle joint (the chill and the wedge) are brought into a straight line, great endwise pressure is produced. The famous Kelmscott books of William Morris, with their heavy woodcut illustrations, were all produced on Albion presses.

The lever hand press reached its zenith with the introduction of the Columbian and the Albion, but in fifty years it was relegated to proofing purposes, and has since been completely superseded by the cylinder proof press. It contributed several engineering principles which are still features of modern engineering practice, and the platen principle of impression is retained in our platen machines. There is even an ultra-modern machine by Victory-Kidder which employs the horizontal flat impression while printing in multi-colour on both sides of the web from the reel, and completes in one operation printing, perforating, numbering, and slitting through the sheet.

Development of the Cylinder

It took nearly four hundred years for the hand press to progress from the screw to the lever principle for impression, and even while the lever principle was being developed and improved, experiments were well advanced for a revolutionary change in the method of taking the impression.

To trace the evolution of the flat-bed cylinder machine it is necessary to go back to the year 1790. The Albion press was first introduced in 1823, but thirty years before that date William Nicholson, an editor, had already anticipated the coming of the cylinder machine, in his patent of 1790. The patent, however, never got beyond the design stage.

It is to Friedrich König that credit goes for making the first letterpress cylinder printing machine. König, a German engineer, came to England in 1806 and spent years trying to harness power to a machine of the platen type which he had invented. It is assumed that later he was impressed with Nicholson's suggestions; and, abandoning his former crude ideas of flat impression, he took out, in 1811, a patent for a single-cylinder machine. This first cylinder machine became an accomplished fact in 1812. Afterwards, König was commissioned by *The Times* to build a double-cylinder machine which was completed in 1814.

This machine was the first printing machine to be driven entirely by power.

SPEEDY CYLINDER PROOF PRESS

Fig. 1. *An easily worked hand press in which the heavy bed remains stationary. This principle is right for the larger hand presses. Note the accessibility of the type forme.*

In 1828, a machine which we now recognize as the first example of the two-revolution principle was invented by David Napier. On this machine the cylinder descended to make the impression and rose to clear the return of the flat type-bed, making two or more revolutions for each impression. This remarkable machine, which actually employed tumbler grippers, was a perfector, the two-impression cylinders being raised and lowered by toggles.

In 1832, an improvement on the Napier press, but on somewhat similar lines, was introduced by Richard Hoe of New York, and this was the first American flat-bed cylinder machine. It is claimed that it had a speed of about 1,800 an hour. For the next twenty years experiments and developments, both in Britain and America, were mostly towards rotary lines, with various ideas for type-revolving machines.

The year 1858 saw the introduction of the first Wharfedale machine which was made by William Dawson for G. W. McLaren, of Glasgow. The pusher bar and flyers were not added until a later date. The name Wharfedale was never registered, neither was the bed-motion of the Wharfedale patented, so many firms have built Wharfedales and at one time there were seven firms in Otley alone (today there are two) making Wharfedale machines, to say nothing of London, Manchester, and other places.

The development of the cylinder printing machine was still further advanced by the introduction of the first two-revolution machine, involving an entirely new principle as compared with the Wharfedale machine (see Chapter 10).

Cylinder Proof Presses

The modern proof press has followed the development and lines of the cylinder printing machine. The impression is by means of a cylinder, the chief advantage of which is found in the fact that pressure is only applied to the very narrow strip directly under dead centre, and making contact with the cylinder as it rolls over the forme. Thus greater pressure is applied with less power, because the resistance area is slight. Further, the design of the press, made

SOLDAN PROOF PRESS

Fig. 2. *A reliable type of modern self-inking cylinder proof press. These presses are very useful for short runs of small jobs, having ample inking and rolling equipment.*

possible by the cylinder principle, readily lends itself to many refinements such as grippers, lays, automatic inking, and make-ready. The cylinder runs on type-high bed bearers, so the press can be used, when required, for pre-make-ready in the matter of underlaying blocks, and also for registering formes which are to be printed on cylinder machines (Figs. 1 and 2).

Short runs of posters, bills and the like are practical paying propositions on these presses, which are much quicker to work than the lever presses.

The Super-speedy Press. This ultra-modern proof press is power driven by a motor hidden within the machine. It has automatic non-contact delivery which needs no adjustment. The lays and grippers are moved into position by finger pressure and have micrometer screws for final setting. Pressure is adjusted by a hand wheel with index pointer and the whole machine is designed on simple operation lines for proofing and urgent small-quantity production by a compositor. It is built in double and quad demy (Fig. 3).

A simple cylinder proof press is manufactured by Victory-Kidder Printing Machine Co., Ltd. Model O, printing surface 13 in. by 18 in. (Fig. 4), is a useful press in any printing office, and particularly so in the composing departments of schools of printing, or offices of advertising agencies. On this press it is impossible to take a pull too heavy or to damage the type or blocks. On the

HARRILD SUPER-SPEEDY POWER PRESS

Fig. 3. *The modern compositor is mechanically minded, and this power-driven press is designed for high-quality proofing and for short runs. After each cycle the press automatically comes to rest. This press is built in double demy and quad demy sizes.*

other hand, a full-size forme pulls up with perfect impression, clear for reading and correction, while two lines of small type for octavo heading print light and clear. The small impression cylinder is permanently packed with resilient material and covered with a harder seamless rubber composition sleeve.

As the cylinder prints both ways, one movement is sufficient for each proof.

Rotary proofing presses (Fig. 5) are available for use with all types of rotary machines. On these presses, the curved plates can be proofed up, under-

VICTORY PROOF PRESS

Fig. 4. *A useful press for taking proofs of small formes for reading and correcting,*

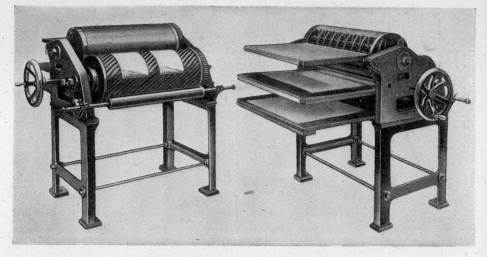

TIMSON ROTARY PROOFING PRESS

Fig. 5. A useful press for proofing curved stereos and electros for register and pre-make-ready purposes. The cylinders are replicas of those on the rotary machine.

laid, and fully tested before reaching the rotary printing machine. The forme cylinder of the proof press is an exact duplicate of the machine cylinders, being grooved and fitted with clips according to the various systems in vogue, to hold the stereos or electros. The impression cylinder is fitted with a blanket, and a tightening bar is provided for the usual impression cylinder dressing; there are simple but adequate inking arrangements. The pre-make-ready made possible by the use of these presses results in a considerable saving in machine time for make-ready, and eliminates standing time for corrections.

PLATEN MACHINES

PLATEN machines fall naturally into two groups: ordinary light or jobbing; and heavy or art. The difference between the two classes, however, is not merely a matter of weight and strength, but also a difference in mechanical principle and capacity.

Ordinary Light or *Jobbing Platen*. This class of machine is definitely limited, as the name suggests, to light jobbing work. Its scope includes circulars, cards, billheads, envelopes, and the many small jobs which every office handles. The simple inking arrangements consist of a rotating disk, three inking rollers, which also serve as distributors, a duct, and a duct roller. The rotating disk cannot give adequate distribution, although on some makes of machines the centre of the disk revolves one way, and the outer rim the other, and thus effects some improvement in the inking.

The platen closes hinge-like to meet the type-bed, and with this movement the relative plane of the platen and printing surface, so important from a make-ready point of view, generally depends on an exact amount of packing on the platen which may bear no relationship to the amount of general pressure required on a particular job. The exigencies of printing often make this exact amount impossible, so where too much is expected from machines of this class, the results are disappointing, involving excessive make-ready, or inferior work.

The trouble associated with this poor mechanical movement of the platen is more noticeable on formes which might be considered heavy for this type of machine. They demand more packing, and this increases the pressure more towards the bottom of the platen than towards the top.

Some makers have given special attention to this problem, which is inherent in the design. Those machines, like Harrild's Bremner, which incorporate wedges or eccentrics to alter the plane of the platen or bed as may be necessary, are the best of this class (Fig. 6).

Heavy or *Art Platen.* This type of platen machine meets all demands for first-class work. The rolling power is adequate for the largest half-tone process work, and one light line of type may be rolled without a suspicion of "wipe." They

have cylindrical distribution with three or four large-diameter inkers with riders, and in some models bottom distribution to obviate roller repeats. For the same purpose, two of the inkers reserve their rolling for the upward stroke. There are, in addition, five distributors, a duct with flexible blade, and a duct roller.

The rigid impression and solid construction of these machines accommodate the largest printing or embossing forme. The platen rolls up to the vertical, and then slides forward with direct approach to meet the rigid type-bed in

BREMNER PLATEN MACHINE

Fig. 6. *A well-designed and solidly built machine, with extra large-diameter inkers, and a device for holding them clear of the forme when the impression is temporarily checked.*

the exact plane, irrespective of the amount of packing.

Unfortunately, this mechanical feature, so good from other points of view, does not lend itself to the high speeds of the clam-shell principle, and it is machines of this latter type which have been developed into the fully automatic platen which is capable of very high speeds.

Fully Automatic Platen Machines. Though the term fully automatic does indicate a certain lack of flexibility in so far as these machines cannot be fed by hand, it is true to say that within the scope of these machines, the range of work covers any stock between 11-lb. bank and medium thick board. Since the Heidelberg entered the British market, and for a long time had its own way, it is gratifying to know that a British machine of somewhat similar design, but with several distinct improvements — the Thompson British automatic platen— has gained very greatly in popularity (Fig. 7).

One of its features is the parallel impression micrometer adjustment, which means that a level impression does not altogether rely on an exact amount of packing. A simple arrangement gives parallel approach from six-sheet board up to manifold. Thicker boards are only accommodated by

reducing the packing; the impression check can be thrown off right up to the last moment.

Quick adjustment of position is obtained without taking the forme out, by altering the grip with two finger screws which move the feeding position backwards or forwards up to a full 12 points. Both side lays are adjustable. Double driving gear gives the machine a smooth balanced action, and the double toggle motion gives dwell and power to the impression.

Register is maintained by a special locking device; the grippers are held rigid both in the feed position when taking the sheet and again in the impression position. The inking arrangements are ample, one 8-in. diameter reciprocating drum, four distributing rollers

THOMPSON BRITISH AUTOMATIC PLATEN
Fig. 7. *Automatic platens are entirely machine fed. The above machine, embodying various improvements in this type of platen, has a locking device for register, and geared inkers.*

(one reciprocating) and three inking rollers with steel riders, and duct fitted with flexible blade. All three inkers clear a full-size forme. The inkers are geared in a novel way to prevent skid, wipe or repeats. Definite adjustment of the roller bearers is made possible by adjusting screws. The machine is easy to operate; all settings are made from the front and there are dials and indicators showing the various settings, making the adjustments almost foolproof. The supply hopper holds a pile 12 in. high. Inside measurement of chase 10¼ in. by 15 in. This platen has a speed up to 4,500 per hour.

Making Ready on Platens

A feature of the work of the letterpress machine printer is its infinite variety. Every job presents its own problems. Generally speaking, all will print well if the impression is level and the rolling right, and the work must be directed to this end. But perfectly sound methods for one job may have to be modified and adapted to suit the next. Nevertheless, certain broad outlines of systematic approach can be laid down which will suit straightforward jobs and also serve as a basis for other jobs. Take, for example, a demy quarto circular, the type of work that would be equally suitable for any type of platen. The following are the various operations of make-ready, given in their correct sequence.

At the Machine. Clean the platen and type bed. Wipe off all grease from rollers, roller trucks and tracks. Dress the platen with one sheet of thin hard board and four sheets of super-calendered paper, 30-lb. double crown. There is no need to damp the top sheet for this job, but it should be pasted along the bottom edge and clipped in. The whole of the packing must lie perfectly snug with the top sheet drawn very tight and

clipped in. Prepare the appropriate ink, and put it into the duct.

Wipe the imposing surface and the back of the forme, place the machine chase round the forme, so that the head of the job is towards the left, and the head of the machine chase away from you as you work. The quoins are placed at the top and right side of the job chase. Wood and metal furniture fill up the space at the lay edges, so that the type falls in the centre of the impression and is locked up *to* the lay edges.

Roller bearers are always useful in platen work, so two of the angle type are used now. Before locking-up, however, the quoins in the job chase are loosened to allow that chase to lie flat while the outer quoins are tightened. Attention is paid to such details as rule joinings, while the inner quoins are being made thumb tight. After planing down, the forme will be lightly locked up, and any tendency to spring can be corrected.

The First Impression. In putting the forme into the machine, it is wedged up to the left side. A glance at the position of the frisket fingers and the impression regulation may obviate danger of damage to forme or packing. If necessary, the frisket and impression block are brought back to safe positions.

The first pull on make-ready paper will now be light in impression, and one or two more pulls will be necessary, as the pressure is gradually increased until there is just, and only just, sufficient indentation to show the irregularities in the impression as viewed from the back of the sheet.

Getting the Lay. The position will first be obtained. Taking an impression on the clean tympan; then, using the copy or instructions as a guide, the lays are carefully fixed. They will be well spaced for accurate feeding, and secure so as not to move during the course of the run.

Setting the Friskets. The job under consideration is not the closest register. Nevertheless, the friskets are tested for shape and effect on the sheet, as one is being brought in to work in margin.

Levelling the Impression. While a sheet is being passed for position and reading, the pull, on make-ready paper which has just sufficient indentation, is taken, and levelling-up work is proceeded with. The work is carried out on the back of the pull, with broad overlapping patches of tissue, or very thin bank, as may be necessary. Every job has its own characteristic impression, but usually on work of this description there will be found three distinct though slight gradations in impression.

Thus the work may consist of a patch of tissue over the first and lightest gradation, and an overlapping patch to cover the first and second gradations. This will bring the impression up to the uniform weight of the third and heaviest gradation, which is left uncovered. Turning the sheet over to the front, a patch can be put on any part which the work on the back will obviously not correct. As little paste as possible is used so as to avoid a lumpy impression. Rule joinings may require a patch on one or other side of the join on the back of the forme.

Sinking the Make-ready. The patched sheet is trimmed to the detail, and secured in position on the top sheet of the tympan. A covering sheet is pasted in at the bottom clip, and the packing, except the two sheets of super-calendered paper, which are discarded, is brought up to cover the make-ready. The new covering sheet is brought under the top clip, drawn very tight, and secured.

The Fly Sheet. A fly sheet will be useful to change occasionally during backing up. It should reach all three lays and be very lightly tipped on with paste. A pull on the paper which is to be used for the job will reveal any slight modification necessary.

Setting the Duct. The duct will now be set to suit the job, slightly pinched at ends. A thin film and long stroke give the best result. If backing up the same day, driers may be added to the ink.

WHARFEDALE CYLINDER MACHINES

OF the stop-cylinder machines, the Wharfedale is the best known and most widely used. It has long been the "bread-and-butter" machine of the commercial printer. Its centre is the vale of the River Wharfe at Otley, Yorkshire.

The great problem which faced the engineers in the design and manufacture of a flat-bed cylinder machine was the reversal of the type-bed. The travel of the heavy type-bed has to be arrested, stopped and reversed without jar or vibration; and it is the type-bed motion which today is the the governing factor on all classes of flat-bed machines.

There are two types of straightforward flat-bed cylinder machines that have grown up side by side: the stop-cylinder (Fig. 8) and the two-revolution cylinder.

Each of these types solves the problem of bed motion in an entirely different manner. In the Wharfedale the bed motion is actuated by means of a crank which gets its throw by reason of being hung on a pin connecting the rims of two large driving wheels; thus, at each end of its throw, there is a gradual slow up, stop and reverse as the crank approaches and passes over dead centre. This rhythmic crank action is the same principle as the pistons of steam and internal combustion engines. It has been compared to the true motion of the pendulum of a clock, which from zero point accelerates gently, reaching maximum speed when it is vertical, then gently slowing down to the end of its stroke. The crank action of the stop-cylinder machine gives a smooth but fast bed motion, and there is no need for buffers or other arrangements to take charge of, or help the bed over its period of reversal.

The cylinder on the Wharfedale moves on one stroke of the bed only. The feed is to the lower edge of the cylinder; as the bed travels from the feed end to the duct, the cylinder is revolved by gears at each end of the cylinder shaft, mesh-ing with gear racks at each side of the bed. For the cylinder to remain station-ary the feed side-gear runs freely on the cylinder shaft, a pawl clutch having dis-engaged. The driving side-gear, which is fixed to the cylinder, has sufficient teeth planed off to clear the rack. The cylinder is picked up by the pawl clutch when the bed is at its extreme end, and therefore stationary, so that there is no shock or jar.

The introduction by Dawson, Payne & Elliott, Ltd., of the Standard high-speed Wharfedale series a few years ago, marked a big advance in this type of design. On these machines the gears are finer cut and the cylinder clutch arrange-ment has been much improved, making the S.W. machines very silent and

WHARFEDALE STOP-CYLINDER MACHINE
Fig. 8. *The Wharfedale is characterized by the simplicity of its design. The perfection delivery is out of action in the above picture, as only proofing is being carried out.*

STANDARD HIGH-SPEED

Fig. 9. *The latest type of Wharfedale machine, fitted with automatic feed and pile delivery. The maximum size of this model is 35 by 22½ in.; and the maximum speed is 2,750*

smooth running at greater speeds. They are fitted with H.T.B. automatic feeders on the larger sizes and Universal feeders on the smaller sizes, and are supplied with perfection or extended pile delivery as preferred. The inking arrangements and impression are good and they can be relied upon for accurate register at high speed (Figs. 9 and 10).

Comparative speeds of the standard Wharfedale stop-cylinder and the modern high-speed two-revolution machines are interesting. They will be found to be in favour of the Wharfedale in the smaller sizes.

The Little Meteor (Fig. 11), with its fine inking system, takes a maximum sheet of 18 by 11½ in.; maximum guaranteed speed 5,000 per hour. The S.W.O. takes a maximum sheet of 24 by 17½ in., maximum guaranteed speed

3,600. The machine is supplied with full or semi-automatic feed and the choice of four deliveries, including extended pile delivery. As the size increases the speeds get more comparable: the S.W.2 maximum size of sheet 30 by 20 in., maximum guaranteed speed 3,250; S.W.3 double demy, speed 2,750. In the larger sizes the advantage is with the two-revolution, the S.W.6 taking a maximum sheet 45 by 35 in., maximum guaranteed speed 2,000 per hour.

Mechanical Adjustments

In describing the various mechanical adjustments possible on different cylinder machines, writers tend to create the impression that these adjustments are everyday occurrences. It is as though printers were engineers who made ready with spanners, or, if about to do a

WHARFEDALE MACHINE (S.W.3)
impressions per hour. This series of Standard high-speed Wharfedales embodies many improvements in design in regard to the cutting of the gears, and the cylinder clutch.

register job, approached the machine with a bag of engineering tools!

The truth is, that these writers have probably worked letterpress printing machines successfully all their lives without the necessity of touching the adjustment of the traverse racks on a Wharfedale, or a register rack on a two-revolution machine. They may never have been called upon to adjust a cylinder to the bed bearers on any type of cylinder machine.

Setting the Cylinder. Unless the cylinder and type-bed are making very firm contact, the cylinder dressing has to be overpacked to obtain proper printing pressure with the forme. This is very bad from a printing point of view, because overpacking a cylinder increases the diameter, and this increases its surface speed. If the periphery of the cylinder and the printing surface are not running in perfect unison, friction occurs and a slur develops—that is where the rub comes. The over-packed cylinder, racing the printing surface, causes a drag on the sheet which creates buckles and creases, distorts the design of the printing and makes register impossible. Often it drags the packing wholesale back from the cylinder bevel. It always causes excessive wear to the forme.

Testing the Impression

If it seems necessary to over-pack the cylinder on moderately light work, and it is suspected that the cylinder and type-bed bearers are not making firm contact, it is a simple matter to test this by cleaning all bearers and then laying a strip of thin glazed bank paper on the bed bearers, putting the machine on

BOWL TRACKS OF THE S.W.2 WHARFEDALE

Fig. 10. *The new Wharfedales, while gaining considerably in speed, lose nothing in solid construction, and the above illustration shows the four bowl tracks of a double crown machine, which ensure the strongest and most rigid support for the heaviest impression.*

impression, and then turning over slowly by hand. The paper should be held firmly throughout. If not, the bearers may be below type high (·918 in.) and need packing with a continuous strip of hard ledger paper. If the bearers are type-high and contact is still not firm the cylinder requires lowering with the set screws.

Cylinder and Feed-board. Any variation in the position of the cylinder to the feed-board, when the grippers close on the sheet, will spoil the register. The grippers are attached to the cylinder and the lays to the feed-board. Any variation between these two must result in more or less grip; in other words, a different margin. To prevent this, the Wharfedale is fitted with a pushing motion, and this pushes the cylinder back to a dead stop before the grippers close on each sheet. On the side of the cylinder brake-drum is a lug. Each time the cylinder comes round, this lug depresses a spring-loaded lever and passes over it allowing the lever to rise up to its previous position.

When the cylinder stops, the pusher bar, which was drawn back to allow the wheel to pass, is pressed forward again by a cam and lever arrangement, and

pushes the lug hard up against the spring-loaded lever. Thus, the cylinder is in the same position each time a sheet is taken. The length of the pusher bar can be adjusted, if necessary, by means of two nuts on the bar.

To adjust, place two pieces of thin paper on either side of the lug, turn the machine until the cam roller is on the highest point of the eccentric cam which actuates the pusher bar. The papers should now be held tightly by the levers. If not, a tiny turn of the nuts will lengthen the bar until this is accomplished. After adjustment, however, turn the cylinder over by hand, and make sure that the end of the pusher bar clears the lug as the cylinder moves forward.

Type-bed Adjustment. When the type-bed is $\frac{3}{8}$ in. from the end of the stroke the feed-board should be at its highest point to the cylinder. When $\frac{1}{4}$ in. from end of stroke the grippers should be closed. When the type-bed is exactly at the end of its stroke and stationary, the pawl clutch should engage, and the cylinder immediately start its move forward. Should the pawl clutch engage before the type-bed has reached the end of its stroke, the traverse racks need adjustment. Adjusting bolts, slots and lock-nuts are located at one end of the traverse racks.

After adjustment of the traverse racks it is necessary to see that the pusher bar is clear of the lug on the side of the cylinder brake-drum as the cylinder revolves.

Oscillation of Cylinder. Any undue oscillation of the cylinder after it has come to rest is bad and may cause the fixed gear to engage the cog rack and turn the cylinder backwards. This may be caused by the wearing of the spring under the cylinder bearing. A slight turn of the screws which go through the frames will stop this oscillation.

Setting Rollers. Detailed instructions are given on page 121.

Two-colour Wharfedale. The two-colour Wharfedale machine embodies all the features of the modern single-colour Wharfedale. It is equipped with a separate inking apparatus at each end of the machine. The two type-beds are in the centre. The single cylinder makes two revolutions, taking an impression from each printing forme in turn. On this type of two-colour machine, label and carton work and the like, where colours overlap, must be made ready largely by way of underlays and interlays, as any variation of pressure by way of overlays would have to apply to both formes. They are tricky machines to work, calling for great ingenuity on the part of the machine minder. The new Standard two-colour high-speed Wharfedales manufactured by Dawson, Payne & Elliott, Ltd., are made in five sizes: demy and three intermediate sizes up to S.T.C.6, quad crown. All but the smallest machine, S.T.C.2, are equipped with perfection delivery. They have geared inkers and distributors; flexible duct blades; ink supply checked with cylinder; and mechanically operated front lays with micrometer adjustment.

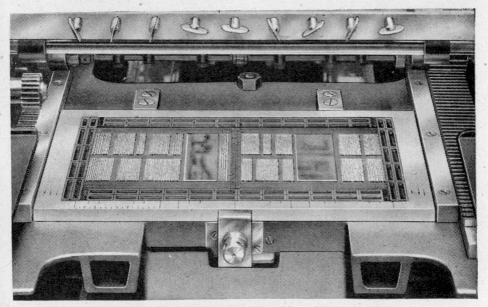

THE LITTLE METEOR: LOCKING-UP ARRANGEMENTS

Fig. 11. *The job is correctly positioned in the machine chase, which is secured in position on the bed of this fast-running Wharfedale by means of a single screw.*

CHAPTER TEN

TWO-REVOLUTION MACHINES

SPECIAL FEATURES.   CYLINDER DRESSING.   SETTING AND TIMING THE LAYS.   THE
CYLINDER BRUSH.   INKING SYSTEM.   REGISTER RACK ADJUSTMENTS.   AIR BUFFERS
AND CYLINDER SPRINGS.   THE PERFECTOR.   TANDEM AND TWO-COLOUR MACHINES.

THE modern two-revolution machine was invented by Robert Miehle, an American, but the two-revolution principle is a development of much older ideas which were suggested by David Napier in his press built so long ago as 1828—thirty years before the invention of the Wharfedale. The two-revolution is a flat-bed cylinder machine in which the continuously revolving cylinder makes two revolutions for each impression. The sheet is printed during the first revolution, and delivered during the second, when the cylinder is raised to clear the forme. The bed motion is remarkable, and generally employs a drive by means of a sliding pinion engaging alternately in two staggered racks secured to the under side of the bed, one above the pinion and one below (see pages 122 and 123).

Crank Drive Control

For the turn, and while the pinion is sliding over, a crank drive takes over control of the bed, and it is this crank approaching and passing over dead centre, which slows up, stops and reverses the bed. Air buffers help to take the shock of reversal and obviate strain. The Harrild two-revolution (Fig. 1) employs the same movement, but a variation of the motion is found in the Otley two-revolution press. On this machine, the even travel is by means of a sliding pinion, but the turn or uneven travel is taken up by

special small reversing pinions (Fig. 4).

One of the best-known machines in Britain is the Miehle two-revolution machine (Figs. 2 and 3), which is manufactured by Linotype & Machinery, Ltd., at Altrincham, Cheshire. The two-revolution principle lends itself to an open design which makes it a comfortable machine to work, e.g. the space between the open feed-board and the cylinder is convenient when working on the cylinder; the high feed-board which leaves the type-bed open and free. The facility of the foot controls, and the sheet clamps and two ratchet bars, aid systematic make-ready, and the forme clamps, racks and bars provide excellent facilities for locking-up arrangements.

When changing a job, work on the principle of matching the new sheet to the machine, not the machine to the sheet. The various accessories, moved from time to time, to suit the different sizes of sheets worked, gradually get into a unique arrangement which can, if the best position for the new sheet is found, be readily adapted to suit any ordinary size of sheet, with a minimum of alteration at the machine.

Machine Adjustments

It should be clearly understood that many of the adjustments, settings and timings to be mentioned with detail later, do not always arise. For instance, the shape of the lay-rests, humoured from time to time, gets right; the height of the feed-board, or the timing of the

114

HARRILD TWO-REVOLUTION WITH INTERFLOW FEEDER
Fig. 1. Note the accessibility to the cylinder for make-ready purposes in this well-known machine. The machine minder has complete freedom of movement for work on the cylinder.

lift of the front lays, unless changing from paper to thick card, or vice versa, seldom needs adjustment; if the grippers are not moved there may be no need to move a stripper finger or a sheet band; when the drop guides or register-fingers are nicely set it may be possible to leave them from job to job, or only move one. It is safe to say that the expert, though he knows how to re-set any part perfectly, makes fewer moves when changing over, than the less experienced minder.

This system of working from job to job, and preserving the settings, can also be applied to the ink duct. By remembering the lie and design of the previous forme, the film of ink can often be better judged, so that a very accurate setting can be obtained right from the start. Few of the devices which need setting on the Miehle are in the nature of refinements; they are mostly necessities to the attainment of satisfactory results.

Cylinder Dressing. Typical moderately hard packing for Miehle machines built before 1936, when the body of the cylinder was fifty-five thousandths of an inch below the cylinder bearers, is as follows:—

	Thous. of an inch
Four oiled manila sheets (each five thousandths of an inch) . . .	20
Glazed linen, reeled round first draw bar	5
Damped stretched manila . . .	5
Semi-permanent packing:	30
Six white super-calendered make-ready sheets (each three thousandths of an inch)	18
Damped stretched thin white super-calendered sheet	2
Manila reeled round second draw bar .	5
	55

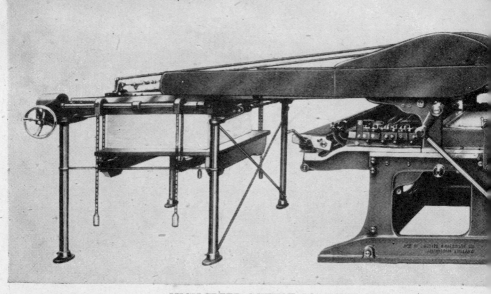

HIGH-SPEED MIEHLE MACHINE WITH BUILT OUT

Fig. 2. *The speed of the improved high-speed Miehles has been greatly increased. This No. 3 (quad crown) produces 3,000 impressions per hour. With the built-out type of automatic*

Since 1936 all Miehle machines have been made to take packing seventy thousandths of an inch thick (this should include all the super-speed models), the idea being to allow extra depth to accommodate a rubber or other form of thick blanket on the cylinder, and for heavy carton and similar work.

Hard or *Soft Packing?* The packing is made harder or softer according to the degree of inequalities in the surface of the forme or stock.

Soft packing provides greater resilience to counteract irregularities in the printing surface or stock, but it also shows the indentation of the impression.

Hard packing produces sharper printing with less indentation, but has less resilience and so cannot altogether overcome irregularities. The make-ready, therefore, requires to be very exact.

Between these two extremes, hard and

soft, a balance can be approximately reached where the firmness and yield necessary are most helpful to the perfection of a particular impression, thus minimizing make-ready.

Presuming that the semi-permanent cylinder dressing packing has already been arranged, crease (one at a time) the seven white super-calendered sheets $1\frac{1}{2}$ in. from the front edge. Paste in (one at a time), front edge only, two of these white sheets. The other five whites and top manila are not pasted at this stage, but are held by the tympan clamp for convenience, during make-ready. Reel the top manila round the second drawbar; smooth out the sheets as they are put up—they must all lie snug and flat along the front edge and round the cylinder with no trace of wrinkles. This work should be done well, for it is the foundation of all that follows.

Before putting the forme on the

AUTO-FEEDER AND EXTENDED PILE DELIVERY
feeder the new pile of paper can be stacked while the old pile is being run off. In spite of its high speed this latest Linotype & Machinery, Ltd. product is a quiet-running machine.

type-bed, the position of the sheet should always be determined on the feed-board. This is done with the machine in the position where the front guides (or lays) have dropped, and the closed grippers are slightly forward and just clear of the lays (this would be on the second, or delivery revolution). Unless the sheet has to be slit, do not stick slavishly to dead centre, but choose a position near the centre of the board where there is an appropriate set of grippers to suit the sheet to be printed with a minimum of alteration.

The grippers should be moderately evenly spaced across the sheet, except those which straddle the lay rests, which should be wider spaced to prevent bulge. The end grippers to be about 1 in. from either end of the sheet. Moving a gripper may necessitate moving a stripper finger and/or a sheet band, and this should be borne in mind and watched.

Transposing a shoo-fly and a gripper is safe without moving a stripper finger. A set of grippers having been determined, move the lay rests to work in the centre of the space arranged between the wider-spaced grippers.

Setting the Lays. Set the front lays lightly on the rests, so that the two legs in each case straddle and clear the rests. The weight of the lays is taken, not by the springy rests, but by the lay shaft lever handle and the stop. Any movement of the lay rests, when the lays drop, is false and will upset the register.

The timing of the lift of the front lays is very important. If the lays leave the sheet too soon, the latter may move before the grippers have firmly got it; on the other hand, if the lays lift too late, they may not clear the front edge of the sheet as it is moved forward by the grippers. In either case, register is lost. The best plan is to time them to lift at almost the latest possible moment just as the grippers catch hold of the sheet, and to make sure that the sheet does not catch them. During the run, be watchful, in case some of the stock is wavy.

Often it is possible to hear the edge of the paper snick the edge of the lay, as the sheet moves forward, or notice a nick down the pile on the delivery board. To time the lays to lift earlier, move the machine until the grippers are in the position in which the lays should start to lift, and lower the lifting finger on the stud. The side lay can now be fixed, true and secure.

Amount of Grip. The amount of grip advisable on the Miehle is important. It should be such that the edge of the sheet just reaches the bevel of the cylinder, about 16 points, and, generally

speaking, it should be equal right across the sheet. To test, place a sheet to the lays and inch the machine round slowly and carefully, ready to stop and apply the foot brake the instant the ear detects any unusual sound, indicating something wrong. When the grippers close on the sheet, stop and observe the amount of grip. If necessary, adjust the front lays until the amount of grip is satisfactory.

Lie of the Sheet round the Cylinder. Continue to inch the machine round with the sheet now in the grippers, but stop well before the grippers open for delivery, and note the lie of the sheet round the cylinder. It should be flat and free from wrinkles. If register is wanted and an absence of slight slurs, special attention must be given to the feed-board and the lay-rests. If the grippers

MIEHLE GEARED INKING ROLLERS

Fig. 3. *The Miehle's full pyramid of nine rollers, when properly set, provides almost perfect inking. The adjustment and detaching of rollers are easily and quickly carried out.*

OTLEY TWO-REVOLUTION REVERSING GEAR AND BOWL TRACKS

Fig. 4. *Three double-width bowl tracks give a wide bed bearing. The small reversing pinions can be seen in line with the air pressure gauge. Note the shock-absorbing air-buffers.*

on either side of the lay-rests are too close to the rests, this will cause a sharp buckle. In opening them out, see that the stripper fingers are not fouled. If the lay-rests are too high, too straight or too long, there will be buckles. The rests are lowered by taking the feed-board down with the adjusting screws.

Short of scraping the cylinder or the printed sheet with the board or the legs of the front lay plates, the feed-board can hardly be too low. In shape, the lay-rests should follow the radius of the cylinder, so that there is nothing awkward in the way the sheet slides off them in its progress to the cylinder. Any unnecessary length can be cut off the lay-rests by an engineer. After any adjustment to the feed-board or the lay-rests, re-set the lays lightly to the rests, with the weight taken by the lever handle on the lay-shaft engaging on the stop as before.

Drop Guides or *Register Fingers.* If engaged on register work, the register fingers will be used; they should be carefully set. Properly set they act as a safeguard against any movement of the sheet during the short period after the lays have commenced to lift, and before the grippers have really taken hold of the sheet, but they can be a real menace to register if improperly set.

To set them, see that grippers are just closed, loosen the stop lever on the feed side of the shaft and set to stop. Then loosen the lever gear end of the shaft and allow the link to rest in its notch on gripper pin lever. The register fingers can now be set down to the apron of the feed-board in such a position as to work in margins. They are tricky to set, the art lying in the ability to set them so that they touch the paper lightly and do not sag at all. Any sag is certain to move the sheets. To time the lift, screw down the set pin until it just makes contact. The fingers will now lift a fraction of a minute after the lays have commenced to lift.

The position of the sheet has already been determined and fixed on the feedboard, and we must match that position with the forme on the type-bed. The pitch lines are towards the end of the type-bed away from the slab. It is possible to advance the cylinder on the Miehle to take oversize sheets, so three pitch lines are indicated on the bed. Advancing the cylinder will be dealt with under a separate heading. The normal lock-up on the Miehle is *from* the lay, and there are four convenient forme clamps for this purpose.

Position and Lock-up

Wharfedale men usually experience a little difficulty with the position and lock-up when first taking up the two-revolution machine. They should proceed as follows: with the forme placed loosely on the bed, with the grip edge towards them, let the grip edge of a sheet of the stock overhang the appropriate pitch line about 16 points, and put the forme in the right position to the paper. To facilitate this, it is an advantage to fold the sheet the narrow way. The space between the back of the chase and the slab or, in the case of a small-size forme, the bar, is filled with short furniture at each side.

The side position can best be obtained by measurement from the edge of a sheet placed in the lays, to the cylinder bearer; and matching this with a sheet on the type-bed, the forme being placed in its correct relative position to the sheet. There are racks on either side of the bed and a straight bar and a sidestick bar to fit them. With these, and the four forme clamps, a variety of locking-up schemes is possible to suit any size of forme in any position on the type-bed. When using the forme clamps, remember the great power of the screw-thread (it is on the same principle as the jack for obtaining

great leverage), and do not lock-up too tightly.

Setting the Grippers. After the job is made ready and the cylinder packing has received its final adjustment, the grippers may be set. While they can be set with the machine in any position in which the grippers are closed, the position recommended is the one where they have just closed and moved forward sufficiently to allow the tumbler to clear slightly the tumbler closing stud.

Having put the machine in this particular position and watched the grippers close, it is unlikely that any confusion will arise in the mind which would lead to leaving the grippers open after setting, when they should be closed. Raise the gripper tumbler a little with the tommy key and insert a strip of manila, about five-thousandths of an inch thick, between the tumbler and the tumbler stop. The grippers are now loosened, and a strip of the stock to be printed is placed under each gripper. Working from the centre on alternate sides, tighten all grippers on the strips of stock; then, by taking a strain on each strip, it is possible to judge the tension on each gripper, and with a little care the tension can be made equal on all grippers.

Having packed-up the tumbler five-thousandths above the stop, and set the grippers down to a sheet of the stock, the grippers will always hold the tumbler off the stop and prevent the stop from limiting the tension. Make sure that no gripper is left loose or moved sideways to foul a stripper finger. Raise the tumbler and remove the manila and leave the grippers closed.

Setting the Sheet Bands. This is another job which is always done when the cylinder is fully packed. Carefully set, the sheet bands hold the sheet up to the cylinder and help to expel air from between the sheet and the cylinder, and thus minimize buckles. They also prevent the back edge of the sheet from tumbling down towards the grip edge and touching the inking rollers. With the cylinder down on impression, and the grippers in view, the bands are set to work in the spaces between the grippers and the shoo-flies. The best results are obtained when the band in the centre is set up close to the packing; and with each succeeding band, either side is set very slightly farther away from the packing. In this manner, the centre band smooths out the sheet from the middle and the other bands allow the wrinkles to pass. The bands must not mark the sheet.

The Cylinder Brush. The function of the brush is to continue the work of the sheet bands, by smoothing out air from under the sheet to eliminate all wrinkles and also to hold up the back-edge of the sheet to prevent it "licking" the forme. Like the sheet bands, the brush should be set up close to the cylinder in the centre.

Testing the set of the brush is done before a forme is placed on the machine by placing three long strips of paper, one in the centre, and one either side, in the grippers; then, with the cylinder down on impression, allowing these to be taken round until the grippers are accessible at the back. Release the strips by means of a tommy key in the tumbler, and test the set of the brush by pulling in turn each strip of paper. Adjustment is made each side by loosening the bolts holding the brush brackets to the side frames, and moving either of the brackets up or down as required.

When the brush is set level on either side by means of the brackets, fine adjustment can always be made by means of the adjusting screw low down in the cylinder brush cam lever.

The Inking System. Nothing contributes more to the attainment of fine

results in printing than good inking. On the Miehle the inking arrangements comprise sixteen rollers in addition to a duct and a large ink slab. There are four large-diameter inkers which all cover a full-size forme, and five riders, arranged as follows: two steel rollers, mounted by two composition rollers, these being mounted by a steel jockey roller. The two steel riders are geared reciprocating rollers. The nine rollers make a complete pyramid (Fig. 3).

For distribution there are six rollers in two sets of three, each set being placed slantwise to aid distribution. The centre steel roller of each set of distributors, which is gear driven, is of small diameter, and this also provides a great aid to distribution. There is a simple lever-locking device which either holds down the inkers and their riders, or raises them clear of the slab or the forme and clear of each other, as desired. The duct, which normally checks with the cylinder, can be set to remain on or off, irrespective of the check.

The ink is fed from the duct by means of a ductor roller or vibrator.

Setting the Rollers

If full advantage is to be taken of the inking arrangements, and the fine finish associated with correct inking be obtained, the setting and adjusting of the rollers is by no means a casual affair. The obvious roller repeat, filling in, missing, and ink squashing out to the edges, are all well-known manifestations of badly set rollers, but a roller wipe caused by a heavy roller or a skidding roller may pass all but the discerning eye, and cause the job to set-off badly. In setting rollers, as in other settings, there is, within narrow limits, always a certain latitude. It is in the play within these limits that character and individuality creep into a man's work.

The inkers can be set to a type-high

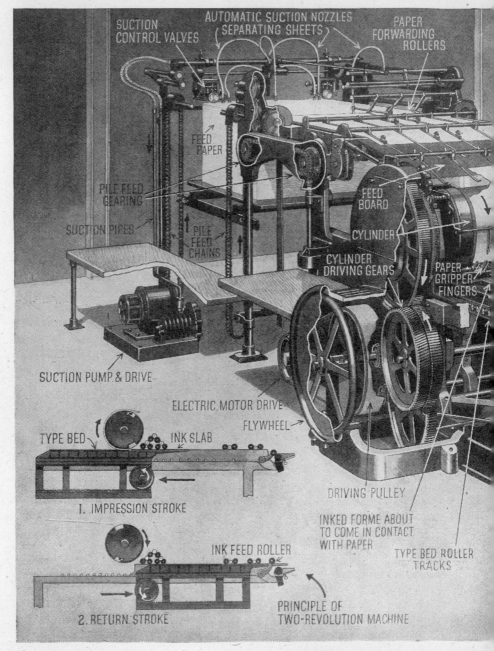

SUCTION CONTROL VALVES

AUTOMATIC SUCTION NOZZLES SEPARATING SHEETS

PAPER FORWARDING ROLLERS

FEED PAPER

PILE FEED GEARING

SUCTION PIPES

PILE FEED CHAINS

FEED BOARD

CYLINDER

CYLINDER DRIVING GEARS

PAPER GRIPPER FINGERS

SUCTION PUMP & DRIVE

ELECTRIC MOTOR DRIVE

FLYWHEEL

TYPE BED

INK SLAB

1. IMPRESSION STROKE

INK FEED ROLLER

2. RETURN STROKE

DRIVING PULLEY

INKED FORME ABOUT TO COME IN CONTACT WITH PAPER

TYPE BED ROLLER TRACKS

PRINCIPLE OF TWO-REVOLUTION MACHINE

WORKING PARTS OF A TWO-

In this instructive drawing, parts of the machine have been cut away to reveal mechanical details and important working parts otherwise hidden from view. The lift of the cylinder for the return of the type-bed on the non-printing revolution of the cylinder, and the bed motion cam, gear and staggered racks are also shown independent of the machine, in the four

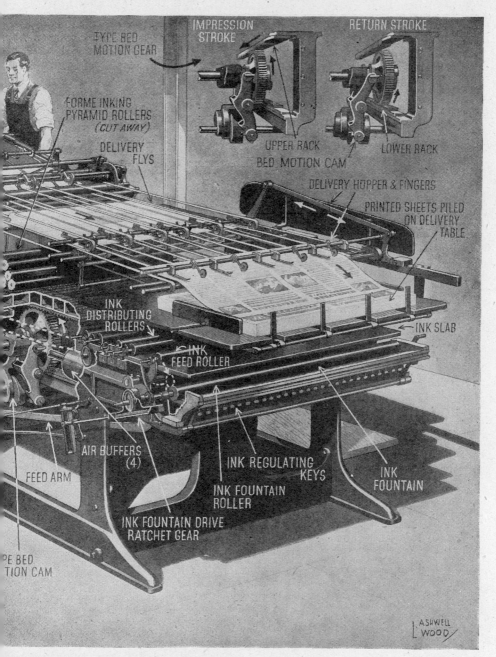

Labels (clockwise):

TYPE BED MOTION GEAR

IMPRESSION STROKE

RETURN STROKE

FORME INKING PYRAMID ROLLERS (CUT AWAY)

DELIVERY FLYS

UPPER RACK

BED MOTION CAM

LOWER RACK

DELIVERY HOPPER & FINGERS

PRINTED SHEETS PILED ON DELIVERY TABLE

INK DISTRIBUTING ROLLERS

INK SLAB

INK FEED ROLLER

AIR BUFFERS (4)

FEED ARM

INK REGULATING KEYS

INK FOUNTAIN

INK FOUNTAIN ROLLER

INK FOUNTAIN DRIVE RATCHET GEAR

°E BED TION CAM

ASHWELL WOOD

REVOLUTION PRINTING MACHINE

explanatory side drawings. Note how the two electric motors are tucked neatly away under the platforms. The ordinary belt and pulley drive and delivery board are shown, but chain or V-shaped drives and extended pile delivery can be substituted if preferred. Every printing stage from the feeding of the sheets to the delivery of the printed sheets is shown.

MIEHLE TWO-COLOUR MACHINE

Fig. 5. *This close up view of a two-colour Miehle shows the arrangement of the cylinders and gives some idea of the massive construction of the cylinder and cylinder bearings.*

roller gauge on the type-bed, but most experienced minders prefer to set them, like the distributors, to the ink slab, and this latter is the better method. Use is made of strips of paper between the roller and the slab to judge the set of the roller. In practice, a narrow strip of paper is used between two wider pieces, the function of the wider pieces being to protect the narrow piece from the tack of the roller on one side, and the tack of the ink on the other. Thus, when the narrow piece is pulled, there will be no confusion between pressure and tack.

The wide difference in the judgment of different men in attempting to set rollers by means of the pressure of the roller on the narrow strip of paper has led the writer to advocate a slight modification in the generally accepted plan of working. Place the roller which goes nearest to the cylinder in the machine; place the three pieces of paper under

one end; lower the roller cup by means of the adjusting screw until the whole weight of the roller is on the slab. Now raise the roller gradually with the screw, while at the same time maintaining a strain on the narrow paper with the left hand. When the weight of the roller on the slab begins to get less, the paper gives a little to the steady strain, and thus tells the worker exactly where the roller is in relationship to the slab. This method will be found very much more positive than any other.

After the four inkers have been set to the slab on both sides, place the steel riders in the machine, lock them, and move machine so that neither slab nor forme contacts the inkers; then set the inkers up to the riders. For this operation help is needed, as the inkers must be brought up from both sides parallel to make firm contact right across the riders: firm contact with the riders obviates roller repeats, too firm contact causes wipe. Move the machine so that the slab is in the extreme position at the duct end; then put all the distributing rollers into the machine, take the composition rollers out of contact with the steel rollers, and proceed to set them to the slab, and afterwards to the steels in a similar manner to the inkers.

Correctly set, all composition rollers should make a flat mark on the slab from 12 to 18 points wide, and this can be tested. The aim should be to get this same width flat between the composition rollers and the steel riders. To set the duct roller, loosen the nut on the stud in slot of duct roller lever on the gear side, and a bolt in slot of the duct roller lever at the near side (the same spanner fits both nut and bolt) so that the roller rests evenly on the slab. For adjustment, set-screws, with lock-nuts, make contact with the bolt and stud. The duct is set to the duct roller. Loosen two nuts in the brackets on either side and pull the duct forward. Move the machine round until the duct roller is in its lowest position, when the duct is pushed lightly back until it is making continuous contact. The screws in the slots are then tightened.

Cylinder and Type-bed

The Register Rack. The function of the register rack is to bring the cylinder into correct relationship to the type-bed just before the cylinder is brought hard down on the impression. It is a short rack which is bolted to the near side of the type-bed in line with the pitch line, and engages with a segment of gear bolted to the side of the cylinder. Before these short gears disengage, the cylinder has been brought hard down on the impression, and there can be no loss of register afterwards.

The correct setting of the register rack is one of the most important settings from the point of view of register, and is to the two-revolution what the pusher-bar mechanism is to the Wharfedale. Once set correctly it seldom needs touching unless the machine develops a knock, or bad register is traced to the register rack. To re-set the rack, bring the cylinder down on the bearers, and if there is a forme on the bed, remove the packing to clear the forme. Now turn the machine forward until the bed is in the rear, and loosen the bolts holding the rack, sufficient to allow movement longways, but not to allow side play. Now *back* the machine by hand until the teeth come into mesh with the cylinder segment gear, taking care that they *do* mesh.

To determine if there is excessive play between the teeth move the rack longways; if there is more play than the thickness of a piece of thin paper, put a strip of hard paper or metal under the ledge so as to raise the rack and eliminate the extra play. If the rack is too high, this may break the teeth, or develop a slur. When the rack is the right height move the machine forward again and tighten the bolts just sufficiently to prevent free movement. Run the machine slowly with the cylinder on impression: a dozen cycles will be sufficient; stop, and further tighten bolts, but not too tightly. Put the speed up to normal; run the machine on impression for six cycles; then stop, and tighten fully.

After setting the register rack, test the machine for register between bed and cylinder by taking several impressions on the draw sheet. The whole point is that the wedge-shaped teeth of the gears must mesh sufficiently deeply to prevent excessive play (they should corrugate a strip of tissue paper, but not hold it); then, the rack having been placed approximately in position lengthways, the machine itself will make the final adjustment (the bolts being loose enough to allow the necessary movement, but tight enough to retain the new position). The bolts are then fully and finally tightened.

Advancing the Cylinder. A unique feature of the Miehle is the provision for advancing the cylinder so that it starts to print in advance of the normal pitch line and so is able to take a larger forme. The cylinder gear is split, making an inner gear and an outer ring gear; the inner gear being keyed to the cylinder journal and the ring gear bolted to it through four arms.

At each point where it is bolted, there is a choice of three holes, one corresponding to the normal pitch line and the other two being each one tooth in advance. To make the change, remove the four bolts and turn the flywheel back until the required set of holes is in line, then replace bolts. On the No. 4 Miehle each hole is $\frac{5}{8}$ in. in advance, but on all the larger size machines each hole is $\frac{3}{4}$ in. in advance of the other. Should the gears stick together after removing the bolts, scotch the inner gear to the framework in order to hold it while the flywheel is being turned.

Altering Roller Pitch

When working to the normal pitch-line all four inkers clear the forme. After altering the pitch, however, only three of the inkers clear the forme; the other should, therefore, be raised and re-set to prevent it reversing on the forme. Notice the pitch lines on the type-bed: the normal one goes right across, the two advance pitch lines are on the right and short. Should a knock develop after advancing or taking back the cylinder, re-set the register rack.

The Air Buffers. The strain on the machine due to the reversal of the bed is balanced by four air buffers, two at either end of the bed, which compress the air in the cylinders each time the bed reciprocates, thus absorbing the shock of sudden reversal. The leather heads of each buffer automatically adjust the air pressure to suit the various speeds of the machine. The faster the speed, the more air is trapped, and the greater the compression. The rims of the leather heads, which are kept pliable with neat's-foot oil, can be adjusted to make firmer contact with the air cylinders by means of a cone-nut in the inside centre of the heads, which will expand the leather. Should the compression be incorrect, though the leather heads are making firm contact, the heads can be brought forward or taken backwards on their rods to increase or decrease the compression.

Cylinder Springs. Though the cylinder on the Miehle is pulled down with a positive motion, it is raised by four powerful springs placed directly under the cylinder boxes. The machine cannot register if the cylinder does not take the full lift. If more tension is required on the impression springs, slack off the set screws in the cylinder spring blocks which support the springs on either side, and lengthen the amount of thread showing on the screw below the spring block. Pressure on each spring must be equal and the coils must not touch under full compression. Too much tension may cause wear. Tighten the set screws to prevent the block screws from moving.

The Delivery. The normal delivery is printed side up. After the sheets are printed the grippers open and the shoo-flies (which should be arranged towards the centre of the space between the grippers, but clear of the stripper fingers) lift the front edge of the printed sheet, while the stripper fingers, raised to clear the cylinder on the printing revolution, drop and engage under the lifted edge of the sheet. The travel of the printed sheet is thus diverted from the cylinder

MIEHLE CYLINDER PACKING

Fig. 6. *Showing the sheet bands on the first cylinder of a Miehle two-colour machine. Note that the full inking is not in use, as the riders are not shown in the illustration.*

along tapes for delivery. The tapes peel from under the sheet which drops on to the pile that may be on the machine-board or extended beyond the board.

On some models the printed-side-up delivery can be changed to flyer-stick delivery which turns the sheets over ready for backing up, and the few simple adjustments necessary to put one delivery out of action and bring in the other, take but a few minutes. Of the two deliveries, however, the printed-side-up is, generally speaking, the best, as it allows the minder to keep a more careful watch on his work. Tapes, guides and stops give good control of the sheets during delivery.

The extended pile delivery is in every way an improvement on all previous methods. It allows several separated sheets to be in process of delivery on the lengthened tapes, and the wet ink thus has more time to settle and dull over before the next sheet touches it. This arrangement, and the fact that there is no necessity to handle the wet work, which is stacked up on a gradually descending platform ready to be wheeled away when full, greatly obviates risk of set-off, and increases output. The extended pile delivery slightly increases the length and cost of the machine, but where there is sufficient room for the extension, the extra cost is fully justified by the advantages gained.

Perfecting Machines

The Perfector. This machine, which is in effect two orthodox single-cylinder Miehles placed together back to back, is particularly suitable for printing general bookwork involving long runs, for catalogues and for magazines. It is an impressive sight to see an eight-crown perfector machine fitted with automatic feed and extended pile delivery, printing both sides of a 60 by 40 in. sheet at speeds between 1,500 and 2,000 per hour. The machine has two impression cylinders, which rotate inwards towards each other, and a taking-off cylinder or drum for delivery and slitting purposes.

Both impression cylinders can be checked independently. The two type-beds come together in the centre of the

BATTERY OF TWO-REVOLUTION MACHINES

A fine example of a modern letterpress machine room with ample daylight and artificial lighting and exceptionally wide gangways. There is a liberal amount of room for stacking and for movement of trollies, and there are no light-obstructing and dust-collecting pipes.

machine and the ink slabs are at either end. As there is absolutely no lag between the release of the grippers on the first cylinder and the take of the grippers on the second cylinder, register on the grip is assured. Offset on the second cylinder is obviated by an anti-offset arrangement which dresses the draw-sheet before each impression with a special fluid containing paraffin wax and oil. The draw-sheet on the second cylinder of a perfector must be of vege-table parchment, so as to prevent the oil from soaking through to the cylinder sheets.

Inks with special characteristics for this class of work have been developed, and these quickly penetrate the absorb-ent paper and finally set bone-hard for binding purposes.

One of the difficulties met with in bookwork is the fluff which comes from featherweight antique paper, which continually collects. If this fluff falls on the rollers it spoils the inking. Brushes are arranged for easy adjustment and removal for cleaning, and a wide tray is also provided which can be readily removed for cleaning by taking out two screws on the feed side. A very tacky roller should be worked next to the cylinder in each case; this roller picks up any fluff which gets on the forme and the fluff finds its way to the duct. The residue of ink containing this should always be removed from the duct before adding a fresh supply of ink. If there is any choice, the forme requiring the heaviest inking is always put to print on the second cylinder.

The mechanical arrangements on the perfector are very similar to those on the orthodox single-cylinder Miehle. The slight modifications which have been necessary with the changed design are all sound, both from an engineering and printing point of view, and any competent two-revolution minder is quickly at home on the perfector.

The Tandem Miehle. More than thirty years ago, the hazards encountered in producing fine process colour work on flat-bed letterpress machines caused progressive printers to look around for methods which would produce a finished result in three or four colours practically in one operation. If this could be done, it would not only solve the problem of paper stretching and shrinking between the printings, but it would also enable the various colours to be modified and corrected to reproduce positive results in the finished product and cut out duplication of certain handling charges.

True, there was the two-colour stop-cylinder machine, but the disadvantage of the superimposition of impression on the one-impression cylinder ruled out this machine for this class of work. It was thus that the tandem idea was born. The practice was for three or four Miehle machines to be lined up and coupled together. They were fitted with either conveyor tapes or a travelling carriage to convey the printed sheets from one machine to the next; slow-down tapes finished the register of the sheets in the lays. Later, special machines were supplied to order by Linotype & Machinery, Ltd., fitted with a coupling arrangement, so that the machines could be worked in tandem or individually as desired. While a measure of success attended the persistent efforts of several well-known printing firms who adopted the idea, tandem Miehles never quite solved the problem of register, but they probably hastened the advent of the two-revolution two-colour machine.

Miehle Two-colour. The Miehle two-colour machine has two impression cylinders. Each forme is made ready on

its own impression cylinder in exactly the same way as on a single-colour machine, without the limitations of the superimposed impression of the two-colour stop cylinder. Register racks are provided between the transfer cylinder and the impression cylinder, and between the impression cylinder and the two beds. The sheet is never out of control during transference from one set of grippers to another. Register is therefore absolute at all points, and the advantages gained from having two impression cylinders are not offset by loss of register in any direction (Figs. 5, 6 and 7).

A brush is provided on the first cylinder to smooth out wrinkles in the sheet, but sheet bands can be substituted if preferred, as a brush cannot be employed on the second cylinder, owing to the wet ink from the first impression. Smoothing out on the second cylinder is carried out by a set of roller-type sheet bands which work in the margins. As a further precaution against smearing the wet ink while the sheet is in progress, the transfer cylinder is fitted with a number of strips with serrated edges which, working between margins, keep the wet surface clear of any contact, and this is quite effective.

The design of the machine makes it very accessible both from a make-ready and washing-up point of view. The mechanical arrangements throughout are similar to the Miehle single-colour, the bed movement being identical.

The development of quick-set inks has greatly favoured the use of these machines and robbed the old bogey, "wet on wet," of much of its terror.

While a pair of No. 3 two-colour Miehles is the ideal equipment for good class four-colour process work, fair results can be obtained on one machine by running the sheets through twice in the usual manner, or by carefully

STREAM FEEDER ON A TWO-COLOUR MIEHLE
Fig. 7. *The sheets are fed in a continuous underlapped stream. As each sheet is taken by the grippers, the next sheet is only a few inches from the register lays.*

dividing the ink duct, using paper half the width, and printing two colours wet on each half of the machine. In this latter way, it is possible to complete a whole four-colour set in one operation.

Test prints help to decide the best order of progression for the colours, but this question has to be considered from various angles: the predominating tone of the finished result and matching the copy, and the slight mingling of the colours working side by side and following one another. The heavier colour of each pair is best printed on the second cylinder, and as far as possible only light colours or heavy colours should be paired side by side:—

Example 1

Near-side 1st cylinder	.	.	.	Red
,,	2nd	,,	.	.	Blue
Off-side	1st	,,	.	.	Yellow
,,	2nd	,,	.	.	Black

Example 2

Near-side 1st cylinder	.	.	.	Yellow
,,	2nd	,,	.	.	Blue
Off-side	1st	,,	.	.	Red
,,	2nd	,,	.	.	Black

Examples of four-colour printing and other colour work, and details regarding colour filters and tint blocks, are given in the Colour Section which is inserted in the chapter on Process Engraving.

The two-colour machine presents no outstanding difficulties to a two-revolution minder, but the following points can be emphasized as applying in particular to this type of machine: both cylinders must be correctly dressed and exactly the same; the grippers on both cylinders must be in exactly the same position in relation to the sheet. This is best done by marking the position of the first set on a sheet and running it through the machine until the second set of grippers take it; these grippers are then moved to the marks.

Position the key-forme first on the appropriate type-bed (heavier colour to print on second cylinder); bring underlaying, interlaying, position and register of key-forme along together, so that when the position is finally determined the forme will not need disturbing again. When the position of the key-forme is correct, the second forme is locked in position on its type-bed, underlaid, interlaid, and then registered.

CHAPTER ELEVEN

MAKING-READY AND RUNNING PROBLEMS

MACHINE MINDER'S WORK.   MAKING-READY METHODS.   INTERLAYS AND OVERLAYS.
VIGNETTED HALF-TONES.   SLURRING PROBLEMS.   RISING SPACES.   CREASING.   PLUCKING.
INK POWDERING.   BAD REGISTER.   AUTOMATIC FEEDERS.   SPRAYING FOR SET-OFF.
STATIC ELECTRICITY IN PAPER.   LETTERPRESS INKS.   ROLLER COMPOSITION.

OF all the processes involved in the production of a book, folder or catalogue, none is more important than the work of the machine minder. In his hands the finished product takes shape. His work includes, as we have seen, the setting up of the machine to feed, take and deliver the sheets; the setting and adjustment of the various parts to maintain accurate register; setting the rollers to obtain perfect inking; setting the ink duct; and the oiling and careful handling of an intricate piece of machinery, so as to avoid breakdowns and maintain its running efficiency. All this has to do with mechanical production and has already been dealt with. It calls for considerable mechanical aptitude and ability.

But much of the work of the machine minder is not mechanical at all. His is the craft of dealing with the various printing materials and surfaces from which he takes his impressions, and with methods necessary to obtain these.

There are many elements which go to make a finished printed work, and in spite of all the pre-make-ready schemes much can go wrong before a forme reaches the printer and his machine. Jobs are seldom straightforward. The Linotype slugs may be bottle-necked, the electrotypes very uneven, the zincos shallow, the stereotypes rough, the mounts untrue, the forme springy, or

the paper bad, and a host of other sources of trouble. But if even moderate results are to be obtained, all inequalities or deficiencies in material, workmanship, or mechanical principle that are inherent or have crept in before the job reaches him, must be dealt with by the machine minder in the process of make-ready, preparatory to running.

Is Make-ready Necessary?

Much has been written about make-ready, and many writers have speculated as to whether it is really necessary. They suggest that if more attention were attached to precision in the manufacture of materials it would do away with the process. While it is true that good plates and mounts considerably minimize work on the machine, this view takes no account of the cylindrical method of taking an impression from a relief surface.

If pressure is spread over a greater area, that pressure is reduced; and vice versa. Regard the cylinder as supplying the pressure and the flat surface of the forme as offering the resistance. The cylinder makes contact with only the narrow strip of the forme falling under dead centre, and the area of printing surface falling within this narrow strip is constantly changing according to the design of the forme. Thus the same amount of potential pressure is spread over a greater or lesser area, and the pressure of an evenly packed cylinder on the various parts of the forme varies throughout an impression, and will always require adjustment.

Making-ready an Eight-page Catalogue Forme. Presuming that the cylinder has been dressed, the rollers set, the position of the sheet determined on the feed-board, and everything connected with the control of the sheet has so far been attended to (as detailed earlier), the back of the catalogue forme is thoroughly cleaned. If the type is Monotype or Linotype there will be small particles of metal adhering to the back, and it will be advantageous to scrape the back with the long edge of a palette knife and afterwards rub with a rag as is done with founders' type. The type bed of the machine is also wiped, and the forme then placed on it with the lay edge towards the pitch line.

Position of the Forme

To get the position of the forme a sheet of the stock is folded and placed in position on the forme, and both are moved together so that the edge of the stock overhangs the pitch line by 16 points. The locking-up bars are used if there is room, and the necessary furniture is arranged. To position the forme sideways a sheet is placed in the lays, and a measurement taken from its edge to the cylinder bearer is matched with the forme on the bed. Forme clamps are provided for locking-up purposes. Unlock the forme so that the chase lies flat before it is locked on the bed. This also provides an opportunity to gauge and underlay all blocks type-high, and test for level. As the blocks are replaced and quoins made thumb-tight, all rule and border joinings are put right and any tendency to spring traced to its source and corrected. A likely source is that the edges of mounts are slightly

undercut. A narrow strip of card pasted along the bottom edge of such mounts will correct this.

While all quoins are thumb-tight, the forme is lightly planed down; isolated parts such as folios are attended to with the fingers to prevent damage by planer. The lock-up, too, is light, as any tendency to spring is accentuated by tight lock-up. A pull is taken and position and underlay are checked up. If the imposition is right and no interlaying is necessary, but the position on the paper and underlays requires slight attention, it is better to lift the forme for any necessary underlaying of individual blocks. If interlays are necessary the required number of pulls is taken and the interlays are then cut.

Cutting Interlays and Overlays

In letterpress the gradation in tone of a half-tone plate corresponds to a gradation in resistance to pressure. The image of the screen, as influenced by the light from the subject photographed, stands in relief on the plate, and varies from pin-point dots in the high-lights to comparatively solid areas in the deep shadows. The object of an interlay or overlay is to balance the variation in resistance by varying the pressure on the different areas. The aim is not to alter the tonal values, but rather to retain, under working conditions, the values already there. Every subject calls for its own special treatment.

To Cut an Interlay for a Vignette. Three pulls are taken, one on art paper, one on super-calendered 30-lb. double crown, and one on glazed bank. Remove the high-lights from the art pull and cut round 6 points inside the vignette edge. Remove solids from super-calendered paper and paste them on the art pull. Remove and discard high-lights and greys from the glazed bank and cut round the darker shadow of

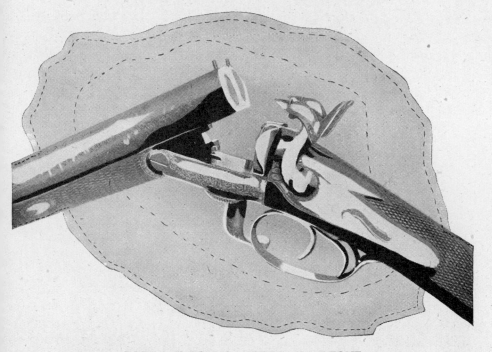

INTERLAY FOR VIGNETTED HALF-TONE

Fig. 1. *A three-ply interlay, pasted together ready to be secured in exact register on the back of the vignetted half-tone plate. The base sheet has only the high-lights removed, and is cut round the outside dotted line, 6 points inside the hard edge. The second sheet has the high-lights and light greys removed, and is cut round the inside dotted line, which follows the darker shadow of the vignette. The solids, taken from the third sheet, are pasted on to the first and second sheets to complete the interlay, which is then pasted in position.*

the vignette; or, if there is no darker shadow, cut away round the figure or article and add this sheet to the interlay.

Patches must be slightly smaller than the detail; cut-outs slightly larger than the detail. Extra patches of glazed bank can be included in the interlay if the plate seems hollow or weak in any part. The whole interlay is then pasted together (Fig. 1). The aim in cutting an interlay is to leave the plate slightly lower at the edges than towards the centre; even in the centre this type of block should be barely type high.

The forme should now be unlocked and the blocks taken out and dismounted. The interlays are pasted in position on the backs of the plates. Use is made of two of the old holes in the plates for re-positioning on mounts, but fresh holes are drilled and countersunk to take the brads and obviate marking trouble on the run caused by brads rising. With vignettes the best results are obtained by working them the thickness of a thin bank under type-high, and this is borne in mind as the blocks are re-underlaid to gauge. They are then replaced in the forme which is re-locked and another pull is taken to check position, underlays and interlays. When correct, a sheet is sent to be passed by the reader for general position while the overlays are being cut.

Cutting Overlays (Figs. 2A to 2E). Best results are obtained with simple overlays rather than elaborate creations. Those cut on thin paper which treat the tones in broad areas, rather than the cutting-out and patching-up of tiny detail, are the most successful.

For instance, a light subject on a solid background, or a dark subject on a light ground, may need an orthodox three-piece overlay. Another plate may have neither actual solids nor high-lights.

The three-piece overlay, however, may not always be practicable, but if

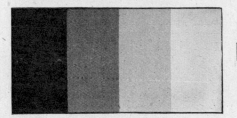

Fig. 2a. *The main tones to look for when cutting a straightforward overlay.*

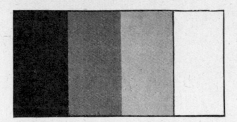

Fig. 2b. *The work on the first sheet of an overlay. The high-lights (white parts) are removed and discarded.*

Fig. 2c. *The work on the second sheet of the overlay. The high-lights and the light greys are removed and discarded.*

Fig. 2d. *Only the solids, or very dark portions, are retained from the third sheet. All other tones are cut away and discarded.*

Fig. 2e. *Shows, in elevation, the finished three-ply overlay, pasted together. Three pieces on the solids, two pieces on the middle tones, one piece on the light greys, and no pieces at all on the high-lights.*

understood, may form the basis of a suitable compromise. The work follows the tonal values of the illustration.

The Three-piece Overlay. Take three pulls on very thin bank paper and, in addition, one on art paper to serve as a guide.

First Sheet. Remove and discard the high-lights.

Second Sheet. Remove the solids (or near solids) and paste them on first sheet.

Third Sheet. Remove and discard the high-lights and greys, and paste the remainder on the first sheet.

This results in three thicknesses on solids or near solids; two thicknesses on middle tones; one thickness on greys, and none on high-lights.

Overlay for Vignetted Half-tone. A slight variation in procedure is necessary in the case of vignetted half-tones; the methods are designed to do away with

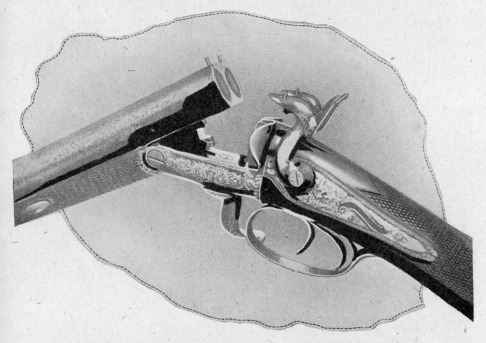

OVERLAY FOR VIGNETTED HALF-TONE: SHEETS 1 AND 2

Fig. 3. *First sheet of overlay with high-lights removed, and the solids, taken from the second sheet, pasted on. It is cut round the dotted line, one point inside the hard edge.*

any semblance of hard edge in the resultant print. Take a hand-rubbing or heavy pull on art paper, 60-lb. royal, and let it clearly show every bit of edge. Now take three pulls on glazed bank.

First Sheet. Remove and discard the high-lights from the hand-rubbing, and cut round one point inside the hard edge (Fig. 3).

Second Sheet. Remove the solids (or near solids) from the glazed bank and paste them on to the first sheet (Fig. 3).

Third Sheet. Remove and discard all but the darker portions of the subject (Fig. 4).

Fourth Sheet. Remove and discard the high-lights and light greys, cut round the darker shadow of the vignette and paste the remainder on to the first sheet (Figs. 5 and 6).

When the forme is passed for position,

and underlays and interlays (if used), also rule and border joinings, are good, and the whole forme free from spring, a pull is taken on super-calendered paper; this, while still in the grippers, is pierced through for registering on the cylinder. It may be more exact to split this sheet up into four pieces, so pierce through accordingly. This will allow the back half of the sheet to be mounted slightly forward, and make up for the difference of printing it above the packing and mounting it below.

The overlays may be fastened to a tight manila immediately above the linen, or they can be mounted on these four sections which are positioned to the bodkin holes in the top one of the two pasted-in sheets on the cylinder (see Cylinder Dressing). Two loose super-calendered sheets are discarded from the cylinder before the top sheet is re-reeled.

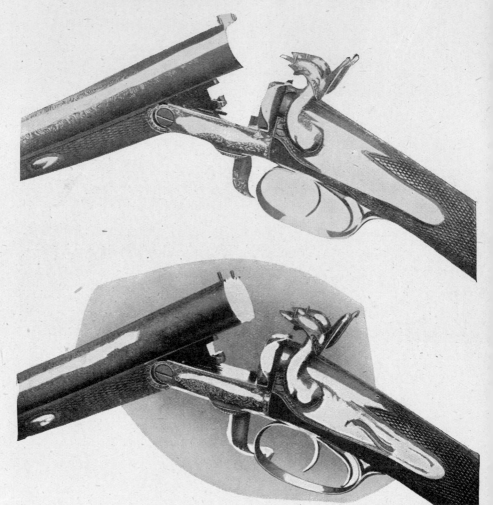

OVERLAY FOR VIGNETTED HALF-TONE: SHEETS 3 AND 4

Fig. 4 *(above). Showing all the darker portions of the subject taken from sheet 3 (the remainder has been discarded). Cut as this, it should be superimposed on sheets 1 and 2.*

Fig. 5 *(below). The high-lights and light greys are removed from the fourth sheet which is then trimmed round the darker shadow of the vignette and superimposed on the first, second and third sheets in order to complete the overlay, as described in the text.*

A pull on art paper is taken and examined, and this is marked as may be necessary for facing up the blocks and then put on one side for the time being. A pull is now taken on super-calendered paper for levelling-up purposes. It should not be too heavy. When viewed from the back the bulk of the impression should be lighter than working weight.

Working with this amount of indentation requires less work to perfect the impression. This sheet should be carefully marked out for two or three broad overlapping patches on each page to

OVERLAY FOR VIGNETTED HALF-TONE: FINISHED RESULT

Fig. 6. *The above result has been obtained by the use of similar methods in the matter of interlay and overlay, to those described. The sharp contrasts of tone brought out on the gun give way to soft gradation on the background. No semblance of an edge is seen.*

bring the light parts up to the heavy, and all pages uniform in impression. When this patching up is done turn the sheet over and face up the blocks by reference to the pull on art paper; also face up any parts which the work on the back will obviously not correct.

It is very important that all paste should be kept in the margins to avoid a lumpy impression, as the art paper will show every little variation. This sheet should be positioned either to the overlay sheet already in position on the cylinder, or, if overlays are mounted direct on bottom tight manila, it should be positioned to bodkin holes, and one loose super-calendered sheet discarded from the cylinder.

Another pull on super-calendered will decide if a further patched sheet is necessary (it probably is), or if the remaining work can be done on the patched sheet already on the cylinder. This second sheet of work will almost complete the make-ready, except for certain spotting up of individual letters.

RUNNING PROBLEMS

IN his work the letterpress machine minder has four main elements of trouble with which he must contend: the forme, the paper, the ink, and the machine. Yet the difficulties associated with these are legion, and no machine-man is immune from trouble for long.

But although he may not always steer clear of difficulties, he may sail out of them if he knows the cause of the trouble he is experiencing. Among the more common difficulties met with in running may be mentioned: (1) slurring; (2) spaces rising; (3) creasing; (4) plucking;

(5) set-off; (6) second printing not taking over the first; (7) work sticking together; (8) ink powdering; and (9) bad register.

1. SLURRING. This trouble can usually be attributed to the following causes:—

(*a*) *Springy Forme.* A springy forme is off the bed and is pushed down during impression; this movement takes place while the paper is in contact with the forme, and causes slur. The spring is caused by faulty material in the forme, but is also often accentuated by a lock-up that is too tight (Fig. 7).

(*b*) *Rocking Blocks* always cause slurring because the printing surface moves on the paper during impression. Warped wooden mounts are usually the cause of the trouble, but bad underlay is also often responsible. When underlaying, blocks should always be well tested for rock and sandpapered down if necessary. A rasp may be used if the mounts are very bad, and a lot can be done to correct a slight rock by the manner of underlaying. The underlay should always be brought right up to the extreme edge of the blocks. Plates which are mounted on metal mounts will not rock

or slur, and this method is always best.

(*c*) *Blocks or Forme Over or Under Type-high.* This will raise the cylinder off the bearers or cause a drag on the sheet and buckles. Both of these faults cause slur and should be guarded against when making ready.

(*d*) *Impression Too Light on Rules or Blocks.* Although this may be regarded as one of the unlikely causes of slur it should not be ruled out as a possibility. The impression should always be firm, otherwise printing is more or less a blur or " shaky," instead of sharp and clear.

(*e*) *Underlay on Large Mounting Boards.* The principle of underlaying on large mounting boards is to strengthen resistance here and allow yield there. When working process plates on these boards, it is often better to correct inequalities in the forme by way of interlays and keep the underlay which adjusts type-height even, so that the board lies snugly on the bed.

(*f*) *Sheet Sagging from Cylinder.* If the sheet should sag it will touch the forme before printing and this will cause slur. On Wharfedale machines strips of

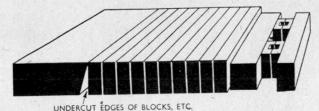

UNDERCUT EDGES OF BLOCKS, ETC.

Fig. 7. *Showing how faulty material will cause spring in formes. The spring is greatly accentuated by tight lock-up.*

EXAGGERATED RESULT OF
TIGHT LOCK-UP WHERE
EDGES OF BLOCKS, ETC.
ARE UNDERCUT

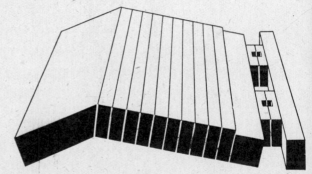

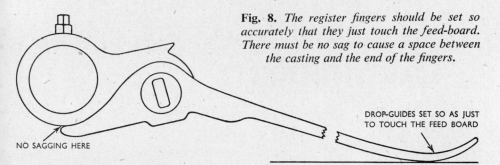

Fig. 8. *The register fingers should be set so accurately that they just touch the feed-board. There must be no sag to cause a space between the casting and the end of the fingers.*

DROP-GUIDES SET SO AS JUST TO TOUCH THE FEED BOARD

NO SAGGING HERE

springy card on the feed-board and working between grippers will hold the sheet up to the cylinder if they extend a little beyond the lays. On two-revolution machines a tape will hold the sheet up to the cylinder and prevent the back edge from licking the forme.

(*g*) *Sheet Buckling in Grippers.* On the two-revolution machine the board may be too high or the grippers on each side of the lay-rests too close. This will, in each case, cause buckles, and the bulky sheet, as in the case of baggy packing, will touch the forme before it actually prints and cause a slur. The remedies are obvious.

2. SPACES RISING. This trouble is often, quite wrongly, attributed to bad justification on the part of the compositor or the composing machine. While it is true to say that Monotype is apt to give trouble with rising spaces, it will usually be found to be the composite formes that are the culprits. More often than not the cause of the trouble can be traced to:—

(*a*) *Springy Forme.* When an impression is taken from a springy forme, the cylinder, making contact with the type-high portion of the forme, forces it down to the bed. Nothing makes contact with the spaces and consequently these are left a little higher. This is repeated until the spaces are so high that they are inked by the rollers.

(*b*) *Rocking Blocks.* When the blocks are not standing true on their bases they are caused to rock under impression and this movement, though it may be slight, will always bring up the spaces round the faulty block. If the block is only a line block the movement may be partly absorbed by the packing and insufficient to cause slur, but it should always be suspected as a likely cause of spaces rising round about it.

(*c*) *Untrue Wooden Mounts.* When the sides of blocks are undercut from surface to base, the other material making contact can square with it only by rising from the bed; this then acts as in (*a*). A strip of card $\frac{1}{8}$ in. wide pasted to the side along the bottom edge of the block will square the block and prevent this (Fig. 7).

(*d*) *Bottle-necked Slugs.* On occasion, and due to some fault, Linotype slugs may be bottle-necked (Fig. 9), i.e. wider at the top than at the bottom, and thus they make contact at the top but stand away from each other at the bottom. Under pressure from lock-up these spaces at the bottom close up and the whole page rises from the bed like an arch. This arch is forced down by the cylinder as each impression is taken, and rises again off the bed. In this way, any whites are brought up until they are high enough to print. The real remedy is to have the slugs recast, but if this is

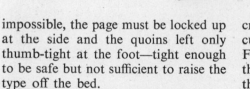

SHOWING BOTTLE-NECKED SLUGS

Fig. 9. *If, when working formes of Linotype, the slugs are slightly bottle-necked, excessive lock-up pressure at the foot of the pages will bring the slugs off the bed of the machine like an arch.*

EXAGGERATED RESULT OF
TIGHT LOCK-UP WHEN
SLUGS ARE BOTTLE-NECKED.

impossible, the page must be locked up at the side and the quoins left only thumb-tight at the foot—tight enough to be safe but not sufficient to raise the type off the bed.

(*e*) *Faulty Furniture* will act in the same way as untrue wooden mounts. When the faulty furniture is located, it should be reversed by turning over. As there is always something in a forme which is untrue and likely to cause spring, the trouble should not be accentuated by tight lock-up; a loose forme cannot spring. Locking-up should be safe but not tight.

3. CREASING. Whatever the design of the forme, creasing is seldom caused by anything other than the following:—

(*a*) *Immature and Wavy-edged Paper.* This is one of the most common causes of the paper creasing on cylinder machines. When the paper comes in contact with the printing surface, as the cylinder rolls over the forme, the extra bulk round the sides of the sheet caused by the wave has to go somewhere. It is pushed back and back until, restricted by the pull of the smaller dimension inside the sheet, it cannot get away, and a crease is inevitable. The best way to cure the trouble is to cure the paper. Failing this, take up the extra bulk of the wavy edge each side with bolsters of thick wrapper round the cylinder, running them from the edge of the paper to within 6 points of the printing design.

(*b*) *Over-packed Cylinder.* This will often cause a crease. The surface of the over-packed cylinder races the printing surface and causes a drag on the one hand and a pull on the other. The bulging paper is often apt to crease. Over-packing is met with when printing off fairly solid plates mounted on large boards, or when the cylinder is not properly down on its bearers.

(*c*) *Grippers not Holding Sheet Tight.* If some of the grippers are not holding the sheet tight—particularly the end grippers at each side—part of the sheet may pull out of the grippers to some extent during printing. This causes extra bulk each side and creasing after the manner of wavy-edged paper.

(*d*) *Spongy Packing* will prevent the sheet from smoothing out freely round the cylinder and is apt to cause a crease on that account. When the nature of a forme suggests the possibility of creasing trouble, hard packing should be put up —and put up carefully.

4. PLUCKING. When, while printing on coated paper, plucking is experienced, it is advisable to reduce the ink with a solid mineral solvent such as solid oil, safe-set, pomade, pedraline, or the like. This will tend to make the ink shorter and decrease the pull on the coating of the paper, and will also help, from a set-off point of view, by driving the ink into the absorbent paper. Boiled linseed oil should on no account be added to ink under these circumstances.

5. SET-OFF. Although set-off is primarily associated with the ink, it has a connection with the impression. Unless the right amount and kind of impression is carried, excessive ink will be needed. If the ink is not pressed to the bottom of the grain in the paper the grain must be filled with ink. Other causes of set-off are as follows:—

(a) *Bad Distribution and Rolling.* Distribution rollers should be properly set and a full stroke arranged on the duct. In this way the ink is well spread out before it reaches the inking rollers. These, too, must be set to roll the forme correctly, as any semblance of wipe will pile the ink on the edges and always cause set-off.

(b) *Wrong Ink.* Good quality ink is much more dense than the cheaper quality, owing to the fact that it has more pigment ground into the vehicle. A thinner film of such ink will give a better result than a thicker film of poorer ink, with less risk of set-off; and this is equally true in the case of blacks as it is with colours.

(c) *Wrong Treatment of Ink.* When reducing ink for coated or other absorbent papers, boiled oil or other tacky solvents should not be used. For art or imitation art a solid solvent such as pomade, solid oil, or pedraline is good.

For ordinary printings or super-calendered papers a few spots of paraffin, well mixed in, will prevent set-off. On tub-sized papers ink cannot penetrate and no reduction of the ink is desirable; reliance has to be placed on a firm hard impression and a good quick-drying ink carrying the minimum amount.

(d) *Ink Drying on Machine.* If the ink is drying on the machine it gathers and gets thicker and thicker. It should be washed up, otherwise set-off is almost inevitable.

(e) *Bad Handling of Wet Sheets.* Great care is necessary in the handling of wet work. Pile delivery is, of course, the ideal. Where this is not available it is an advantage to run the sheets direct into trays on the machine, and lift down on the tray without any movement between the sheets.

6. SECOND PRINTING NOT TAKING OVER THE FIRST. When a second printing has to be super-imposed, the first working must be kept soft. If the first working is reduced with boiled oil, or if paste driers are added, the second working will not pick up. If reduction is necessary use a spot of raw linseed oil; if the addition of driers is needed, a few spots of terebene may prove helpful if the paper is absorbent.

7. WORK STICKING TOGETHER. This trouble occurs on label work printed on esparto or litho paper, in cases where there is overlapping of colours, and they remain bright and sticky on the surface of the paper, and dry by oxidation. Excess of driers should be avoided in the earlier workings to keep them moderately soft, and with the later workings the work should be shaken up three or four hours after printing, just as the ink has become tacky. Once properly disturbed at this stage the ink will not stick again. This work should not be stacked too high, as considerable heat is generated during the drying process.

8. INK POWDERING. When working with heavy pigments such as white, or chrome, the ink will often dry and then powder off to the touch on art and other paper. With any heavy pigment the ink should be worked as stiff as possible. Certainly nothing of a penetrating nature should be added to drive the vehicle into the paper and leave the powder dry on the surface without a binder.

9. BAD REGISTER may be attributable to the following causes:—

(a) *The Machine or Setting up of the Machine.* Bad register may be fundamental to a machine or only due to the faulty setting up of the machine. When two machines are involved, with one machine following another, it is necessary to match exactly everything to do with the take on both machines. Lays, sheet-bands, grippers, and wheels should be in identical positions on the sheet. Amount of grip, height of feed-board and cylinder dressings should be the same and the speeds of both machines kept constant.

If, in spite of these precautions, the register is out along the grip edge, the fault may be due to the front lays lifting too early or too late. They may not be down to the rests, or they may be down too hard and springing the lay-rests. The front lay plates may be too vertical. The correct angle is a slight slope outwards so as to clear the edge of the sheet as the lays rise on a radius; a groove in the lay plate will also move the sheet as the lays rise. If the front-lays are set too far out, allowing too much grip, the grippers are liable to disturb the sheet as they close; the drop guides sagging on the sheet will push it from the lays (Fig. 8). If the grippers do not hold the sheet, or some of them are bent out of shape and knocking the sheet as they close, this is equally bad. On open formes the paper may sag in spite of the brush, and this will cause loss of register towards the back. Tape round the cylinder will prevent this; it should be looped round the sheet-band shaft, run between grippers and in a gutter of the forme, and secured to the bar under the back section of the feed-board.

If the cylinder is over packed this will cause distortion of the printed sheet, the over-packed cylinder surface trying to race the printing surface drags and distorts the sheet during printing.

When register cannot be obtained on the draw sheet, however, it may be due to one of the following faults: register rack may need resetting; cylinder not fully down on bearers; air buffers not functioning; if out across the cylinder it may be due to end play in the cylinder or side play in the type bed. To correct any end play in the cylinder, remove the bolt and large cylinder shaft washer, take out a paper packing washer and substitute a thinner one. To correct any side play in the type-bed, set the outside gibs tighter against vertical side guides.

(b) *Paper Stretching or Contracting.* If paper for register work cannot be properly cured, it should be hung in the machine room for at least twelve hours before printing. Paper stretches more across the web than in the machine direction (on some papers, nearly as much as eight times); therefore, where register is all important on a job, the longer dimension of the paper should run in the direction of the web. In this way, the greatest stretch takes place along the narrow width and the trouble is minimized.

On heavy carton work, a change in the direction of the web will alter the position about 3 points right from the grip. This is probably due to the different lie of the sheets on the feed-board, and its influence on inertia as the grippers take the sheet. The wrappers of these boards are usually marked with an arrow to indicate the direction of the web, but the direction can be easily detected while handling.

(*c*) *Wavy Paper*. When register is perfect along the grip but out along the sides and back, it is usually caused by buckles. Wavy-edged paper is one of the causes of buckles, and to cure this trouble, bolsters round the cylinder (as for creases) are effective, but maturing is better.

(*d*) *Untrimmed Lay Edges* may sometimes be the unsuspected cause of bad register. An untrimmed lay edge is an unknown quantity, and no two sheets stand up to the lays in the same way if they have a feather edge. For exact work, paper should always be trimmed.

(*e*) *Pull of the Ink*. Variation in register is sometimes caused by the pull of the ink. On large sheets of solid label work any variation in the consistency of the ink, or of the quantity carried, changes the pull on the sheet, and this, as the minder of any two-colour machine knows, will upset the register.

AUTOMATIC FEEDERS

BEFORE hand feeding could be said to limit in any way the output of sheet-fed printing machines, British inventive genius had already applied itself to the prodigious task of producing a mechanical device to perform the operations previously carried out by hand, backed by the human brain. The device must be capable not only of stripping the sheets one by one from the top of a pile and conveying them to the grippers of the printing machine—it must adjust each sheet accurately to the lays to obtain perfect register. It must be capable of tripping and stopping the machine when normal feeding conditions vary, as when sheets stick together, or with torn sheets. The device must be sufficiently versatile to handle various sizes of different stocks with quick change over. It must be accurate and reliable in running at high speed, in order to turn out first-class work and to avoid frequent stops.

How successful the inventors were in their task, may be judged by the great number of automatic feeders in use, and by the quality and quantity of the work they turn out. No wise printer today would buy a printing machine without buying an automatic feeder for it. In many directions mechanical production must be inferior to hand work, but in this case the automatic feeder takes over the tedious job and does it better than it can be performed by hand. And what a picture to watch the separation of the sheets by a large auto-feeder; the flick of the elegant and dainty combing operation, the float forward of the sheet like a veritable magic carpet!

The separating mechanism is the most important feature of automatic feeders. Some of the earlier successful automatic feeders were of the friction type, i.e. friction was used to fan out and separate the sheets. But this does not signify that the principle of suction is something new in sheet control; it was one of the early successful methods tried for feeding, and the principle was utilized for the delivery on the old lithographic machines.

Friction feeds have their points: the Cross feeder is really continuous. The Dexter is well named. For small sheets, automatic feeders employing only suction and blast are satisfactory; the L. & M. front separation may be mentioned as an example. The Universal is excellent for sizes up to demy.

Fig. 10. *H.T.B. automatic stream feeder showing one side of the back-combing mechanism.*

Progress has been very rapid in the development of automatic feeders; the latest types combine friction with air-suction and blast for the separation of the sheets.

A difficulty which all automatic feeders for the larger sizes of printing machines had to overcome, was the great distance which the sheet had to travel down the two large feed boards, from the pile to the lays, in a little more than one second. This difficulty was completely overcome by the introduction of the stream feed which feeds the sheets down the feed board in a continuous under-lapped stream (see Chapter 10, Fig. 7). There are several good stream feeders to choose from: the H.T.B., L. & M. and Interflow are three of the best-known makes. A description of the operation of an automatic feeder, as given below, may prove useful.

The H.T.B. Feeder

The separating, lifting and forwarding of the sheets are done on the following principle. Two hollow blower feet, or, as they are sometimes called, second-sheet stops, descend on to the rear edge and some distance in from the corners of the pile. The blower feet press slightly into the pile, and their air orifices are directed forward over the pile. Rotary combers now descend on to the rear corners of the pile and comb the top sheets inwards so as to form humps between the blower feet and the combing wheels. The lifting suckers, of which there are two, now descend and are positioned above the humps by means of adjustable stops which rest on the uncombed portion of the pile.

When the lifting suckers are thus positioned, they suck up the topmost sheet. The blower feet now rise, followed by the combers and lifting suckers; and, in lifting, the suckers are caused to move outward, towards the top corners of the pile, for the purpose of stretching the sheet. At the same time the blower feet move backwards to clear the rear edge of the rising sheet and when clear, they move inwards, below the sheet, and downwards on to the rear edge of the pile (Fig. 10).

Meanwhile, the sheet is transferred to a set of forwarding suckers of which there may be two or more. These are situated about $1\frac{1}{2}$ in. above the rear edge of the pile and have a reciprocating movement of about $2\frac{1}{2}$ in. towards the front and rear of the pile respectively. When the separated sheet is transferred to the forwarding suckers from the lifting suckers, it is drawn backwards slightly. At the same time the air blast to the blower feet is switched on, blowing a current of air between the separated sheet and the pile. The sheet is then forwarded on this cushion of air until it enters between the drop wheels and tape roller, which are situated in front of the pile, on the conveyor portion of the feeder. Smoothers are used over the sheet to guide it between these wheels and the tape roller, and there is also a flap or jogger which guides the sheet from below.

When the sheet is safely under the

drop wheels the air blast and suction are switched off, releasing the sheet for conveying down the layboard. The cycle of operations is repeated, other sheets following the first in underlapped formation, and spaced 6 to 12 in. apart.

On reaching the front lays, each sheet is adjusted to the side lay in turn. The side lay is of the hammer or finger type. The finger only falls when the side lay is on its return stroke, thus it cannot disturb the sheet at the front lays, by falling on the sheet before it starts on its return stroke.

To eliminate the problem of torn sheets, or sheets stuck together, a special detecting device has been fitted. A detecting finger is set to within $\frac{1}{2}$ in. of either side of the sheet as it passes over the main tape roller; and if a sheet is not in its correct position, it will foul one of these fingers, causing the machine to be stopped.

The separator is the flexible head type, that is to say, lifting sucker, comber, and second sheet stop units are independent of each other, and they can be adjusted to any position to suit the condition of any pile or stock. A hand wheel is fitted to the separator for starting purposes.

If a sheet does not register at the front lays, detecting needles are arrested in their movement forward by the fact of the sheet not being in correct position.

Should a sheet become caught in the stripper mechanism of the press, special cut-outs are fitted to detect such occasions which, in turn, trip and stop the press and feeder.

SPRAYING TO PREVENT SET-OFF

THE older methods of spraying the freshly printed sheets with molten wax to prevent set-off have given way to the more effective and cleaner methods of the cold fluid sprays. These latest spray fluids contain certain inert substances such as gum or starch, with a solution of water and spirit as the vehicle. The fluid is sprayed in the form of a fine mist on to each printed sheet as it comes to rest on the pile.

The rapid evaporation of the vehicle during transit from the spray gun leaves minute solid particles on the freshly printed sheet. These dry particles not only prevent set-off by holding the sheets apart, but also, by allowing access of air between the sheets, aid actual drying by oxidation. Subsequent workings do not suffer in any way from the spray, all traces of which finally disappear completely. According to information up to the moment, no injurious effects are suffered by workers through spraying. This question has been the subject of investigation by the British Federation of Master Printers.

Air Compressor

The usual equipment comprises an air compressor large enough to maintain the maximum number of spray guns likely to be in operation at the same time, and a main air line running through the machine room with branches to each machine. Smaller air compressors of a portable type are also used, in which case the whole set, including compressor, air receiver and $\frac{1}{4}$-h.p. motor, are mounted on to a pressed steel base, supported on rubber feet; the spray guns may also be portable or fitted on the printing machine (Fig. 11).

In operating the spray guns, although there are few adjustments, these are very important if best results are to be

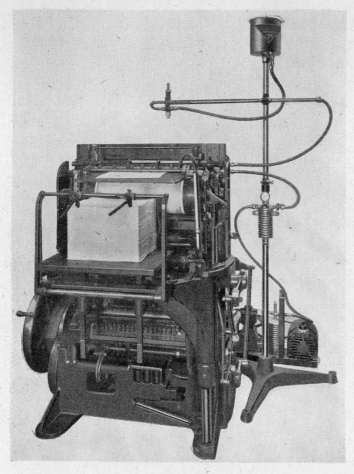

AERASPRAY UNIT, ATTACHED TO VERTICAL MIEHLE

Fig. 11. *The entire anti-set-off plant is portable. The air compressor and $\frac{1}{4}$-h.p. electric motor are mounted on a pressed-steel base. The spray unit with tripod stand is also portable.*

and other smooth absorbent papers require a light-grade mix with fine particles; and heavier grades containing a higher percentage of solid content are more suitable for non-absorbent papers carrying ink which must dry on the surface by oxidation; also boards and other heavy stocks and jobs requiring considerable inking.

But as the mix is broken up into fine particles by the air in the dashpot, their size depends also on the proportions of air and mix; more air and less mix for small particles, less air and more mix for large particles.

The particles of mix should always be dry when they reach the printed sheet, otherwise they will flatten out and will not prevent contact between the sheets. The same principles apply here: more air and less mix for drier particles. The shape of the spray and the height of the gun above the sheet are adjusted to allow the spray to cover the wet ink.

A wider spray, or a spray delivered from a higher position, will naturally deliver drier particles.

The portable "Aeraspray" unit illustrated, or the evenspray "Kitten" portable, will also solve set-off problems,

obtained and set-off entirely eliminated. An understanding of the principles involved in the process will help operators with the adjustments. The spraying fluid or mix is made in different grades, which contain higher or lower percentages of solid content. A light-grade mix will produce finer particles and larger particles are produced by the heavier grades.

Generally speaking, papers like art

STATIC ELECTRICITY IN PAPER

STATIC electricity is one of the major production problems in the printing industry. There can be few letterpress machine printers who have not experienced the troubles and delays which are associated with printing on paper charged with static electricity. The sheets cling tenaciously to the pile, feedboard, cylinder or platen, and feeding, either by hand or by automatic, is almost impossible. The effect of static electricity on the delivery of the printed sheets is often even worse, the sheets going back to foul the sheet stops rather than leave the sticks; and on tape delivery, going round with the tapes instead of dropping on to the pile.

Those sheets which do deliver often come down crooked, and fasten tightly on to the pile as soon as they touch, jogging is impossible and set-off inevitable. When the paper is in this bad condition, register is bad, and output deteriorates. The trouble is also bad on rotary machines printing from the web. Static electricity in paper has been the subject of a very thorough investigation by the Printing and Allied Trades Research Association (PATRA) to whom the writer is indebted for much help.

Nature of Static Electricity

When the ancients first discovered that by rubbing a piece of fossilized gum called amber, they could produce a force which would pick up light non-conducting objects, they were experimenting with static electricity. Friction between two different surfaces generates static, and it can be generated by the quick separation, or bringing together, of two different surfaces, and by pressure. The charge generated is higher if conditions are dry, therefore static is more troublesome in winter than summer.

In the winter months the low relative humidity indoors tends to dry surfaces; they become poor conductors and the static accumulates on the generating surfaces. On the other hand, the high relative humidity of summer moistens surfaces; they become good conductors and the charges leak away to earth; these conditions can be imitated by the principle of artificial humidification.

Static charges may be either positive or negative. When a charge is generated on two surfaces by pressure or friction, one surface will have a negative charge and the other a positive charge. The same kind of charges repel one another, but bodies charged oppositely are attracted to each other. If full contact is made the charges are neutralized. A charged body, if it is a non-conductor, remains charged in ordinary air; if the air is made a conductor, the charge is lost. If an earthed conductor with a pointed end is held near a charged body, it is discharged.

Friction and Pressure

A great deal of friction and pressure is associated with paper both in the course of its manufacture and in the process of printing. Thus, the paper may be charged either in the paper mill, or on the printing machine. As paper is a non-conductor the charge generated remains on the paper—in the form of static electricity.

Generally speaking, coated papers generate less static than uncoated, and uncoated papers made from rag fibres, generate less charge than those made from mechanical wood fibres. Paper that is conditioned to contain not less than 3 per cent moisture will be freer of static.

When paper is hung in the machine room from metal racks for twenty-four hours the static is greatly decreased.

Moisture is a conductor of electricity and there is no doubt that paper stored and printed in a moist atmosphere gives little or no trouble from static, because the charge is able to leak away to earth. American printers, who study the subject of raw materials more than we do, equip their machine rooms with humidifiers and so control the moisture content, irrespective of atmospheric conditions outside. A range of 45 to 60 per cent relative humidity (normal summer conditions in England) has been found most practical. Where ventilating systems are installed, humidification is a simple problem. PATRA has an experimental humidity controlled room in which temperature and relative humidity are automatically controlled. A humidistat supplied by British Thermostats Ltd. regulates the humidity; it can be set at any relative humidity within the range of 50 to 90 per cent. The total cost of all the plant was under £200 for this small room, and the cost to run it approximately twelve shillings per week. Temperature and humidity recommended by PATRA are 65 to 70 deg. F. and 65 per cent relative humidity.

Many earthing methods have been tried by distracted machine-men struggling against something quite outside their control. The methods take various forms, but the principle is the same throughout: to pick up the charge from the paper surface and run it to earth.

One of the best earthing devices is a tinsel bar. A thick copper earth wire is connected to each end of a wooden dowel round which tinsel is wound, being connected at each end to the earthing wire. This can be hung or fixed as close to the sheet as possible. Rubbing with glycerine or french chalk surfaces over which the sheet passes is also resorted to, but these ideas, though helpful on occasions, are not completely effective and they should be regarded only as palliatives.

A common device in America is the use of open gas flame and electric strip heaters at the delivery end. Experiments have been made to eliminate static electricity by incorporating materials in the paper during its manufacture to make it a conductor, but the difficulties in this connection have not yet been completely overcome. The most effective method of overcoming static troubles to date, is to fit the printing machines with static neutralizers. When they are correctly fitted and maintained, they are effective.

LETTERPRESS INKS AND ROLLERS

IN the general desire for speed, printing has of necessity had to fall into line; and as possibly the slowest factor in the process is the drying of the ink, developments have been directed to the speeding up of this important stage. The drying time of letterpress inks based on oxidation of linseed oil media is reduced by the addition of various metallic driers, but there is a definite limit to the extent to which this can be done. The advent of synthetic resins and solvents, relatively unknown a few years ago, has opened up a new field of inks which set quickly under ordinary working conditions and allow rapid backing, cutting and folding to be carried out, and the principle is applied to multi-colour as well as monotone.

With the increase in the number and variety of materials available to the ink maker, great strides have been made in printing on difficult surfaces such as cellophane, glassine and bakelite as distinct from paper. But the inks have to be specially formulated to ensure that the ink keys on to the non-absorbent surface. Further increase in the rate of drying can be effected by higher temperatures. To obtain this, heat can be applied by means of electric heaters, gas, or other means. Ozonized air has been tried as a means of increasing the rate of oxidation, but practical difficulties have restricted developments in this direction.

Other types of inks have been introduced which depend on the principle of the setting of waxes and resins at different temperatures. These are maintained fluid in the ink duct by the application of heat, and they set on coming into contact with the cool paper. In America, the development of new inks now known generally as heat-set inks has made it possible to use rotary web magazine presses more in accordance with the speeds of which they are capable. They rely on the principle of drying by evaporation and consist of a concentrated pigment, synthetic resins and a volatile vehicle, such as petroleum oil, combined so as to form a thermo-plastic fluid. The printed web is subjected to heat which vaporizes the oil and is then chilled by passing over water-cooled drums which absorb the heat and reduce the plastic residue to a hardened surface on the paper. As the ink does not vaporize at atmospheric temperatures it does not dry on the rollers.

American magazines, such as *Life*, with a weekly production of 2,800,000 copies, are now printed with these heat-set inks on specially designed Hoe rotary web presses, all equipped with short heating ovens 4 ft. long for the instantaneous drying of the ink on coated paper which is perfected and folded on the presses. Gas heaters have also been added to existing machines with good results. The flow of gas to the heaters is automatically controlled by the speed of the press, and the heaters are fitted with automatic electrical ignition and shut-off devices, and fresh air and exhaust ducts to recover the solvents.

The subject of printers' inks is fully dealt with in Chapter 29.

Development of Composition Rollers

From Gutenberg to Stanhope, a period of nearly four centuries, saw no change in the methods and materials used for inking the forme, which was done with sheepskin balls stuffed with horsehair. These ink balls were dabbed and rolled together to distribute the ink, which was transferred to the type in a similar manner.

With the introduction of the cylinder machine arose the necessity for the roller, but the seam of a sheepskin covered roller left a streak across the forme. Nicholson, Stanhope, König, Cowper and other inventors of the time, tried vainly to develop a method of inking the type by roller, but their methods naturally followed the methods used in the manufacture of the ink balls. Wooden rollers were covered with horsehair; and sheepskin, cloth and silk were all tried for the outer covering.

Composition rollers were invented about 1818 and overcame the difficulty. The early composition was made from glue and treacle and was similar to the composition used in the Staffordshire Potteries at that time for dabbers for decorating pottery. This composition was satisfactory while it was fresh, but it became very hard and shrank badly, due to evaporation of the moisture in the glue, which destroyed its gelatinous nature. The casting was done in brass tube moulds, and later split iron moulds were used. The molten composition had to be poured in from the top, and this was a disadvantage because air bubbles were trapped and often left blow holes. The great difference between the old

MAKING COMPOSITION ROLLERS

Fig. 12. *A simple spinning-type lathe used in the manufacture of Ideal dried-oil composition rollers. The unset composition is poured in via the specially designed tail stock, and the composition sets inside the spinning tube, and thus a solid roller is obtained.*

and modern composition rollers is the introduction into the formula of glycerine and the gatling-gun system of casting. Glycerine has an affinity for moisture which it draws from the air. It is not volatile, and is therefore inclined to increase in bulk, and in this way it counteracts the opposite inclination in the glue. The gatling-gun system of casting consists of a number of brass moulds of various diameters, each in an iron tube, and all set in a cylinder or gun. Hot and cold water supplies are connected and the melted composition is forced under pressure into the heated moulds from the bottom upwards. Cold water then takes the place of the hot water to obviate delays for setting.

Scientific Progress

Today, scientific and chemical progress has provided a large variety of roller compositions with characteristics to suit all modern conditions of

processes, machinery, and also climate. Infusible qualities have been developed in gelatine composition and rubber, and rubber-like synthetics have been utilized for commercial letterpress and rotary machines.

An interesting development is the Ideal series of roller compositions, manufactured by Ault & Wiborg, Ltd., which cover the entire field of letterpress printing (Figs. 12 and 13). Ideal Graphic is a special non-melting composition to stand up to the wear and tear of fast-running letterpress machines. An Ideal rubber roller for newspaper and other rotaries is made under licence from the Goodyear Rubber Co., and a patented Ideal process roller combines the advantages of both rubber and gelatine.

The base of this roller is made of rubber or such suitable material and has a guaranteed life. It is made on the printer's own stocks to a diameter of $\frac{1}{16}$ in. below the finished diameter required; the base is then coated with a thin layer of glue, which process can be repeated as often as desired, and at a very small cost, as much of the old glue can be washed off and remelted. ·This process ensures a perfect roller at all times, which can be run at high speed in the hottest weather, and the combination of base and thin coating is proof against shrinkage or expansion.

Rubber litho and rotary letterpress rollers have become increasingly popular in view of the ease with which they can be used, both as regards setting and cleaning. Usher Walker, Ltd., supply both rubber and synthetic rubber rotary rollers and also several infusible compositions to suit modern developments. Their Azuroll composition roller is not only unmeltable, but it has a high degree of immunity from shrinking and swelling, and on this account is specially suitable for high-speed machines.

When gelatine rollers are first cast the composition is very moist and tender; they require a period in which to dry out and toughen before they are in condition for use in the machine. This period will vary. In cold weather evaporation is rapid and seasoning will only take a day or two; but in hot humid weather when the air is heavily charged with moisture new rollers will get worse.

Winter composition which contains more glycerine never gets really hard. These rollers become soft if used in the summer, and in humid weather get very tender. On the other hand, summer rollers, containing less glycerine, get harder the longer they are kept, and if used during the winter become very hard and shrink badly. Composition rollers should, therefore, be ordered for the season in which they are to be used.

Seasoned rollers not in use should always be covered with machine oil to prevent ageing. When printing small formes, composition rollers should never be allowed to run hot and dry on the ends; a little grease at either end of the duct will nearly always prevent this.

VULCANIZING RUBBER ROLLERS
Fig. 13. *The rubber is received in sheets of ready-mixed composition which is carefully wrapped on to the roller stock, and this is then vulcanized. The man shown in the illustration is in the act of sliding a rack of rubber rollers into the vulcanizer.*

CHAPTER TWELVE

LETTERPRESS ROTARY DEVELOPMENTS

NEWSPAPER MACHINES. MAGAZINE PRESSES. COLOUR WORK. SPECIALITY PRINTING. WRAPPER CONTAINERS. ROTARY CARTON-MACHINES. JOBBING WORK ROTARIES.

FROM 1846 onwards, newspaper machines were developing towards the rotary principle. First with various ideas for type-revolving cylinders by Applegarth and by Hoe, and later with the introduction of the Bullock press of 1866 and the Walter press of 1868, we have the complete rotary principle in embryo—curved stereotypes and reel feed. Though the Walter press contained only one printing unit for one reel of paper, the elements were there, and the natural development to accommodate huge editions has been in multiple units.

There seems no limit to the number of units which can be either built up in decks or placed in line. A newspaper installation may include Hoe super-speed presses consisting of sixty unit-type printing sections and fifteen super-speed folders (Fig. 1). Hoe presses, many of them fitted with multicolour units for colour sections, are installed in the machine rooms of many of the great national and provincial dailies throughout the world. The new Hoe anti-friction presses are guaranteed for a running speed of 25,000 cylinder revolutions per hour.

Another British manufactured newspaper press is the Victory high speed. This is a machine which also embodies all that is modern in newspaper design. The units can be assembled in line or superimposed in single or double width to meet individual requirements. They are made by Victory-Kidder, Birken-

head. There are many other newspaper machines, made by Goss and similar well-known firms, each with its own special features and developments.

Magazine and Book Printing

The capacity and performance of the rotary magazine presses is startling. Magazines are printed on Hoe rotary presses at 24,000 copies per hour. The production of telephone directories at H.M. Stationery Office is on Victory-Kidder presses, which operate for weeks on end at a speed of 15,000—64-page signatures—per hour (Fig. 2).

R. W. Crabtree and Sons, of Leeds, have developed an all-size rotary letterpress machine specially for book printing. The machine prints from the reel and delivers signatures of 8, 16 or 32 pages, as the case may be, cut and folded to page size up to a total of 256 pages, in one revolution of the cylinders. A number of these presses has already been installed.

But America is the home of magazines and enormous circulations. Letterpress and two-colour work, and black and one-colour letterpress magazines, are printed and perfected on Hoe rotary presses equipped with drying ovens to dry the special heat-set inks. Multicolour rotaries and methods have been brought to a high degree of perfection by the introduction of the Cottrell four-and five-colour presses for printing colour sections and covers. The colours

HOE STANDARD PRINTING UNIT

Fig. 1. *The machine weighs 25 tons, yet it can be barred round by finger pressure. This unit, which is four pages wide, is guaranteed to turn out at least 50,000 copies per hour.*

are printed wet on wet with inks which have been specially developed for the process. They are either sheet- or reel-fed, but the delivery is flat.

On the sheet-fed type one set of grippers holds the sheet throughout. There is only one impression cylinder and the plate cylinders, with own inking, are grouped around it. There can be no make-ready on this cylinder, but the McKee system is used whereby the plates—electros or stereos—are bumped up, and the necessary variation in pressure is in the plate itself. This system need alarm no one. Some of the finest four-colour results on two-revolution machines are obtained by the use of interlays between the plates and the solid mounts without the use of overlays, and this is the same in principle.

Speciality Printing

Modern industrial and other developments on mass-production lines have necessitated similar methods for the associated printing. The ever-growing demand for printed wrappers and containers for food and other products, and the enormous sales of commodities brought about by national advertising, have found old reciprocating flat-bed methods of printing too slow. Speed is the most insistent demand today, and rotary methods provide the means.

Machines are built specially to suit individual requirements, but certain parts are standardized for easy replacements and additions.

The man in the street, when he buys his bus ticket, may be interested to know that it was probably printed on a Victory rotary ticket machine, from a web $2\frac{3}{4}$ in. wide at a speed of about 300,000 tickets per hour. The machine has four printing units, two-face (front and reverse), numeration and series.

His cigarette packet would possibly be printed, cut and creased on a Thrissell Simplex with rotary cutting unit capable of cutting, creasing and/or scoring 10,000,000 packets before it needs re-knifing (at three-quarters original cost). Three-colour wrappers can be printed at the rate of 1,000 per minute on the Victory three-colour special-purpose rotary machine. This type of Victory special-purpose rotary is suitable for printing margarine wrappers at 2,000 per minute; bread wrappers at 1,200 per minute; security forms, licences and tax forms at 2,400 per minute; and football pool coupons, folded in triplicate ready for envelope, at 72,000 per hour. The machines print from stereos, electros, rubber plates, manganese bronze or steel engraved cylinders.

Rotary Carton Machines

Thrissell's Simplex cutter and printer, which has been referred to, is for the production of cartons in long runs. Its all-rotary principle ensures maximum speed with accurate register. It is built on the unit principle which makes it very versatile for different combinations of operations, direct letterpress and letterpress offset, and other classes of work. It prints from electros, stereos, or engraved steel cylinders for long life.

Rotary carton machines lack the flexibility of the flat-beds for short runs, but where the runs are long, or where the cutting sizes and shapes will suit a number of different cartons, rotary is the method for maximum output. A multi-size carton machine made by Timson's, Ltd., of Kettering, will solve many problems where a variety of

VICTORY MAGAZINE PRESS

Fig. 2. *Five of these presses are installed at H.M. Stationery Office for the production of Telephone Directories. They run a 64-pp. sheet at the rate of 15,000 copies an hour.*

TIMSON ROTARY PRESS WITH CENTRE DELIVERY

Fig. 3. *These presses are built from standard parts to customers' own requirements for printing wrappers and labels, cartons and stationery, including folding, numbering, gumming, perforating, punching, slitting, cutting, creasing and counting.*

cartons is needed for special purposes.

The printing and cutting cylinders of this machine are arranged in order that they may be removed and changed with the minimum of trouble. It is a three-unit press to print one, two or three colours in register—and the carton is delivered free from waste.

Printers who specialize in numerical and stationery printing, for order forms, invoices, cheque forms, and duplicate books, are well catered for as regards rotary machinery, and comparatively little of this class of work is now printed on flat-bed machines.

The usual operations of stationery plant include printing and book numbering. Both front and back of the paper can be printed, and the other operations usual for this class of work are carried out, such as perforating down or across; hole punching for filing; pasting, slitting, inserting or collating; applying one-time carbon, and folding (Figs. 3 and 4).

It may not be long before the speed and economies of rotary methods will be enjoyed by the commercial printer on work which was formerly only attempted on flat-bed machines. There are two sheet-fed two-colour rotary machines of somewhat similar type which will come very much to the fore in Britain in the near future.

One, the Cottrell Claybourn two-colour rotary press with continuous stream-feed, pile delivery and Claybourn grooved plate cylinder, has splendid inking arrangements, the inkers and distributors being interchangeable. Easy to handle, it will turn out first-class process work, equal to the best two-revolution standards at speeds up to 5,500 sheets per hour.

The other machine of like capacity is Timson's Ketterina (Fig. 5), with pyramid inking. Three rollers of different sizes ink the forme, which is double rolled before each impression. The sheet does not leave the grippers until

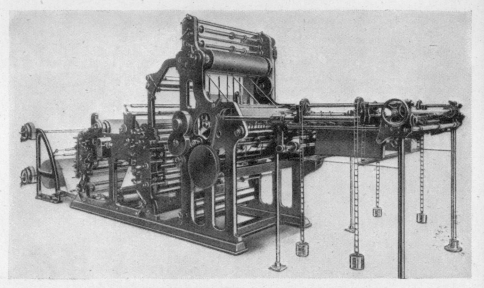

TIMSON ROTARY PRESS WITH PILE DELIVERY

Fig. 4. *A rotary press for the production of two-colour letterpress work from the reel, but delivered in flat sheets. It is also built for perfecting or for printing additional colours.*

printing is complete. This machine prints all substances including very light weights and is fitted with automatic feed of any selected make. The delivery takes six sheets between impression and extended pile. Curved stereos or electros are used and stereotyping equipment is available with rotary proof press for pre-make-ready. The machine is made in 38 in. by 48 in. and smaller sizes.

KETTERINA TWO-COLOUR ROTARY PRESS

Fig. 5. *A sheet-fed two-colour rotary press with automatic-feed and pile delivery. This press is suitable for general jobbing and fine quality work in which long runs are involved.*

CHAPTER THIRTEEN

MODERN PLATE-MAKING METHODS

REASONS FOR DUPLICATING. USE OF HIGH QUADS AND FURNITURE. BACKING THE
STEREO MOULD. WET AND DRY FLONG. PLASTER MOULDING PROCESS. PACKING
OUT FOR CASTING. COMPOSITION OF STEREO METAL. CASTING AND FINISHING
ROTARY STEREOS. NICKEL-FACING. WAX AND LEAD MOULDING FOR ELECTROS.
BUILDING AND BLACKLEADING. BACKING UP THE ELECTRO SHELL. NICKEL- AND
CHROMIUM-FACED ELECTROS. CURVED ELECTROS. WAX ENGRAVING.

BOTH stereotyping and electrotyping are duplicating processes and the reasons for duplicating are several. For example, it is desired to speed up the production of printed matter at the machining stage. Repetition of the type or original blocks by the processes under consideration enables the printer to prepare a multiple forme and to print the subject four, eight, sixteen or more to the sheet, according to the number of copies required and the time or the machine available.

Rapid Duplication

Alternatively, it may be necessary to produce the same subject matter in identical form at the same time in a number of different places, a requirement associated with national advertising campaigns. To meet this need the foundry can, in a few hours, produce the required number of stereotype plates, each a replica of the original. The quantity required may run into several hundreds and frequently does so in view of the fact that the number of morning and evening papers, periodicals and magazines in the Press Directory of Great Britain exceeds 5,000.

The saving of wear and tear on

expensive type and original blocks has also to be considered. For the relatively small cost of an electro or stereo an original block is insured against the risk of deterioration or accidental damage which use on the machine would involve; and by the same means, type, especially founders' or display type, is released for other purposes with a consequent economy in time and capital outlay.

The process of stereotyping was invented in 1727 by William Ged of Edinburgh. The method, comparatively simple of description, calls for skill and care in application if the high standard of result of which the process is capable is to be achieved.

Use of High Quads

Formes intended for foundry duplication should, if possible, be made up with high quads in any large, open spaces. High quads also make an excellent foundation to which halftones or zincos can be fixed, instead of being made up into the forme on their wood mounts. The advantages of metal instead of wood beneath the cuts are obvious. The originals can easily be attached by soldering, or pinning to metal bases, or by pinning to the comparatively soft metal of the quads. If using pins—the warning is not so superfluous as might appear—make quite sure that the pins go into the quads and not between them.

Adhesives of any sort are not recommended, because a reaction is set up by the heat and pressure of the drying press, resulting in the spew of the adhesive to the mould face.

Failing the pinning area on a block it is always better to solder on to a solid metal base, giving an overall type-high thickness.

In preparation for stereo moulding the forme must be imposed for foundry —if this has not been done in the composing room—i.e. type-high metal clumps, as bearers for the mould, must be placed close to the work round the four sides, arranged as shown in Fig. 1, so as not to bind on one another at the corners. With the quoins loosened the

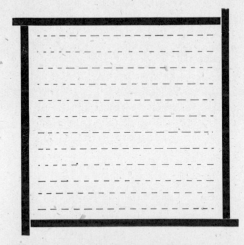

Fig. 1. *Method of imposing type-high metal clumps round a page ready for stereotyping.*

forme is planed, to ensure that all the letters are down on their feet, and that any low or unlevel illustration blocks are brought up to the correct height.

After retightening the quoins the surface of the matter is vigorously brushed with a soft brush to remove any foreign matter from the cups of the letters and elsewhere, and again very lightly brushed over with a thin oil to facilitate the release of the mould. Any large open white spaces should be filled in by laying a strip of thin card or stereo backing in them, in order to prevent too great a dip in the mould in such areas. This precaution will be unnecessary if high quads have been used as indicated above.

Wet and Dry Flong

The forme is now ready for the application of the flong, as the moulding material is generally termed. Flongs are divided into two classes—wet and dry, and each has its own particular application. Wet flong is usually prepared in the foundry, preferably not too long before it is required for use, and is composed of tissue and blotting paper conjoined by a special paste. To a sheet of blotting are pasted two sheets of tissue on each side. A further sheet of blotting is then pasted to one side and on the other side two more sheets of tissue. The final flong is therefore composed of alternate layers of blotting and tissue with a blotting base and a tissue face (Fig. 2). It must be understood, however, that every stereotyper has his own method of preparing the flong, which may vary in detail from the method described.

The flong is prepared on a flat metal table, or a litho stone is equally suitable, and as each sheet of tissue or blotting is pasted down a heavy cast-iron roller is rolled back and forth across the surface (Fig. 3). By this means complete amalgamation of surface is achieved between blotting and tissue and any air bubbles or irregularities dispersed. A comparatively tough tissue, specially

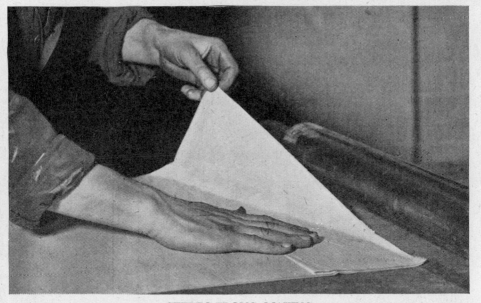

STEREO-FLONG MAKING

Fig. 2. *The base sheet of blotter having been pasted, the tissue is drawn by passing the hand to and fro. The roller is used to squeeze out surplus paste and air bubbles.*

made for the purpose, is used; the more ordinary soft tissues are apt to cause splitting of the mould if more than a very few casts are required.

Beating the Flong

The flong thus prepared is laid, tissue side downwards, on the prepared forme and beaten in with a stiff bristled beating brush. If several casts are to be taken from the mould it can be reinforced at this stage by the pasting on of an additional sheet of blotting or backing paper, and beating in is resumed. The forme, covered with several thicknesses of blotting or moulding blanket, is placed in a hot press under pressure and thoroughly dried out (Fig. 4).

The time taken preparing and drying out the mould by the methods just described, and the ever increasing rapidity called for in newspaper production, was largely responsible for the introduction of the alternative dry flong

method of moulding. It is fair to say that much of the great improvement in newspaper illustration during the last decade or so is due to the efforts of the flong makers to meet the needs of this development.

Dry flong divides into two sub-classes, the wholly dry and the damp. The former variety is moulded in a completely dry state. Before the hydraulic presses were introduced, the forme, with the sheet of flong on the surface, was placed on a mangle consisting of a moving table passing under a roller. In this way the flong, under considerable pressure from the roller, was forced into the type and was then ready for immediate use. This method was only suitable for type matter and the coarsest screen half-tones. Greatly improved results are obtained from moulds produced in an hydraulic press.

The alternative variety, although still generally known as dry flong, is

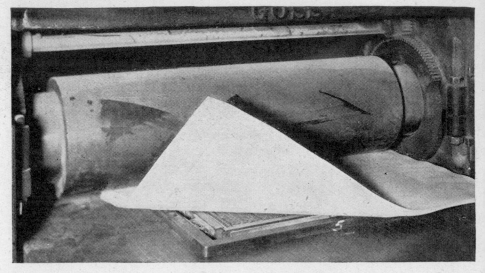

AMALGAMATING THE FLONG

Fig. 3. The forme, dry flong, and blotting paper, which eases the impression, passing under the mangle by means of a slow-moving table, ensuring uniformity of impression.

used in a partially damp form. In preparation for use it is kept in damping boxes known as humidifiers or humidors, which maintain the correct degree of moisture content in the sheets of flong, so that it is ready for immediate use at any time.

Basically the same as the completely dry variety, it differs by the incorporation in its face in the course of manufacture of a smooth paste which, in the moistened form in which the flong is used, is soft enough to take an adequate depth of both half-tone and type matter and to preserve the perfectly smooth surface essential to satisfactory half-tone reproduction (Fig. 5).

Plaster Moulding Process

It is necessary at this stage to make some reference to the plaster moulding process. By means of this method the very finest half-tone screens, up to 200 line, are successfully duplicated. Where plaster moulding is specialized in, it is claimed that not only is the full depth

of the screen obtained in the stereo but that it is indistinguishable from the original in printing quality. For this reason plaster cast stereos are largely used for three- and four-colour half-tone printing without loss of register. Furthermore, because the delicate moulding medium retains all the characteristics of the dot formation of the original, there is no disturbance of that balance between the respective colours which is the basis of satisfactory three-colour printing, and good register is maintained.

The process may be said to be almost entirely in the hands of specialists and requires considerable skill and experience for its effective operation. The plaster is mixed with water to a fluid consistency and poured upon a backing paper slightly larger than the subject to be moulded.

Side gauges are used to determine the thickness of the plaster film on the surface of the paper, the superfluous material being removed by a steel straight-edge, which also imparts a perfectly level face to the mould.

When, in the opinion of the moulder, and this is almost entirely a matter of experienced judgment, sufficient moisture has been absorbed, the paper with its plaster film can be lifted and laid face downwards on the forme or block. It is then transferred to a cold press, covered with several thicknesses of an absorbent type of paper, and under light pressure allowed to dry. The softness of the moulding material, and the fact that a cold press and a very moderate pressure are used, remove the necessity for mounting originals on metal in mixed formes, and preclude any damage to the finest faces or overhanging letters.

Having produced our mould by one of the three methods described, it is now prepared for casting by packing out (Fig. 6). By this is meant filling in the hollows in the back, corresponding to whites in the face, by pasting in strips of thin card or similar substance. The use of high quads in such places, already recommended, eliminates much of the necessity for such treatment, which is designed to prevent the weight of metal, when casting, depressing hollow parts of the mould and so adding to the amount of work required in routing and finishing.

On receiving the mould in this condition the caster pastes to its leading edge a strip of brown paper of sufficient

RELEASING THE STEREO MOULD

Fig. 4. *The stereo mould being released from the forme. The drying blanket, in the form of blotting paper, has absorbed the dampness from the flong, which dries rapidly.*

P.T.G.—F

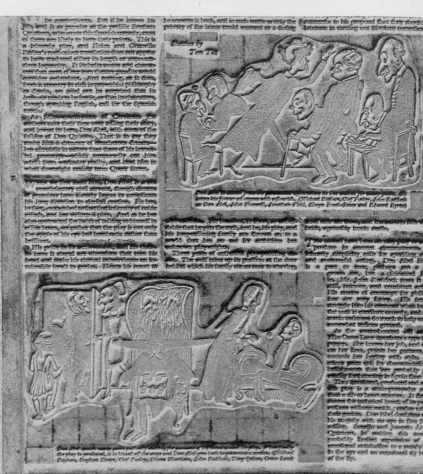

PAPIER MÂCHÉ STEREO MOULD

Fig. 5. The face of a papier mâché stereo mould showing the impression obtained by the moulding press. Every indent is reproduced when the metal cast is taken from the mould

length to reach from the position the mould will occupy to the pouring lip of the casting box. This acts as a guide for the molten metal as it is poured into the casting box, and assists in the removal of the mould from the cast in fit condition for further casting.

Further drying on the hot plate is required at this stage, otherwise the moisture in the paste will cause defects in the cast. The mould is laid face upwards on the flat surface of the casting box, held in position by the gauges which determine its thickness, usually 12 points with an allowance for back-planing (Fig. 7). Over the gauges is then laid a ribbed casting board, a wood pulp board into which transverse ribs have been impressed. This provides similar ribs on the back of the cast and assists the back-planing machine by reducing the amount of metal to be shaved off.

The metal used in stereotyping is an

alloy of tin, antimony and lead, the tin varying between 5 and 10 per cent, antimony 15 per cent, and the balance lead. The tin content selected to be used is, or should be, determined by the general nature of the work to be produced. If a large proportion of the foundry output is in half-tone, particularly in the finer screens, the tin proportion should be in the region of 10 per cent, as the function of the tin is not only to add toughness to the metal but also to increase the sharpness of the cast—a very desirable factor in a fine half-tone plate.

The pot temperature for stereotyping should be approximately 300 deg. C.; a higher temperature leading to abnormal dross formation and a lower one to a separation of the constituent metal

PACKING OUT A STEREO MOULD

Fig. 6. *The back of a stereo mould packed out with small pieces of card to give support to the hollow portions during the casting process. Packing out eliminates a considerable amount of finishing work on the plate and reduces the work of the routing machine.*

STEREO CASTING BOX: OPEN

Fig. 7. *Showing mould with paper tail attached. Gauges of the required plate thickness are placed over the clumps of the mould.*

to the point where two different metals are joined will generate a measurable electrical reaction, varying with the degree of heat.

Not only is a correct metal temperature necessary for maintenance of a satisfactory state of the metal within the pot, but satisfactory casting is also largely determined by it. Too hot a metal will cause the liberation of gases in the mould which, in spite of the drying to which it has been subjected, still contains a certain amount of moisture. The escape of this moisture under the influence of excessive heat produces a porous face in the plate and may also cause irretrievable damage to the mould. On the other hand, the box should be kept hot, otherwise the metal will solidify irregularly and too rapidly, and air holes be formed within the cast beneath the surface, giving rise to depressions and other defects in the printing plate.

crystals. The rough-and-ready means of testing the heat of the metal by the amount of scorching induced in a strip of paper, useful as it is in the absence of more accurate methods, is not to be recommended. It is worth while to install a pyrometer for this purpose, an electrical heat measuring instrument of simple yet robust construction. In appearance a long metal rod with electrical connections, its operation is based on the principle that heat applied

The mould is placed in the casting box (Fig. 8) as low down, i.e. as far away from the pouring edge as possible, in order to provide a long tang to the cast. The purpose of the tang is, by its weight, to force the metal beneath it into the detail of the mould. Because of its greater volume the tang does not solidify so quickly as the metal in contact with the mould. It therefore provides a reservoir of fluid metal from which the cast is fed as it cools: in its fluid state it also provides a means of escape for the air displaced from the box during the pour, and prevents this from becoming trapped in the plate.

If care be exercised in separating the mould from the cast it will come away undamaged, and the mould will be in fit condition for further casts if desired. The tang is sawn off to within half an inch or so of the work and the plate then passed to the finishing department. It is then back-planed to the required thickness, usually 12 points (pica).

The planing machine (Fig. 9) consists of a travelling bed actuated by a worm screw drive which carries it slowly beneath a knife set at an angle in a heavily constructed head. The bed is capable of minute adjustment, and the plate can be planed to accuracy within very narrow

tolerances. One fine and one finishing cut is the usual method; it is also desirable to place a piece of thin card (of known thickness so that the bed can be adjusted accordingly) between the face of the plate and the bed of the

STEREO CASTING BOX : CLOSED

Fig. 8. *Showing the gauges protruding from the mouth of the box. The molten metal is being poured into the lip between the paper tails.*

BACK-PLANING THE STEREO

Fig. 9. *The stereo is placed face down upon a card to prevent face damage. The knife passes over and levels the stereo, which is held firm by front and rear rollers. Plates can be planed to any thickness from 6 point to type-high by raising or lowering the bed.*

machine to avoid a metal to metal contact. During the cut the plate is held firmly on the bed under pressure from a spring-loaded cover plate.

Before planing, the leading edge of the plate should be bevelled on the back, on a bowling machine (a revolving disk containing knives for squaring up edges of plates), so that it comes easily and smoothly under the plane knife. It is to provide room for this bevel outside the printing surface that the recommendation was made earlier to cut off the tang not closer than within half an inch of the work.

The function of the finisher is to examine the plate after the superfluous metal has been removed on the routing machine (Fig. 10), so as to remove with appropriate tools any shoulder left by the router-cutter and similarly to deepen any parts of the plate likely to black-up in printing, i.e. any shallows in line work or the cups of larger letters.

Large solid areas may require a little burnishing or bringing up from the back; corners of rules, or breaks in straight lengths of rule, may need joining, and other defects may need correcting. Pinholes are next punched or drilled in the plate to facilitate mounting, and any burrs raised on the back of the plate by the punching tool must be removed by a rough file, otherwise the plate will ride on the mount.

Rotary Stereotyping

Rotary stereotyping (Fig. 11) for commercial and other purposes follows generally the same technique as flat casting. Present-day marketing conditions of consumer goods call for the production on a large numerical scale of cartons, packages, and end and side labels. Since the sizes and designs of these are constant in relation to any particular product, and the demand continuous, they are particularly suitable for production by rotary printing machines.

In a multiple job, repetition of the same design of label on one cylinder, only one original block need be made, and a master plate is prepared in the foundry containing a predetermined number of flat stereos laid down with the required spacing on a metal moulding plate or slab.

A calculation of the known shrinkage factor will enable the master plate to be made up with that slightly larger spacing required to bring the margins between the subjects on the rotary stereo to precisely the size desired. Similarly, if the originals are process blocks, they can be made to a formula size in excess of their nominal size to allow for shrinkage.

In the case of zincos containing a number of subjects it is an advantage not to rout away the marginal whites

ROUTING MACHINE IN USE

Fig. 10. *Cutting away the high parts of the stereo that are not required for printing. The router cutter revolves at great speed, while the plate is secured by the machine clamps. The guide of the cutter is secured by the arm. Routing requires considerable skill,*

CASTING ROTARY STEREO PLATES

Fig. 11. *This autoplate machine requires five men to operate, and casts plates at the rate of four per minute. It contains a $7\frac{1}{2}$-ton furnace pot and mixer, and a built-in electric motor. Rotary plates are used for commercial as well as newspaper printing.*

before moulding (beyond, of course, a clear indication of what is and what is not work). Naturally this adds somewhat to the amount of routing required in the stereo, but it assists in retaining the correct curvature of the mould in the box and in the resultant cast.

Casting Difficulties

Open whites tend to form chords of an arc when the mould is bent into the curved casting box, and the plate thus tends to depart from a perfectly circular form. Bevels for the attachment of the plate to the machine cylinder are formed by the undercut of the casting gauges. Ribbed casting boards are used as in flat casting, and the increasingly high standards of accuracy, to which the plate-making industry is constantly tending, call for boring the inner circumference of the plate.

Boring is analogous to back-planing of the flat plate and is carried out by one of two methods. The plate is laid in the semicylindrical bed of the boring machine where a knife, revolving longitudinally on a central spindle, scoops away the superfluous metal to the required thickness. Alternatively, a disk, fitted with a number of cutters along its edge, and revolving rapidly, travels along a worm thread arranged axially to the plate, cutting the core in the process. The effect is the same by both processes, the latter being somewhat slower, but having more theoretical advantage in the matter of accuracy.

Where very long runs are required, and also as a resistant to the corrosive and in some cases abrasive effect of certain inks, stereo plates can be nickel faced. It should be emphasized that no further finishing of the surface of the plate can be undertaken after the nickel facing is applied, without risk of the nickel peeling off when the plate is in use. It follows that subjects requiring to be shot-up flush to the work (such as solid tint blocks) should have this operation performed before facing.

Nickel depositing is performed by immersing the plate in a bath containing a solution of nickel salts. Across the bath are laid brass rods in electrical contact with the positive and negative poles respectively of a dynamo. The plate to be coated is completely immersed in the solution, suspended by hooks from the brass rod on the negative side. Opposite to it, suspended from the positive rod, is an anode of pure nickel in the form of a flat sheet; or a set of oval-shaped anodes can be used. The passage of the current disintegrates the anode and deposits a skin of nickel on face and back of the plate.

Nickel will deposit upon, but will not firmly adhere directly to, stereo metal, and this condition is overcome by first giving the stereo a thin coating of copper by a similar method in a copper cyanide bath, with, of course, a copper anode. Given correct solutions and current control, strict cleanliness at every stage of the operation is of paramount importance. The plate must be thoroughly cleaned before depositing is commenced, and also swilled in hot water in passing from the copper to the nickel bath.

The method of cleaning must be one that will remove every trace of grease, and the operator should avoid any direct handling of the plate, moving it from bath to bath by means of the hooks. The usual method of cleaning is by means of a vigorous scrubbing in a hot solution of potash or caustic soda.

More effective in result, and less unpleasant to the operator, is a chemical degreasing plant using trichlorethylene. This is a fluid with a very low boiling point, vaporized in a special form of tank from which, if correctly operated, the vapour is unable to escape. After a few minutes exposure to the vapour the plate is withdrawn effectively cleaned, dipped in running water and transferred immediately to the copper cyanide tank.

ELECTROTYPING

THE process of electrotyping has for its purpose the duplication of the same class of originals as stereotyping and for the same reasons. Electrotyping is the longer and more expensive process, and therefore is not suitable for such work as newspaper reproduction and for press advertising purposes, for which stereotyping is invariably used.

The oldest method of electrotyping is by wax moulding. If the original be a forme it is unlocked, imposed with type-high clumps or bearers and levelled as described earlier. Any spaces below the level of the type shoulders, and any hollow quads, are filled in with plaster (this is termed floating the forme) to prevent the entry of the wax and so cause difficulty in detaching the mould. Strips of nonpareil (6 point) metal are used for bearers when moulding from unmounted original blocks.

The wax, mostly composed of beeswax, which is to become the mould, is melted and poured on to a moulding tray—a flat metal slab with holed projections at one end for subsequent attachment to the rods of the depositing bath. The wax is poured in semi-molten form and it will find its own level, flat and smooth, if poured on an even-standing bench. When solid, but still warm, the wax is placed on the prepared forme which has previously been brushed over with fine graphite powder. Surmounted by the moulding tray, the forme is placed on the table of an hydraulic moulding press and pressure applied varying with the area and nature of the work.

When the mould is released from the forme the superfluous wax squeezed up by this pressure is removed with a thin knife-like tool, and the mould, now integral with the tray, passed to the bench-hand for building. This process has for its purpose the sinking of the open spaces in the plate which would otherwise have to be routed down to secure adequate printing depth.

As the term implies, building consists of building up high spots on the mould, which, conversely, become low spots on the shell next to be grown upon it. The building up is done by running a piece of wax into the desired places, much as solder is run with a soldering iron, and with a very similar instrument, though much smaller and with a sharper point.

Recently, more up-to-date and hygienic methods of so-called wax moulding have come to the fore. For instance, a process has been invented by two English electrotypers, in which a waxed-face material is made up, which eliminates the floating of formes and the building up of the tray. There is also a commercial wax material which is used in the same manner as stereo flong —by placing the wax side down and pressing into the type or original.

In preparation for the depositing bath the mould is blackleaded in order to give it a metallic face and so, by increasing its electrical conductivity, to assist the initial growth of the shell. Graphiting is carried out in an air-tight box to prevent the very fine powder used in the process from impregnating not only the work but the workroom. Within the box are mechanically vibrated brushes which impart a bright, smooth surface of graphite to the mould. After being sprayed with water to remove any stray particles of powder, sprinkled with fine iron filings and copper sulphate, the mould is ready for depositing.

The depositing vat (Fig. 12) operates on the principle already described, but the solution is of copper sulphate and the anodes are of pure copper. The copper shell, which is to become the surface of the finished electrotype, is allowed to grow upon the mould until the desired thickness is reached. This can vary within very wide limits according to the run required from the plate. This stage having been reached, hot water poured on the back of the shell readily detaches it from the mould.

Backing-up the Shell

The shell, a thin but tough film of copper, rough on the back but bearing on the face a reproduction of the original forme, must now be backed-up, i.e. brought to the standard thickness of a printing plate by the addition of suitable metal to the back. The metal used for backing electrotypes is much softer than that used for stereotyping, a usual formula being tin 2 per cent, antimony 3 per cent, lead 95 per cent.

That the shell and the backing metal shall remain in inseparable contact during the working life of the electro is an essential consideration, and to ensure this the back of the shell is tinned before the backing metal is run on. The shell is placed face downwards in a shallow tray, and a piece of thin tin foil, cut to the same size, is laid on the back of it. The tray is lowered to the surface of the molten backing metal which rapidly raises tray and shell to approximately its own heat, at the same time melting the tin which runs into and adheres firmly to the rough back of the shell.

The backing metal is then poured over the whole, and when cool and extracted from the tray, the shell is found embedded in metal of a thickness of about ⅜ in. The printing surface of the shell is unaffected, having previously been protected by the application of a suitable greasy paste.

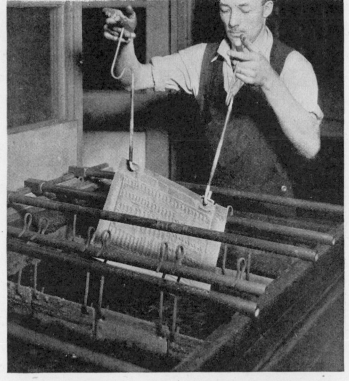

DEPOSITING THE ELECTRO MOULD

Fig. 12. The wax mould is blackleaded in order to give it a metallic face, and to increase the growth of the copper shell.

One essential condition of a satisfactory printing plate is perfect flatness and parallelism between front and back surfaces; and to produce this, slabbing is resorted to, as the plate in its cast condition is by no means flat (Fig. 13).

Slabbing

In slabbing, the back is first roughly skimmed in a machine in which the plate is held firmly under rollers which force it forwards under a knife travelling backwards and forwards on a reciprocating holder. This produces a certain degree of flatness, and the rest is the responsibility of the slab hand.

By means of a variety of tools—a cast-iron surface plate, various punches, callipers, hammer, and straight-edge—the plate is worked to a level surface. Where the straight-edge discloses a hollow on the face, the callipers mark the back immediately beneath it; and the punch and hammer, discreetly applied to the marked area while the face is in contact with the surface plate, gradually eliminate the hollow. Every part of the area of the plate is tested for level and treated accordingly.

What has taken a few lines to describe is a process calling for considerable skill and judgment on the part of the operator and may involve half an hour or more of careful manipulation. Only too easily are fine letters spread or highlight dots on a fine screen tone increased

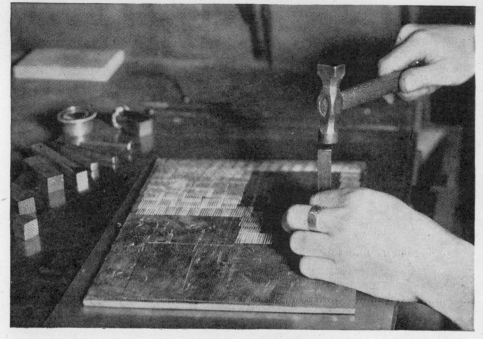

SLABBING ELECTROS

Fig. 13. *The electro is placed face down on a polished slab and tooled over with a serrated punch or slabbing hammer, levelling out any unevenness or sinks that occur upon the face.*

slightly in size to the detriment of the printed result from the plate. When the operator is satisfied that the standard of accuracy has been reached the plate is again back-planed, to 12 point or other specified thickness.

Lead Moulding

Lead moulding is frequently used in place of wax, particularly for electro-typing half-tones. It is claimed to provide exact duplication of the finest half-tone printing surfaces and is consequently much favoured where three- and four-colour reproduction is concerned.

Lead moulding has in many cases displaced the wax mould for reasons of hygiene, as the graphite preparation for lead, as compared with wax, is cut to a minimum. Greater pressure is required for the moulding of lead and it is possible

with due care to obtain excellent results from type and originals alike.

The comparatively soft lead sheet which forms the moulding material is forced into the forme under heavy hydraulic pressure, and a mould of delicate precision is obtained. Upon this the copper shell is deposited in the same way as in wax moulding.

Where a specially hard surface is required, to withstand more than ordinarily long printing runs, a nickel shell is sometimes deposited on the mould before the copper, and a direct-deposited nickel-electro is the result. Alternatively, the usual copper-shelled electro can be nickel-faced. This is termed a nickel-faced electro. The two classes of plate are distinct and should not be confused.

Chromium facing can be applied to

either electros or stereos for the production of abnormally long runs or for working on very hard stock. Chromium being one of the hardest metals known, and practically immune from corrosive or abrasive effects under printing conditions, chromium facing is particularly suitable for repetition work where the subject is in continuous demand.

Curved Electros

Electrotypes for rotary printing are first produced as flat electros and backed to the thickness required by the cylinder of the rotary press, which may be anything up to $\frac{3}{8}$ in. The necessary curvature is produced by passing the plate between rollers, usually three arranged pyramidically, the top one rather smaller than the two at the base. The rollers are turned by hand or power gearing and the plate fed with the face towards the two bottom rollers. As downward pressure is applied upon the apex roller, revolving on the back of the plate and slowly driving it forwards, the perpendicular distance between the roller centres is decreased and the curve formed. Gradually increasing pressure is applied until the correct curve is obtained to fit the cylinder.

Wax Engraving Process

Another method of electrotyping, mainly used for letterpress map work, is the wax engraving process. In this process the key or outline of the map is laid down direct on the wax mould, and the names of places are impressed in the wax by hand from type which is specially selected for this purpose. By means of a ruling machine, lines are drawn on the wax to indicate seas and oceans; and cross rulings and stipples are used for giving gradations of tone. When the outline and lettering have been completed on the wax a photo-print is taken for correction purposes, and any necessary alterations can be made in the wax.

After correction an electro is made from the wax mould in the usual way.

If the map is to be printed in colour the tints for each colour plate are laid down by the same method as the key, and an electro is made for each separate colour plate.

The wax engraving method is, however, more suitable for maps printed in black and white than for colour work, owing to the difficulties in making the frequent corrections which are necessary to keep maps up to date.

Recent Developments

Having dealt at length with the main methods of duplication there has yet to be written a very brief survey of the latest developments in plate-making that assist the particular style of printing to which these are suited.

There is the rubber stereo for use when printing with aniline inks. This is a mould consisting of a similar make-up as described earlier in reference to the wet flong. The mould is strengthened by reinforcing with a cement plaster.

In some cases a plastic mould is used. A piece of unvulcanized rubber, cut to size, is brushed with french chalk to check any adhesion, and placed upon the mould. This is then placed under a hot hydraulic press for a few minutes to vulcanize the rubber. Gauges are used under the press to obtain the correct thickness. These stereos are fitted to the fit beds or curved cylinders of the printing machines by means of a special adhesive.

Another method, claimed in some circles as effective, is the plastic stereo. Several assortments of plastics have been tried and used. Both these later developments in plate duplication have shown some excellent results in halftone, colour and type, but they do not lend themselves to all classes of print.

CHAPTER FOURTEEN

THE PROCESS AND ITS PROGRESS

SENEFELDER'S DISCOVERY. DISADVANTAGES OF STONE. USE OF ZINC AND ALUMINIUM.
MACHINERY IMPROVEMENTS. OFFSET PRINTING ON METAL. ROTARY MACHINES.
CHEMICAL DEVELOPMENTS. INKS FOR COLOUR WORK. PLATE-MAKING METHODS.

LITHOGRAPHY is the youngest of the major printing processes, and much uncertainty exists in regard to certain of its phases by many who practise the craft. Inventions are often the result of a gradual accumulation of specialized knowledge, and processes usually evolve with little regard to specific dates; but lithography has both a date and an inventor.

Johann Aloysius (or Aloys) Senefelder was born at Prague, Bohemia (now Czechoslovakia), on November 6, 1771, and at an early age, moved to Munich, Bavaria. From 1796 and for two years Senefelder made "several thousand different experiments" using relief and recessed images, and in 1798 the planographic method of printing was evolved and brought under practical control. Senefelder was not a good artist, so he invented a drawing machine; he found writing in reverse a real trial, and overcame this by writing and drawing on cartridge paper and transferring the drawing to the stone. This developed to coated transfer paper which the far-sighted Senefelder regarded as the greatest of his inventions (Fig. 1).

By this means lithography was raised to a premier duplicating process—a position which it still holds. Through bitter opposition and ridicule from other printing interests, lithography moved on to ever increasing usefulness.

Lithography spread with remarkable rapidity and by 1820 it was being practised in most of the European countries.

Senefelder travelled Europe, inaugurating the process in the chief cities and supplying materials and equipment.

Improvements were continually being made and the scope of the process widened. A tint was added to chalk drawing in black and this led to the use of coloured inks in lithography.

Alternatives for Stone

It was soon found that stone was a cumbersome printing material, and several alternatives were suggested and used by Senefelder. These included zinc, with dilute phosphoric acid and gum as an etch. It was nearing the end of the century before the trade generally took kindly to zinc, although samples of good six-colour work, which were printed from zinc plates in 1846, are still extant. Senefelder also devised a means of spreading stone solution on a flexible card or paper base so that this "plate" could then be treated as stone. It is therefore strange to find a British patent taken out for this process as late as 1901. Senefelder used intaglio cylinders for printing calico, and he suggested the rotary principle for lithography.

Lithography owed its continuance largely to its dual appeal as an artistic and an industrial medium. Its existence was thereby assisted through precarious times when the pendulum of popularity swung violently, or when one of the competing printing processes enjoyed a temporary period of ascendancy.

For over sixty years lithographic printing was done on hand-operated presses (Fig. 2), but Senefelder was certain that all the operations could be better carried out mechanically.

The first lithographic machine was operated in the year 1852. Sigls's fast machine was subjected to the usual scorn and derision given to the pioneer. It had a reciprocating bed carrying the stone, a cylinder with grippers for the sheet, a feed-board, damping rollers and inking rollers. The fly-

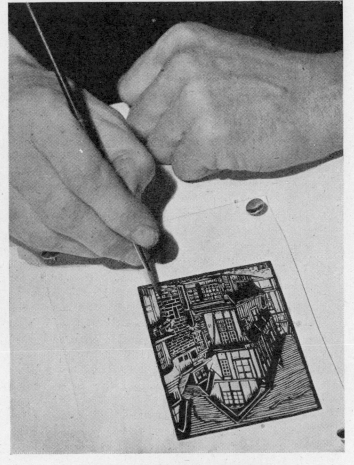

MAKING A DRAWN TRANSFER

Fig. 1. *The drawing is made on specially coated paper, using lithographic drawing ink. This will then be transferred to a prepared lithographic printing surface for use as an original.*

wheel was turned by hand. The machine, however, was too revolutionary to find immediate favour.

A period followed (1864-1875) in which flat-bed machines (Fig. 3) were made by several makers in Britain and others in France and Germany, and it was difficult to find enough skilled men to work them. This mechanization of the trade brought about a minor revolution. These machines needed much work to keep them running; and

as much of the artistic work had depended on hand manipulation for its full effect, there was soon a large increase in commercial printing which entirely overshadowed the exclusively artistic production.

Then came a time when labour was divided into grades according to degrees of skill, and the reproducing artist did most of the ground work on stone, while the creative artist completed the drawing. Thus began the commercial

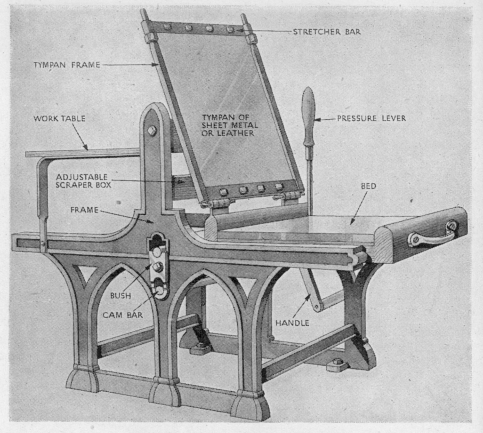

STRETCHER BAR

TYMPAN FRAME

WORK TABLE

TYMPAN OF SHEET METAL OR LEATHER

PRESSURE LEVER

ADJUSTABLE SCRAPER BOX

FRAME

BED

BUSH

CAM BAR

HANDLE

SIDE-LEVER LITHO TRANSFER PRESS

Fig. 2. The tympan is closed over the stone and the bed pushed forward. Lowering the pressure lever to the horizontal position forces the carriage and stone upwards against the scraper. As the handle is turned, the bed is slowly driven through the press. The lever is then returned to the vertical position, thus releasing the pressure on the bed.

reproduction period in which much of the work produced was clever but artistically paltry.

First Offset Machine

A lithographic landmark was erected in 1875 when Robert Barclay patented the offset printing process for printing on metal sheets. This first offset machine to be put to general practical use had the usual reciprocating bed carrying the litho stone to and fro, and in addition two cylinders, one above the other,

similar to the arrangement of a mangle. The lower cylinder was covered with a specially prepared card on which the print was taken from the stone. The sheet of metal then passed between the two cylinders and received the impression on the under side, by transfer from the card. After many experiments rubber sheeting was used, and the process has remained in constant commercial production since 1877. The rubber-covered cotton sheet, or blanket, is the result of long experiment and improvement.

The reciprocating motion of the litho flat-bed machine is clumsy, and the rollers are comparatively noisy. Changing the direction of the bed absorbs considerable power, while the return journey is but a preparation for printing, taking almost as much time as is actually used in printing. It is well to remember that the printing engineer had a certain amount of experience available for the devising of printing machinery, for in 1814 *The Times* had a successful letterpress machine which printed over 1,000 sheets per hour.

Rotary Principle

The next stage in machinery development was the adoption of the rotary principle. Progress was continuous if not spectacular. Work of a pioneer and progressive nature was constantly being done by individuals and small groups, though the higher standard of production attained by their efforts was not quickly established as trade practice. This was largely due to the conservative craftsman who had no vision of the wider field of potential lithographic application. The use of zinc plates became more general, while the newer aluminium surface was also being used. Plates of both metals were used on flat-bed machines as an alternative to stone.

This technical and practical progress with thin flexible printing surfaces paved the way for the rotary type of machine which appeared towards the end of the nineteenth century. The idea of such a machine had been conceived many years before the first practical machine came from New York, and the general design was soon utilized by all lithographic machine manufacturers in Great Britain.

The construction of the direct rotary type of machine (Fig. 4) was simple, retaining the cylinder and the delivery apparatus of the flat-bed machine, while the stone bed and ink slab were replaced by a second cylinder. This rotary principle produced a smoother and quieter-running machine, and the sheet output was practically doubled while retaining the same peripheral speed as the flat-bed.

FLAT-BED LITHO PRINTING MACHINE

Fig. 3. *The hooks near the flier-sticks are to suspend the delivery cylinder when stiff card necessitates taking-off by hand. All operations are mechanical except the feeding.*

DIRECT ROTARY LITHO PRINTING MACHINE

Fig. 4. The damping system is seen at the bottom left; the inking system is over the plate cylinder; the feed board is at the top right with the delivery board below it. The cylinders have a coarse gear which engages deeply when in the printing position but less deeply when tripped, so that in this non-printing position a cylinder clearance is maintained.

It is strange that the offset principle should have been used for nearly thirty years for tin-printing before it was generally applied to lithographic printing on paper, but once the direct rotary machine was established the introduction of the offset rotary was simplified. Again the tin-printing section was the pioneer, and the Mann Standard tin-printer was in commercial production in 1904. This machine, though still being manufactured, is essentially a hand-fed machine and must soon make way for the automatically-fed type.

The three-cylinder rotary-offset machine is now firmly established, and evolution rather than revolution marks the further course of lithographic machine changes. By reducing the impres-sion cylinder of the Mann Standard rotary tin-printer to half the size of the plate and blanket cylinders, and by modifying the feed and delivery, the very useful two-revolution paper-print-ing litho-offset machine appeared.

From this same basic design came the two-revolution two-colour and perfect-ing litho-offset machine, which prints either two colours on one side of the sheet or one colour on each side of the sheet simultaneously.

The single-revolution machine—that is a machine having all cylinders of the same diameter—is the type which found favour both with American and Conti-nental designers. The plate cylinder is uppermost and this arrangement retains the automatic feeder low down on the machine. This style allows for building two-, three- and four-colour machines on the unit principle.

Two-colour machines may be said to be modern standard practice; three-colour machines have much less general use, while four-colour machines are little used except in America where they are used extensively for the production of remarkably good work, notably fruit-can labels. This is highly specialized work and the design has to be prepared to suit the peculiar technique of the wet-printing process.

Machine Design Progress

The reasons for the recent rapid progress in machine design are due mainly, not to the unaided efforts of practical lithographic printers, but rather to the general developments in other spheres, which have contributed to the advance of lithographic practice. For instance, the science of metallurgy has supplied improved metals for use with progressive engineering design; cotton experts have produced a special base for the offset blanket; while chemists have spent many years evolving the present remarkable rubber surface, and still later the more remarkable and more efficient rubber substitute. Metal plates have been improved in purity of substance and uniformity of rolling, while chemists specializing in ink and paper have embarked on an endless task in an effort to fulfil demands. The necessary chemicals and materials have improved in quality and uniformity, and high scientific standards of purity now obtain.

Packaging Labels

As modern packaging processes control more and more the design and method of printing the labels used in this class of work (e.g. the wrapping of safety razor blades), a great degree of accuracy and uniformity is called for both in making-up the printing plates from which such work is printed, and in the cutting of the printed sheets. For the purpose of obtaining labels of uniform and accurate size some American makes of guillotines are controlled by means of photo-electric cells.

Multi-transferring Machine

To ensure fine accuracy in the spacing of the image on the printing plate a multi-transferring machine is available which uses the offset principle, and transfers the image from a small original plate to the machine plate with micrometric accuracy. The image is transferred to pre-arranged positions, and as many plates as may be required, or all the colours of one job, or any number of colour sets, can be made with the same high degree of precision. This machine is fully described and illustrated in Chapter 19.

The adoption of the Harris four-colour offset machine in America created an urgent need for making sets of four printing plates, the accurate fit of which could be guaranteed. To this end the Traung hydraulic litho transfer press came into being. This transfer press uses a roller instead of the normal sliding scraper, and the pressure can be pre-set and is indicated in pounds per square inch on a pressure dial. Power is supplied by electric motor with push-button control giving inching, forward, and reverse motions, and there are automatic safety stops in both directions. (see also Chapter 19, Fig. 1).

The changes in lithographic printing methods, equipment and materials during the present century have made unparalleled demands on the ink-maker. From the slow flat-bed machine which leisurely and amply inked the printing forme in two directions, to the unidirectional rotary machine, was but a short step; but to the offset rotary machine and the demand for great concentration of tinctorial power in a minimum thickness of ink film, was a far cry calling for much intensive and highly skilled research.

The wide variety of stocks created by the papermaker, from unsized rag to metal foil, and also of transparent cellulose; the varied uses of printed wrappings from greasy foods to soaps; the effects of light, temperature, exposure to varied weather and atmospheric conditions, are but some of the many problems which have been solved.

Not the least achievement of the inkmaker is the provision of lithographic silver ink for the production of a metallic surface on paper. Satisfactory lithographic gold printing inks are looked for but are not yet generally available; but there can be few lithographers who will not welcome the introduction of a practical gold ink as an alternative to the unhygienic metal powder which pollutes the atmosphere and clogs the respiratory passages in a way which calls for the closer attention and control of the officials at the Home Office.

Photography and Lithography

The two chief additional features which make modern lithographic printing of such a high standard are: (1) the combination of lithography and photography; and (2) the more recent improvements in the making of printing plates, notably the so-called deep etch plate-making methods.

Anything which can be photographed can be lithographed, and the days are gone when the letterpress photo-engraving fine etcher held the advantage in tone production and correction. The present period is one in which lithography holds still greater possibilities, and wide-awake craftsmen are exploiting this to the full —but too many others are not!

Modern photographic process is considered more flexible than fine etching by the photo-engraver, for the tonal values of the photographic plate can be both increased and decreased. Much is left to the skill of the retoucher, but instruments are available for measuring the size of the half-tone dot. Values of each colour plate to produce any desired result can be measured and should be known and not guessed.

Chemical dot reduction methods also produce photographic plates with definite printing values which can be repeated as many times as required on the printing plate. These photographic plates are not over-sensitive even to large percentages of variation in exposure. This is in marked distinction from the atrocious stain, chalk and pencil additions which are so often unskilfully attached to the plate. Such methods break up the half-tone formation, and hold back the light locally so that a satisfactory printing image is not obtained on the printing plate. Nor are these unsatisfactory photographic images under full control during printing down, and they lend themselves to manipulation and thus to varying printing results due to many variable factors, not least of which is the mood of the operator.

The alternative to this obsolescent method is the dot reduction process, in which the tonal values are corrected on the photographic plate, thus producing a nearly perfect positive, which is then used with a deep-etch method of plate-making to produce the printing plate.

In this method the dots on the photographic plate remain firm and of a good shape, but the size is changed by chemical means to give a greater or smaller printing surface to the tonal result required. Many duplications can be made from such plates and there is a minimum scope for variation. Accuracy of tone rendering is thus fully obtained.

CHAPTER FIFTEEN

PRINCIPLES OF LITHOGRAPHY

ARTISTIC, COMMERCIAL AND SCIENTIFIC ASPECTS. CHEMICAL REACTIONS. LITHO-
GRAPHIC STONE. USE OF GUM ARABIC. IMAGE FORMATION. IMAGE CONTROL.
ETCHING AND ITS EFFECTS. ACIDS AND SALTS. NATURAL, FOUNDATION AND
CHEMICAL PRINCIPLES. ZINC AND ALUMINIUM PLATES. DRAWING ON METAL.

LITHOGRAPHY may be considered from three aspects: (1) artistic; (2) commercial; (3) scientific. The artist treats lithography or lithographic surfaces as media through which to express his ideas. It may be largely fortuitous that this method opens a wide field for commercial exploitation; but to the artist the creation is what matters, and of the chemical reactions (if any) he is blissfully ignorant. To the lithographic printer the control of production in quantity and quality is the main concern.

From Senefelder to the present day the lithographer has always imagined that he is in control of a highly complex chemical process. If this is so, it is strange that so few lithographers have even the most elementary knowledge of chemistry. It is stranger still that, despite the increasing complexity of modern production; of higher printing speeds; of the constantly widening use of new synthetic materials; the adoption of more satisfactory ways of plate-making; and the need for precise control of solutions, materials and conditions, the lithographic printer is usually entirely ignorant of chemistry and physics.

Much research work still remains to be done on lithographic problems and it is hoped that detailed investigation will not be long delayed. Meantime, a simple explanation of the basis of lithographic printing may clear up certain obscurities. The subject of lithographic printing on stone will first be considered, as offering the simplest approach.

The first principle on which lithographic printing is based is the entirely natural fact that grease does not mix with, nor is it wetted by, water. Grease and water are naturally repellent. No chemical action whatever is involved in this natural principle.

The illustrations in this chapter (Figs. 1 to 5) show in sequence the drawing and proofing of a lithographic job.

Lithographic Stone

The stone which is used in lithographic printing is a very fine-grained, compact limestone (calcium carbonate, $CaCO_3$). Although limestone is deposited freely all over the world, it is only in the Jura Mountains, Bavaria, that the superfine quality required for lithography is found. This stone is assumed to have an affinity for certain substances, because of the peculiar effect which is produced when these substances make contact with the stone. The effect is such that, after the applied substance has been dried, if the whole surface of the stone is kept slightly moistened, and then rolled over with a roller charged with an even film of printing ink, the printing ink will adhere to the previously applied substance, but not to the moistened surface. This substance is thus said to form an image.

In the course of continued rolling and pulling of proofs it is found that the

DIRECT DRAWING ON STONE

Fig. 1. *This image is for direct printing and is therefore drawn in the reverse position. Clean paper prevents the hands from touching the surface, while strips of thin card slightly raise the straight-edge from the stone to prevent smearing. The fingers of the right hand rest on the ruler to assist in maintaining a light, even contact of the pen with the stone.*

image loses its sharp definition and becomes thickened and the lines woolly, while the non-image section becomes increasingly soiled with the waterproof printing ink. Measures have therefore to be taken to prevent growth of the image.

After the image-forming substance is applied to the stone and dried, the whole of the surface of the stone (including the image) is coated with a solution of gum arabic dissolved in water. The water is then evaporated from this deposited solution by fanning, and a dry, even film of glossy-looking gum is left on the surface of the stone.

If this gum is well washed from the stone with clean water and a sponge,

the moisture reduced to a very slight film with a soft rag or damping cloth, and the rolling continued as before, it will be found that the non-image sections will keep free from ink deposit, and the image will retain its definition during the pulling of far more impressions than was the case without the gum. Indeed, the gum treatment is essential in commercial practice or when several identical prints are required.

Effect of Gum

It follows from this that the gum has had some effect on the stone, even though it would appear to have been removed when washing with water. Gum arabic is used in this way because it produces a water-attracting film on the surface of the stone. As lithographic stone is slightly porous, the gum solution penetrates the fine surface pores of the stone, and this absorbed or penetrated film remains in intimate contact with the stone, even when the excess or surface gum is washed off with water. The absorbed or combined gum film is hygroscopic or water-attracting and, therefore, when it is in a moist condition it repels the waterproof ink.

If the stone is left without gum for a prolonged period the combined film deteriorates on contact with the atmosphere. Therefore, when the stone is not in actual printing use, it should be covered with an amount of gum which is generously in excess of what can be absorbed by the stone, and thus the combined film is renewed and retained in effective condition.

The image-forming or ink-attracting substances also penetrate into the stone, and these two opposite forces of ink attraction and water repulsion, and water attraction and ink repulsion, produce and maintain the conditions which make lithographic printing possible.

The *foundation principle* may therefore be subdivided into (*a*) image formation, and (*b*) image control, i.e. the desensitizing action of gum arabic.

Lithographic images are very often

DAMPING THE STONE

Fig. 2. *Clean water is used, and this may be applied by first wiping a sponge across the stone. A cotton damping cloth is then used in broad sweeps to smooth out the water over the whole surface until the thinnest controllable film is obtained before applying the roller.*

INKING THE IMAGE

Fig. 3. The roller is worked to and fro on the dampened surface. The stone may have to be damped and rolled several times before the image is properly charged with ink.

formed by the action of fatty acids on the printing surface. The popular explanation assumes a chemical reaction between the fatty acid and the printing surface. This widely held view is neither proved nor probable. Images can be formed with chemically neutral substances, which thus precludes the possibility of the formation of chemical salts. Also, the salt thus formed would be unstable and would hydrolyse—that is, it would be split up on contact with water.

Similarly, it is generally supposed by lithographers that some acidic radical of gum arabic exerts a chemical influence on the non-image section of the stone. This again is not proven and is highly improbable, since if the so-called active acid is removed from the gum solution and the solution made chemically neutral before application to the stone, the practical lithographic effect is the same.

As chemically inert substances do not readily enter into chemical reaction this old theory would seem to demand revision in the light of modern knowledge. It may be that in the case of printing from stone, the simple explanation of absorption suffices ; but it is more probable that this absorption is combined with adsorption, which may be described as a strong physical attraction, or an action in which no definite chemical compound has been formed and which yet produces an effect which is not very easily resolved or reversed.

Printing can be carried on immediately after the image is formed and the gum solution is applied, but it is found that there is still a tendency for the ink-repelling forces to be less strong than desired. To overcome this, and to make the gum film still more effective, the image is inked up generously. It is then dusted with finely powdered rosin, which acts as an acid resist. The whole stone is then washed over with a dilute solution of nitric acid. This operation is termed etching, and 1 to 3 per cent nitric acid solution is sufficiently strong for normal purposes.

This acid solution attacks the exposed surface of the stone immediately on application, causing slight effervescence and producing a finely granular condition on the surface of the stone. This open condition of the stone surface allows a deeper penetration of, and provides a stronger anchorage for, the subsequent gum solution which is then applied and fanned dry. Due to a combination of a more firmly established hygroscopic film, in conjunction with a better water-retaining surface due to slight roughness and greater surface porosity, the stone is now in the best possible printing condition.

Etching Results

Certain matters arising out of the etching operation should be noted. If the acid solution is too concentrated, or if a normal strength of solution is applied excessively, the surface of the stone will be dissolved to a degree which leaves the image in obvious relief. There is also the added possibility that when producing this exaggerated effect the image may be undermined and made weak.

This relief effect is not usually required and indeed should be guarded against; but it can be used to advantage (a) when direct printing is being done on hard paper (thus applying localized pressure); and (b) when carrying out the relief method of transposition, i.e. when changing the ink-attracting sections of the stone to ink-rejecting and water-attracting sections, and changing the water-attracting sections to ink-attracting and water-rejecting (i.e. hydrophobic) sections.

It should also be noted that the acid removes the stone to a greater depth than the gum has penetrated, with the result that the stone is again lithographically sensitive, so that further work may be added by drawing or transferring.

Chemical Reactions

The application of a dilute acid to stone is in no way an exclusively lithographic procedure, but is an elementary chemical operation the effects of which can be calculated and controlled. When an acid which has been diluted with water is brought into contact with the litho stone, the stone and the acid react to form a salt. This resulting salt may be either soluble or insoluble in water according to the kind of acid used. Oxalic acid, for example, forms a water-insoluble salt, and the film so formed is utilized for making temporary image deletions and for keeping stone edges clean during printing operations.

Nitric acid in contact with stone forms a water-soluble salt, and during the action gas is given off (as seen by the effervescence), and the change from acid to salt solution may be demonstrated and experienced by tasting the etch before use and the liquid remaining on the stone after effervescence has ceased.

This action, and the normal etching operation on stone result from the replacement of a weak acid from a salt by means of a stronger acid. An acid is a compound containing hydrogen, some or all of which may be replaced by a

TAKING THE PRINT

Fig. 4. *The paper is placed in position, the tympan closed, pressure is adjusted by the screw key through the threaded rod on the press head, and then applied by lowering the side lever. The turning of the handle actuates a friction cylinder and the press bed is forced along under the scraper. Raising the side lever releases the pressure.*

metal to form a salt. Acids are mostly water-soluble and have a sour taste.

A salt is a compound which is formed by the replacement of the hydrogen of an acid by a metal, and there are several different methods of producing salts. Salts are usually neutral to litmus, while acids turn blue litmus paper red.

Limestone is calcium carbonate, the chemical formula for which is $CaCO_3$. The formula for nitric acid is HNO_3. The chemist would therefore express the reaction which takes place during the etching of lithographic stone in this way: $CaCO_3 + 2HNO_3 = CO_2 + H_2O + Ca(NO_3)_2$.

This simply means that when stone is

acted upon by nitric acid, carbon dioxide (carbonic acid gas) is given off, and water and calcium nitrate are formed. As the calcium nitrate is entirely soluble in water, and is readily removed from the stone after the etching is completed, the stone is thus left in a condition for he addition of further work or the best acceptance of gum.

Lithographic Principles

The principles on which lithographic printing is based may therefore be summarized as follows:—

(1) *Natura' Principle.* The fact that grease and water do not mix; or, that grease is not wetted by water.

(2) *Foundation Principle.* This has two parts: (*a*) image formation. Certain substances affect the stone in such a way that they attract waterproof printing ink; (*b*) image control. Gum arabic inhibits further image formation by establishing a film which has a preferential attraction for moisture. This control of the image is increased in effectiveness by the application of a

(3) *Chemical Principle.* This is most important in all lithographic work.

Stone Substitutes

Litho stone, quarried at Solnhofen in Bavaria, is very largely superseded in the modern application of lithographic printing due to the need for increased speed to compete with contemporary processes. The heavy slabs of stone require the ponderous flat-bed type of printing machine, and the urgent modern requirement is for a flexible surface which lends itself to the rotary method of printing. Experiments are constantly being made to improve the control of printing surfaces and to find new ones. Highly complex metal alloys have been evolved and used in sheet form during recent years and these will have wider distribution in the near future. Not only metal, but plastic plates have been introduced. Their planographic use will probably continue to be restricted.

Electrolytically deposited surfaces, using metals of contrasting properties, are highly effective.

Zinc and Aluminium

The metals which have become established through long trade usage are zinc and aluminium. Both are entirely satisfactory as lithographic printing surfaces, but some craftsmen have a marked preference for one and some for the other. Usually craftsmen favour the metal of their first experience.

The principles of lithography apply in a general way to printing from both stone and metal, but certain differences must be pointed out. Stone is porous: it absorbs water and does not oxidize. Zinc and aluminium readily oxidize and do not absorb water. Therefore the metal surfaces are treated with an abrasive to produce an even, granular effect.

This mechanical treatment is known as graining, and the coarseness of the grain is largely decided by the grade and quality of the abrasive which is used. The purpose of this grain is threefold: it serves to retain a film of moisture; it serves as an anchorage for both the image and the non-image films; and the texture makes possible the production of tonal values by the chalk method of direct drawing. Graining increases the surface area several times and produces a condition in which the various chemical solutions which are used react much more readily (see also page 195).

Direct Drawing on Metal

The production of the direct drawing (Fig. 1) and the transferred image is practically the same on metal as on stone. Before applying the image, the plate is given a sensitizing bath. Nitric-alum solution is used in the case of zinc, and the effect is to deposit a film of basic aluminium sulphate on the surface of the metal.

Aluminium has a natural film of aluminium oxide and needs no further treatment if washed thoroughly and used in the state in which it is taken out of the graining machine. Usually the plate is given a dilute acid bath to remove traces of grease, e.g. fingermarks, which may accumulate. In the case of both metals an aluminium compound (chiefly aluminium oxide) is retained on the surface.

Although there is no appreciable penetration into the metal of either the image-forming or the water-attracting materials, the forces of attraction are so strong that they withstand the friction of printing work to a remarkable degree.

The etching operation on plates is in marked contrast to that on stone. There is wide variety in the etching solutions which are used, but they usually contain an acid such as gallic, chromic or phosphoric, or phosphate salts such as ammonium dihydrogen phosphate. Gum arabic is also often used in the etch, but this is optional; and pure gum arabic solution may be applied after the etching. Gum in an etch retards the action and it also assists local control.

The purpose of the etch is to form a chemically neutral phosphate salt on the non-image sections of the plate and so to change the ink-receptive nature of the surface to a condition which will not readily attract printing ink.

After etching for from one to three minutes (according to the type of etch which is being used), the etch is removed and a thin film of gum solution applied evenly to the whole of the surface of the plate and dried quickly. The application of the gum thus has a cumulative effect in building up a more vigorous and durable water-retaining section, which then controls the image by means of its opposite and balancing actions.

REMOVING THE PRINTED SHEET

Fig. 5. *The printed sheet is removed from the stone. The quality of the print is critically noted and, if imperfect, the treatment is modified before taking the next impression. It may be necessary to adjust ink, pressure or roller manipulation, either separately or in combination.*

CHAPTER SIXTEEN

VERSATILITY OF LITHOGRAPHY

VARIETY OF LITHO WORK. SPECIALIZATION. SHEET-METAL PRINTING. REPETITION WORK. FINE ART REPRODUCTION. PRINTING ON GLASS AND SILK. NEWSPAPER PRINTING BY LITHO. OFFSET SECURITY PRINTING. MAP AND CHART WORK. AUTO-GRAPHIC TRANSFERS. AUTOLITHOGRAPHY. LITHO POSTERS.

THE range of work that is produced by the lithographic process is exceedingly wide, but despite its remarkable versatility there are types of work which are more suited to letterpress and to gravure printing methods.

Lithographic printers, therefore, usually concentrate on certain types of work. Those who are highly specialized generally produce the higher qualities of work over their limited range. Similarly, those who produce a greater variety may do so both with less highly specialized craftsmen and with equipment of more general utility. Furthermore, there are extensive variations in the standards of individual craftsmanship and also in the standards which are set and maintained by different firms.

Many limiting factors determine the range of work which a firm of lithographic printers may undertake; for example, the general requirements of the small provincial town or locality; the equipment used, e.g. large work for large machines; automatic feeders for long runs and high speeds; and so on. The general type of work may decide the greater suitability of hand or photographic methods of plate-making.

Specialized Litho Printing

Sheet-metal printing again demands not only special lithographic machinery, but elaborate and costly machinery for treatment after the printing is completed. This specialized branch of printing is subdivided into high-class metal box production, toys, general work and crown corks. This further division is rendered desirable not so much by difference in lithographic procedure as by the need for special organization and equipment for fabricating the printed sheets. Similarly, carton making requires special equipment; maps and charts (see page 191), decalcomanie transfers (to glass, etc.), fabrics, ceramics and music all need some special technique. The last subject is dealt with in Chapter 26.

Repetition Work

The balance of personnel in the various departments also depends on the types of work which are undertaken. When repetition work forms the major part of the production a small studio staff is required relative to the machine-room staff. Such repetition work would include labels, business stationery, cartons, packages, and all such work where printing plates are readily made from standing originals, and when fresh runs or editions are constantly required.

Work which is mainly completed in a single edition will require a much larger studio and planning staff. Advertising folders, periodicals, book jackets, children's books, book illustrations, magazine covers, illustrated catalogues, are typical examples of work which needs more preliminary preparation in relation to machine production.

Fine-art reproduction is yet another

aspect of lithography which demands a very high degree of skill, while continuous stationery requires, in addition to a special type of printing machine, a supply organization extending well beyond the actual printed material.

Printing on Tissue, or Glass!

Not only is the lithographic process versatile in the variety of work which it can produce, but it is remarkable for the variety of materials on which it can print. They range from tissue paper to card or fibre board, from glassine, celluloid and flint paper to deep-grained cover paper. Any flexible metal which can be obtained in sheet form of constant thickness can be printed at fairly high speeds, while printing on glass and other rigid materials is as much in the day's work as is printing on silk and other fabrics. The nature of the image to be printed may consist of line or chalk, mediums and half-tone, separately or in combination.

Although the printing of daily newspapers is outside the present scope of lithography, the uninterrupted weekly production of *The Australian*, Melbourne, since 1929 may be instanced as but one outstanding achievement, both of organization and production, in this direction. The web rotary offset is a project for which the near future can confidently anticipate a considerably extended use.

Part of the very extensive mail-order catalogue business of America (of which there is no counterpart in Britain) is printed from the web by litho-offset at very high speeds, two colours being printed on one side of the web and one on the other. The sections are delivered ready for collating with the various other sections of printed matter which go to make up this type of publication.

The coloured covers of periodicals which are exhibited on our bookstalls in bewildering variety are sufficient indication of the high state of technical excellence and production control which four-colour photo-lithography has attained at the present day.

The delicate wash drawing; the subtle pencil shade; the variety of the tonal chalk; the vigour of the charcoal stick; the clean lines of the pen drawing; the density of the woodcut; the charm of the etching; the dignity of the engraving; the appeal of the poster; the goodwill of the greeting card; and the complexity of security printing: all these are but indications of the extremely wide scope of lithographic productions.

Security Printing by Offset

Lithography enters the field of security printing in a limited way only, and a very large percentage of such work is done by a small number of specialist firms. Background tints are often produced by this method and the pattern may vary from a straight line to an intricate design or micro-lettering. Usually the original is engraved in plates of steel or copper, and transfers are taken from these to make up the machine printing plates (see Chapter 18). A micro-letter ground would more readily be prepared by setting type by Monotype, and photographically reducing an impression to the required size.

Where such a ground is required to be printed in a fugitive ink, the printing plate would be etched into relief and printed without the dampers.

Backgrounds of this kind may be printed in a single colour or in "rainbow" tints by dividing the ink fountain. Black text is usually overprinted.

Examples of security work by lithography are: bank and currency notes, cheques, share certificates and stamps.

Security printing by photogravure methods is described in Chapter 25.

MAP AND CHART PRINTING

MAP printing is usually carried out by specializing firms. Diagrams, plans, charts and the like, which do not usually call for the same degree of accuracy, may frequently be produced by lithographic firms which do not so specialize. The principles and operations which are involved in the printing of maps are the same as those which are used in the ordinary process of lithography. When maps are printed in several colours, great care has to be taken to ensure that the various colours are in close register. This necessitates mechanical accuracy in the printing machine; skill and care in feeding where this is carried out by hand, and close control when an automatic feeder is used; and the need for preserving the dimensions of the paper throughout the printing of the job. Paper is a hygroscopic substance, and it can be deformed either by mechanical stretch or by changing its moisture content. If the relative humidity of the printing room atmosphere were to remain constant, few of the present problems would arise, or they would be reduced to controllable proportions. One of the most obvious problems is that of misfit due to the changing dimensions of paper. The old-fashioned method of dealing with this trouble is that of exposing the paper to the

GEOGRAPHICAL ARTIST AT WORK

Fig. 1. *The preparation of the key or outline drawing of a large-scale map for photographic reduction. The coast outline is first drawn and the details are afterwards filled in. Place names are frequently patched in from type proofs, instead of being drawn by the artist.*

atmosphere of the printing room some hours or even some days before the printing begins. As the relative humidity of the atmosphere of the room is seldom under close (if any) control during this hanging period this treatment has obvious limitations to its efficacy. Modern methods call for the use of controlled air-conditioning and paper maturing machines.

Preparing the Drawings

The map draughtsman (Fig. 1) prepares from geographical material a large-scale drawing of the key or outline which is usually printed in black. Name places may be drawn directly on this outline, or they may be drawn on the plate by the litho artist (Fig. 2), but frequently they are set in type of suitable sizes, and impressions pasted in position on the key drawing. The completed drawing is then photographed to the required size for reproduction.

While engraved plates have not now the same extensive use which they previously had as originals, they are still used by some geographical firms.

LITHO ARTIST CORRECTING A MAP PLATE

Fig. 2. *Drawing place names by hand on the printed plate. Note that this map is prepared for direct printing. The lettering is first outlined, and then written in with the brush.*

CORRECTING AN ENGRAVED COPPER PLATE

Fig. 3. *In making corrections to copperplate originals the surface of the portion to be corrected is scraped to form a gradual hollow and the metal is beaten up from the back until the surface is level. The position of the correction to be made is marked with callipers.*

From these large engraved plates, areas can be selected for a particular map, and special features can be added to or removed from the printing plate.

Fig. 3 shows the method of making corrections to an original engraved plate. Where an alteration is to be made, the surface is scraped to form a gradual hollow to the depth of the original engraving, and the metal is then beaten up from the back until the surface is level. Callipers are used to mark the back of the plate in order to indicate where it has to be beaten. A printing plate may also be made by the lithographic draughtsman from a draft

key prepared by the geographical artist.

Colour Plates for Maps

The colour plates in map printing are prepared by a combination of litho drawing and transferring. Offsets of the outline (i.e. dye or coloured chalk impressions) are made on clean printing surfaces to form a guide for the draughtsman or "tinter." Where the colour is to be solid, or where line work is required to indicate roads, rivers and boundaries, these are drawn by the litho artist in the usual way, while tones or tints are obtained by transferring rulings or mediums. The areas which

P.T.G.—G

TWO-COLOUR ROTARY OFFSET LITHO MACHINE

Fig. 4. *Maps being printed on a Crabtree two-colour offset. The Elless stream feeder is seen in the foreground. A diagram showing progress of the sheets is shown on page 237.*

are to be ruled or tinted are left "open" on the clean plate or stone, and the rest of the surface is covered thinly and evenly with gum solution by the tinter. The gum solution is dried and the plate passed to the lithographic transferrer who runs down transfers of generous area, which have been taken from suitably engraved plates. The ink of the transfer forms an image only on the ungummed section of the printing surface, and the overlapping portion is washed away with the surplus gum. A variety of tones may be obtained by superimposing one colour over another. Also the strength of colour can be increased by double transferring of mediums at different angles and thus obtaining cross-ruling or patterns. Engraved stipple and other varied patterns can also be used in the same way. Maps may also be drawn on Kodatrace or other transparent material, and this tracing used as a positive from which to make printing plates by the Vandyke or similar so-called reversal method. The method of producing maps for letterpress printing is described on page 173. Offset rotary machines are used almost exclusively for lithographic map printing, and large maps may need to be printed in sections. Fig. 4 shows a sheet of atlas maps being printed on a two-colour Crabtree rotary offset machine, the sheets being automatically fed by an Elless stream feeder. This class of work usually involves long runs in four to eight printings, and the two-colour machine effects a considerable saving in cost and simplifies register control.

Graining Metal Plates

The metal plates in most general use for lithographic map and general printing are made of zinc or aluminium. These plates may be used many times by cleaning and re-preparing. Unlike stone, metal plates are prepared both physically and chemically. Physical treatment is necessary due to the non-absorbent nature of the metal.

The reason for graining is to form a roughened surface. This roughness has the advantages that such a texture effectively retains moisture; the films produced by counter-etching, image formation, etching and gumming, have a firmer anchorage; tonal values are possible by the use of lithographic crayon. The method of re-preparing a used zinc plate for a further image is as follows. The ink is removed by an ink solvent, the plate placed on a flat surface, moistened with caustic solution and the old work rubbed with a suitable pad and a small quantity of fine abrasive. Alternatively, after the ink is cleaned off, the plate may be immersed in a caustic bath until the old image is destroyed.

The plate is then washed with water, and in addition it may be given a passing bath of weak acid to neutralize the caustic and thus induce a better rolling motion to the marbles. The plate is then fastened to the clean trough of the graining machine (Fig. 5), covered with steel, porcelain or glass marbles of half to one inch in diameter, sprinkled with a suitable grade of powdered abrasive such as carborundum, and the machine started up. This very noisy operation is continued from thirty to sixty minutes, after which the plate is removed from the machine and well washed front and back. Many factors determine the final quality of the grain. Preparation is often treated too casually.

PLATE GRAINING MACHINE

Fig. 5. *The trough of a plate graining machine showing the marbles which cover the plate. The tray is first completely covered with marbles and a generous number then forms a second layer. Graining forms a roughened surface on the plate, which retains moisture.*

AUTOGRAPHIC TRANSFERS

THE method of lithographically producing autographic transfers does not claim to be artistic, but is strictly utilitarian. Once the transfer is made, a print can be produced within a very few minutes. The method was used in the earliest days of the process and was demonstrated by Senefelder.

Autographic means self-writing; and the matter to be printed is usually written by the customer and the required number of prints is then made by means of this original transfer. There is no limit to the number of prints which can be obtained, and the method is useful for saving the time of a writer who requires to make a personal appeal to a number of people in the same terms. Examples of its application are: invitations to private functions which may require only a small number of copies; appeals of a semi-private or philanthropic nature, where the personal approach is desired. This may involve a run of hundreds or of many thousands.

A more usual application of the autographic transfer is in the production of specifications containing a great amount of detail, and where the number of prints required is so small as to make other means of production prohibitive on account of cost.

Wartime destruction of printing houses which carried foreign types makes this method of production of peculiar interest and importance to those nationals, domiciled in a strange country, whose language has characters not native to their own (Fig. 6).

The materials used to produce autographic transfers are very simple. The ink is the normal lithographic drawing ink as used for direct drawings on stone and plate. The paper must be hard-sized so that the ink remains on the surface and is not absorbed in the paper.

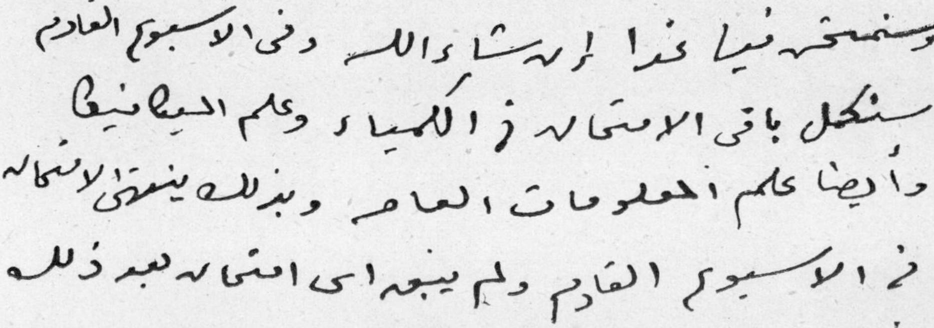
وستمتحن فيها غدا إن شاء الله وفي الاسبوع القادم
ستكمل باقي الامتحان في الكيمياء وعلم الميكانيكا
وأيضا علم المعلومات العامة وبذلك ينتهي الامتحان
في الاسبوع القادم ولم يبق أي امتحان بعد ذلك
في هذا العام . أسأل الله الدعوات الصالحة .
سلامي للجميع والسلام

EXAMPLE OF AUTOGRAPHIC TRANSFER

Fig. 6. *Part of an Egyptian letter originally written as an autographic transfer.*

It is important that the distribution of ink shall be even, and the thickness of line fairly uniform, or at least not excessively fine. Great care must be taken not to fingermark the paper, for although perspiration marks may be invisible on the transfer, they would transfer to the printing surface and make a very strong image. Measures must also be taken to prevent smearing the ink. When the ink is dry, the transfer is ready for the lithographic printer. Line drawings and diagrams may also be added.

Two unusual features of this type of transfer are: (1) the transfers will remain active over long periods of time; (2) so long as the image is not deformed by smearing or running of the ink, a transfer can be used more than once, and in favourable circumstances a transfer may be used several times.

Transferring to the printing surface is also unique in that it has to be accomplished by a single pull through the transfer press. When the transfer is fresh the treatment is simplified, and all that is necessary is to place the transfer to position on a slightly moistened stone or plate, and pull through the press once only under firm pressure.

As there is no adhesive on the paper on which the transfer is written a second pull through the press would probably cause a double impression, and spoil both the transfer and the image. The appearance of the image on the printing surface will probably be disappointing; but in all probability it will ink up quite well if the rubbing-up method is used. To do this, sprinkle a few drops of turps on the ink slab, make a small pad of soft cotton rag, and rub or work this into the turps and ink alternately until the rag is charged with a thin film of thin ink. Gum the entire printing surface with a thin film of gum and rub firmly over the image with the ink pad.

Several details should be noted. Use turps very sparingly. Little ink is required on the rag. Difficulty in inking up may be due to excess gum; if so, reduce the consistency with water, also reduce the quantity to a minimum. The opposite effect, of ink adhering to the non-image section, may be corrected by increasing the consistency of the gum but still retaining a minimum quantity.

Touching up or local improvement of the image should seldom be required on this class of work, but there may be dirt, which will readily be removed by polishing with snakestone, after which the stone should be gummed and dried.

Roll up with a thinner ink than would normally be used, and take impressions. If many impressions are required, or if the image has to be printed on the machine, the usual process of rolling up and etching should be carried out.

Stale Transfers

If this attempt has not been successful and the transfer has been preserved in good condition, a second attempt may be made. The same method may be used or slightly more elaborate treatment given. Also a transfer which has become old would be treated with a little more elaboration as follows. Lay the transfer face down on a clean sheet of paper and damp the back with a dilute solution of nitric acid, say 1 per cent. This has the twofold object of making the paper limp, so that it makes a more intimate contact with the printing surface during the single pull through the press, and of causing the ink to be more active, so that the maximum image-forming effect is obtained. Also, the surface of the stone or plate may be coated with a thin film of pure turps, or turps to which has been added a trace of carbolic acid. When this has evaporated almost to dryness, the transfer is placed in position, pulled through the press and treated as explained above.

AUTOLITHOGRAPHY

FROM its earliest days the process of lithography developed along two complementary lines. It was primarily intended to provide a method of printing at a lower cost the type of work which can be drawn with brush and pen, and particularly where the required number of prints was limited. Such work was usually done on a stone surface which was highly polished. But it was soon found that the surface could be given a grained finish which lent itself admirably to being worked upon with chalks for gradated tones.

With the development of suitable technique, varied and beautiful effects became possible. In addition, this new form of art allowed the artist to have numerous reproductions of his pictures as a result of one creative effort.

Such direct drawing on the stone gave the artist a peculiar freedom which became lost, or in some measure artificial, in a reproduction by an interpreting artist.

This direct drawing of an original picture on the printing surface (which may now be either metal plate or stone) is known as autolithography (Fig. 7). Some early work of this kind is of such excellence that it has set a standard of artistic merit by which later work produced by this process has been judged.

Confusion of Terms

The terms lithography and lithographer are used in two entirely different ways, and this leads to much confusion.

Those who prepare the printing formes and produce the printed work on the lithographic machines are called lithographers or lithographic printers; while the workers who produce commercial work on the printing surface as direct drawings are called lithographic artists.

On the other hand, from the earliest days of the craft there has developed and practised contemporaneously with the organized trade, a minority of independent artists who have used the lithographic surface as just another medium through which to express their artistic impulse.

It is clear that there is a wide difference between the two crafts. Such differences and segregation are unfortunate, for if working contacts with the whole of these craftsmen could be maintained as a complementary combination, it could result in the production of work which would be æsthetically satisfying, technically inspiring and commercially profitable.

Need for Co-operation

This lack of close co-operation between art, craft and commerce has led to various sporadic attempts to make improvements. During recent years the need for modernized design for lithographic production has been fully recognized, and artists of high standing have been commissioned to produce their designs directly on the stone or plate for machine printing. Outstanding artists have also frequently been commissioned to produce sketches or paintings which have been reproduced on the printing surface by lithographic artists.

Litho posters have been particularly successful in this way. The autolitho posters of Spencer Pryse were produced in a very economical number of workings, but they exhibit a wonderful variety of form and colour and they never fail to carry the personality of the artist.

Contemporary autolithographers are too numerous to mention, but the book illustrations, book jackets, posters and commercial work of Barnett Freedman, the book illustrations of Clarke Hutton, and the fine prints of John Copley set a high standard.

Some very fine series of productions have also served to bring this method into prominence during recent years, such as the London Transport Board and Postal Services posters.

Future prospects for autolithography are good, for this method should form a healthy contrast to the increasing per-fection of the various photo processes.

Lithographic stone is particularly sympathetic to this kind of treatment, and as limited editions have been produced for purely artistic purposes the cumbersome nature of the stone has not been a serious drawback. But in the modern application of autolithography for commercial production metal plates are being used to an increasing extent.

DRAWING BY AUTOLITHOGRAPHY

Fig. 7. *A reproduction reduced to about one-third the size of the original autolithograph. This excellent portrait was drawn from life directly on to a grained lithographic stone.*

CHAPTER SEVENTEEN

LITHOGRAPHIC ROLLERS

MAIN TYPES OF ROLLERS. PREPARING A NAP ROLLER. WATERPROOFING THE SKIN. TREATMENT OF SKIN TEXTURE. IMPORTANCE OF SCRAPING. USE OF DRYING INKS. STORING AND RESTORING. GLAZED ROLLERS. COMPOSITION ROLLERS.

THREE main types of rollers are used by lithographic printers and all have their advantages and limitations. They may be classed as follows: (1) nap rollers; (2) glazed rollers; (3) composition rollers.

The nap roller is the oldest type. It is by far the most important single tool which the transferrer uses and it will long remain so, for it has no challenger in this field. Modifications have been tried from time to time but with little success. A nap roller is invariably used for pulling retransfers. For this purpose the roller must be matured and in the best possible condition. Nap rollers are also used for general transfer press work.

To bring a nap roller to suitable condition for use, long and skilful preparation is required. This preparation must be done in the workshop, for this type of roller is not purchased ready for use. The treatment given to a new nap roller to prepare it for work may be divided into two sections: (a) making the skin waterproof and supple; (b) bringing the surface texture, grain, or nap, to an open condition.

Assembling the Parts

The hand roller may be purchased as a unit and ready for this preparatory treatment, or skin and stock may be purchased separately and put together.

The skin is made from the hides of young cattle, and is known as french calf. Uniform texture is essential and the skin is sewn in tubular form with the flesh side or nap outside. The join is carefully made so as not to mark the printed work, and the sewing is inside so that it is least noticeable when in use. Around both open ends, small holes are closely punched at uniform distances and through these holes the fastening cord is threaded. The skin should be longer than the stock by an amount sufficient to allow of fastening at each end (Fig. 1).

The base or stock is of wood, and special care should be taken to choose a stock in which the cylinder body and the handles are turned from the same block. Otherwise handles have a habit of coming loose or adrift. Any attempt to reset them perfectly truly is largely a waste of time.

The tubular skin is also larger in diameter than the cylindrical base, to allow for a slightly resilient packing. Two or three layers of flannel should be sufficient to make a tight but cushion fit. Care should be taken to sew on the flannel round the stock, in such a way that the joins are obscured as much as possible, and they should be evenly spaced round the roller to obviate double seams making a bulge or ridge. The ends of the flannel are fastened firmly and neatly with strong thin thread or cord. The skin should then be drawn over the covered roller and made a tight fit and the ends fastened securely (Fig. 2).

A little french chalk will assist as a

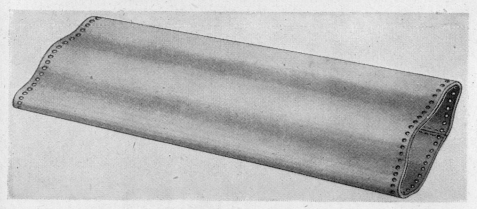

NAP ROLLER SKIN

Fig. 1. *A new nap roller skin before preparation and assembly on the stock. Note the inside sewing, the punched ends and the rough outside texture. The skin must be larger than the stock.*

dry lubricant if difficulty is found in getting the skin to position. Mechanical aids are available for the purpose of drawing on roller skins, but these should be used with great care. A sliding hand grip is usually much better than mechanical aid, for it is less drastic on both the skin and the underpacking.

Making the Skin Waterproof

The completely assembled roller is now ready for the next treatment, which consists of oiling the skin to make it waterproof. This may be done in several ways. Tallow or vaseline may be rubbed into the skin, or a non-drying oil such as olive, castor or neatsfoot may be used. Oil must be applied uniformly, in small quantities, and at intervals, so that it penetrates the skin evenly, but not excessively.

Some workers prefer to roll the oil in from the ink slab, but excess should be carefully guarded against, for it would cause the skin to stretch. If the roller is not to be further prepared for some weeks, it may be rubbed generously in vaseline or tallow and stored. This is a safer way than using oil, for the less-fluid lubricant penetrates very slowly and not in excessive quantity; but pene-

tration may be hastened if it is so desired, by warming gently and rubbing in with the hand.

The next treatment is the preparation of the skin texture or nap and the removal of loose fibres and dirt. An oiled roller may be ready for further treatment in a day or a few days. When tallow has been used and the roller is ready for the next process, the excess tallow should be carefully scraped off.

Rolling in varnish is the next treatment. This may be done either by starting with thin varnish and gradually changing to stronger grades, or by first using strong varnish and gradually reducing it. Perhaps the latter way is generally better, but satisfactory results can be obtained both ways. When the stiff varnish is first used, it requires considerable physical effort to roll on the ink slab. During the first rolling the varnish will be quickly reduced as it mixes with the surplus oil or tallow from the skin. The slab should be scraped and more strong varnish added. A surprising amount of loose fibres and dirt is drawn off the skin by the tack of the viscous varnish. Such deposit should be scraped from the slab at frequent intervals with a push knife, more varnish added and the rolling continued with deliberation and persistence.

Gradually, the skin will assume an even texture not unlike velvet in appearance, but unlike velvet in that the way of the grain lies in a definite direction. Usually, this grain direction, like the coat of an animal, is obvious enough; but occasionally there may be a doubt in the minds of those not used to such rollers. The way of the grain must be decided very positively; and it is an advantage to indicate the direction by a mark, such as a file or a cut mark on the handle, to ensure scraping in one direction only, and that direction the smooth way of the grain.

Scraping a Nap Roller

The final quality of a nap roller is largely determined by the uniformity and care in scraping, particularly during the breaking-in operation, and also during the first few months of actual use. The importance of the simple scraping operation cannot be over-emphasized and it is seldom sufficiently appreciated. With care, a roller will last a lifetime: but it may also be spoiled by unskilful scraping before it has been brought to best condition for use.

The knife which is kept for roller scraping should have a fairly flexible blade, sufficiently long to hold the handle in one hand and the opposite end of the blade in the other. The blade should not be sharp, and a palette knife or an old table knife serves this purpose quite well.

The roller handle which points the direction of the grain is pressed firmly against the body of the operator while the other handle is placed against a suitable groove (either on the press or at the base of the ink slab), and at a lower height, so that the roller is at an angle of about 45 deg. The knife is held firmly in both hands and the edge of the blade

is applied to the lower end of the roller and at an angle of 90 deg. and drawn firmly, evenly and deliberately across the skin to the near end of the roller.

Varnish will be removed from the skin where the contact has been made. The accumulated varnish may be deposited on the slab or on a piece of waste paper, but the more usual way is to wipe the varnish near the top of the roller and to the right of the scraped section. At the same time the roller is turned in an anti-clockwise direction by the amount of the scraped portion, thus preparing for the next scrape. This action is repeated until the whole surface of the roller has been covered. Any varnish which has become deposited over the end should be scraped up cleanly with the knife.

Improving the Texture

The purpose of this scraping is to remove dirt and loose fibres from the skin and to smooth out the texture of the nap. Rolling in strong varnish should alternate with scraping until all loose fibres are removed. Thinner grades of varnish may then be used and the scraping continued until the skin is soft and the grain even and clearly noticeable. Be patient; be persistent; spread this task over several days, but do it *very* thoroughly.

It must now be decided for what colour the roller is to be used. For colour proofing on grained stones or coarsely grained plates a set of yellow, red, and blue rollers is often kept. A thin, non-drying ink of the general hue decided upon should be applied to the roller in a fairly large quantity and allowed to stand.

If a black roller for general purposes is required, the roller should be used on a rough class of work for some weeks and scraped regularly and carefully

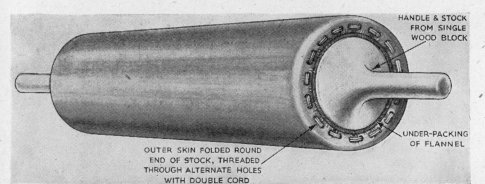

NAP ROLLER COVERED

Fig. 2. *The assembled hand nap roller now ready for further preparation. The skin shown in Fig. 1 has been fastened round the padded roller stock, and the ends of the cord fastened.*

during this time. The condition of the skin should gradually improve until after a few months it may be suitable for more exacting work, and even for pulling retransfers.

As normal treatment, the nap roller should be scraped each morning, and then during the day as may be required. The reasons for this are: (*a*) to restore the open condition of the nap, for this becomes clogged in the course of use; (*b*) to remove stale ink, due to contact with excessive water; (*c*) to change the consistency of the ink, as when changing from one type of work to another; (*d*) to remove dust, fibres, dirt and such accumulations from damping cloths, paper or other sources; (*e*) to remove drying ink to prevent it hardening.

Use of Drying Inks

It is often necessary to take proofs with drying inks which must on no account be allowed to dry on the roller. When the proof is taken or at the end of the day, whichever is the earlier, the roller should be scraped well and a copious supply of thin non-drying ink added and the roller well knocked up. It may now stand overnight or for a shorter period if wanted for other work.

A nap roller which is not to be used for a long period should be treated as follows. Scrape cleanly and carefully to remove as much ink as possible and to bring the nap to the best possible condition. Apply vaseline thickly and rub in with the hand leaving the skin well covered. Tallow is sometimes used, but this tends to cause scum when used subsequently. Oils should not be used as they cause the skin to stretch.

Roll the roller in a sheet of bank or similar paper to preserve from dust and grit, and store resting on the handles and without any other contact.

When a skin has been allowed to get into bad condition skilful treatment can do much to improve it. Such a bad condition is a reflection on a craftsman and should not be allowed. Prevention is far better than cure in this case and the little regular care and time spent on roller maintenance are well repaid in constant high-grade service.

Glazed Rollers

Nap rollers have many advantages over others; indeed no other type of roller is comparable with the nap for quality of work. But changing from one colour to another offers real difficulty. Compromise has therefore to be made in the many cases in which a set of rollers for the primary colours and black is not practicable. Glazed rollers were the first answer to this problem, and these are particularly useful for short runs of colour work when washing up is frequent.

Glazed rollers are made from nap rollers by coating them with a hard-drying ink. The general method is as follows. Scrape clean and remove all traces of non-drying ink. Mix a natural drying ink such as burnt sienna or burnt umber with some drier to workable consistency, and coat the roller evenly by rolling on the slab. See that any inequalities in the skin are filled with ink, and leave this base rough as a key to the final coating. Place in a rack and allow to set firmly for some hours or overnight. Mix a thinner, hard-drying ink and coat again. Roll on a wet stone to give a smooth surface to the roller, and put aside to set hard. Such rollers are washed with paraffin in the same way as the slab and knives.

Glazed rollers are economical in that only one hand roller or one set of ma-chine rollers is necessary and these can easily and quickly be changed.

Although hand rollers have been specifically mentioned, these remarks apply equally to machine rollers with suitable modification in control. For example, machine rollers are set in position in the machine and run under power. They are then taken out and placed on a suitable rack for scraping.

Composition Rollers

As machine speeds increased it became necessary to try to combine the sympathetic contact of the nap roller with the economy and convenience of the glazed roller. This has resulted in the very efficient composition or vulcanized oil rollers, which are produced under such trade names as Gestite, Ideal and Mintite. These rollers leave little to be desired: they are soft enough to feed the finest work at the highest speeds; firm enough to retain their shape; constant in dimension; not affected by water; may be smooth or have various grains; and they wash thoroughly with paraffin.

FINISHING COMPOSITION ROLLERS

After the formation of vulcanized oil and rubber rollers, they are put into a lathe and ground accurately to shape and required size by means of a special grinding wheel.

CHAPTER EIGHTEEN

TRANSFERRING METHODS

PREPARATION OF ORIGINALS. STORAGE OF STONES AND PLATES. DUPLICATING METHODS. RETRANSFERRING BY HAND. RECIPES FOR RETRANSFER INK. TRANSFER PAPERS. RULING OUT AND PATCHING. PREPARING MACHINE PLATES. ETCHING.

THE method of lithography already described, is not that which has caused the trade to develop to its present dimensions and versatility, and which is complementary with modern relief and gravure processes. This more general aspect of lithography is one of reproduction from a master image, usually known as an original. The original image may be obtained in several different ways; for example, as a print-down from a photographic negative or positive on glass, film or paper; as a direct drawing on stone or metal; as engraved plates or by other suitable means. Transfers from letterpress type and blocks are also used in combination with any other form of lithographic transfer or retransfer.

Treatment of Originals

The method by which the original image is produced is not of importance, but the quality and condition of the image are of the greatest significance. Not only should this original be initially perfect, but normally it should be so treated and stored that the perfect condition is long retained.

One of the few remaining justifications for retaining stone as a printing surface in modern lithography, is in its use for originals. Storing of original stones and plates is a matter requiring the most careful and constant attention. The system of indexing and storing should be such that it is but a matter of a few minutes to find any original and to have it in condition for production.

When an image is so large that it has to be printed singly, the usual way of producing the image on the surface for machine printing would be by direct drawing. Such work is not usually produced in exceptionally large quantities. But smaller work such as labels or cigarette cartons and the like cannot be produced singly, nor would the large numbers required be printed from the original drawing, even if this were convenient, for the original image would soon suffer deterioration.

Method of Duplication

The method generally adopted is to produce by most suitable means a first, or master, or original lithographic image on stone or plate. From this image impressions of a special kind are taken and suitably mounted on a sheet of appropriate size. This sheet of retransfers is then pressed into contact with, or transferred to, a clean stone or plate of suitable size for the machine on which the job has to be printed, and after certain preparatory treatment this machine plate is ready for printing. The original image is retained for future use.

Ideal Training for Learners

Duplicating by the method of hand retransferring tends to be looked down upon as being out of date and less worthy of attention than some of the more modern methods of lithographic plate-making. It is quite true that there are many more modern, spectacular and easier methods of making plates than by hand transferring. It is also highly desirable that these should be more widely known to the trade, but this old method is unique in the scope which it offers to the learner to understand the process, and to acquire image manipulation and control.

By this means, more satisfactorily than by any other, the eye is taught to appreciate fine differences in print quality, while the hand learns fine methods of control and modification. When the first stages of craftsmanship are learnt in this way, all other stages are simplified. In the opinion of the author, all lithographers should spend the greater part of their apprenticeship in this way irrespective of later specialization.

Transfers and Retransfers

A *lithographic transfer* is an impression or drawing which has been made with special ink, usually on a specially-coated paper. This surfaced paper is a convenient carrier of the image-forming ink, and is the means whereby the image is carried to a lithographic printing surface, or from the surface of an allied process to a lithographic surface.

Any impression which can be transferred to a lithographic surface for the purpose of producing a lithographic image is called a lithographic transfer. Examples of such transfers are:—

(*a*) A drawing made with lithographic drawing ink or crayon on one of the many varieties of specially prepared transfer papers.

(*b*) Drawings or writings made with lithographic drawing ink on hard-sized paper, as in the case of the autographic transfer, or in the autolithographic drawing shown in Chapter 16.

(*c*) Type, blocks or other letterpress matter. Lithographic retransfer ink would be used in conjunction with a

suitable transfer paper. Berlin transfer paper is particularly useful for pulling transfers from half-tone blocks.

(*d*) Photo-litho transfers. For these a very smooth gelatinized paper surface is used with retransfer ink, and the resulting transfer is subsequently treated as a retransfer.

(*e*) Engraved plates. Scotch paper is used for these. It has a rough bulky coating and is used in conjunction with a hard pitch-like ink which is rendered viscous by heating the plate. During the taking of these transfers the paper is caused to take on a high gloss.

(*f*) Music transfers. The plate is of pewter into which the image is punched or cut; the ink is fatty and becomes soft at low temperatures. A good quality and substance printing paper is used. This has no special coating.

A *retransfer* is an impression which has been taken from a lithographic image using special ink and paper, for the purpose of duplicating on to another lithographic surface.

Retransfer ink usually contains a comparatively large amount of fatty acid. Neither the kind of fatty acid nor the amount is critical, and therefore a wide variety of recipes is used. Press black forms the base of this type of ink, and the thorough incorporation of a small amount of oleic acid or lavender oil would give results, but these would not be of the most satisfactory kind and would be used only in emergency. Greater elaboration is therefore usual and the following two recipes may be taken as typical :—

	Parts		Parts
Tallow	2	Tallow	2
Castile soap	2	Mutton suet	4
Palm oil	1	Palm oil	1
Stearin	2	Stearin	1
Press black	8	Press black	8

Note that soap is used in one recipe and mutton suet in the other. Both are satisfactory. This ink is supplied in very stiff consistency so that it can be reduced by the transferrer to suit all kinds of work.

Transfer papers are made in a very wide variety to suit all kinds of lithographic work. A suitable base paper of even texture is coated with a water solution or suspension of various materials which are carefully chosen according to the type of coating required, from the following fairly comprehensive list: albumen, dextrin, flake white, flour, gamboge, gelatin, glue, glycerine, gum arabic, plaster of paris, starch, syrup.

For single-colour work, rolled scotch transfer paper is very serviceable. The ingredients would consist of flour, plaster of paris, starch, gelatin and glue. Gamboge may also be added as a yellow colouring. This is doubly coated and plate pressed when dry, to give a smooth surface.

Everdamp transfer paper is deservedly popular throughout the trade. It is made in two kinds, opaque and transparent. The advantages of this type of paper are that it takes a very good impression with little ink, it adheres to a dry surface during transferring, and the paper parts with the ink readily to the new surface to which it is transferred.

Pulling Retransfers

The greatest care should be bestowed upon original images at all times. Stones should have a clean impression firmly gummed over the surface when they are put into store. This serves to identify the image and helps to preserve it from damage by friction. Metal plates should be stored in suitable cupboards and guarded against scratches, kinks and oxidation.

The original to be reproduced is placed on the press, gummed and dried. Whenever there is cause to leave an original it should invariably be gummed and *whenever a metal plate is gummed it should be fanned dry as quickly as possible* to prevent oxidation.

The roller and ink may now be prepared. The ink is of a greasy nature and the general tendency of the retransferring operations is slightly to thicken the final result. Ink for this duplicating purpose should therefore be stiffer than ink for any other treatment of the same image. For fine work the ink should be as stiff as can be worked. The ink may be reduced slightly for solids, while for combined work precedence is given to the finer work, for the solids can be manipulated later if necessary.

When washing out an image of this kind it should be remembered that the image is firmly established, and that the final result must not be thickened. Little ink should at first be applied to the roller, and the image must be worked up gradually so as to preserve the detail.

Some transfer papers carry a heavier ink charge without deformation than others, and some require much greater pressure to obtain a firm impression. When a satisfactory retransfer has been pulled it should be marked and placed face up so that all other retransfers can be compared. Imperfect retransfers should be scrapped immediately. Good retransfers can be placed face down on a clean sheet. They may be laid in small lots and need not be spread out too widely, but it is essential not to smear the ink, to prevent the collection of dust, and to guard against deterioration of the image in any way.

Pulling retransfers calls for a considerable amount of physical exertion, manual dexterity and critical observation. The two latter qualities can only be acquired by long and patient application and effort. To pull a single retransfer may not need outstanding skill; to pull two identical retransfers is much less simple, while to pull twenty identical retransfers is a job calling for crafts-manship. Such craftsmanship is well worth attaining.

A few more retransfers than are actu-ally required should always be pulled. This allows for spoilage, and for more critical observation in the quieter con-ditions of the patching bench.

Etching an original image on stone should be a last expedient. The less the acid is used the longer the image is likely to last. The need for acid is an indica-tion that control is less than complete, and other means of correction should first be resorted to.

After etching, always apply gum im-mediately and generously and dry tho-roughly. Gum can be applied at any time, always to advantage. Metal plates may be etched as required, for this does not induce a relief effect; but counter-etching should be reduced to a mini-mum, as it flattens the grain and thus impairs the water-retaining properties.

RULING OUT AND PATCHING UP

THESE retransfers have now to be arranged in such a way that they will appear on the printed sheet with correct and equal spacing. The remark-able flexibility of the lithographic pro-cess is largely lost once the image is on the machine printing plate, and the greatest care must therefore be exercised before reaching that stage.

The wide range of work which is pro-duced lithographically precludes a stan-dard and stereotyped approach to the layout operations, and each job has to be considered individually or as belong-ing to a certain class.

The tools which are used are simple, and the following list caters for practi-cally all classes of work: straight-edge, ruler, set-square, dividers, scissors, pen-knife, hard pencil and runners or paral-lels. Engineers' scribers are very useful, and one end may be used as a stabber, the other as a cutting tool. A ruling pen also has its uses for precise or intricate work. The sizes of these tools will, in some measure, depend upon the usual sizes of sheets used, but they should not be too small.

The adhesives depend on the trans-fer papers. Glucose or treacle would generally be used for light paper such as french, while paste would be used on heavier papers. The greatest care must be taken to keep the adhesive from the face of the retransfers, and a minimum should be used to prevent spreading to the plate during transferring. Re-transfers can also be affixed to a suitable base by stabbing. This method has certain advantages but it is frequently overworked.

Ruling schemes should be simple, clear and comprehensive and all lines ruled at 90 deg. Fingers should not touch the face of the transfer paper, and every care must be taken to prevent smearing the ink.

Paper sizes are measured in inches and certain sizes are standardized. Despite this, paper may vary discon-certingly in size from one wrapped ream to another of the same consignment. It is well to have this in mind when ruling out a sheet, for compensation can often be made.

Gripper room must always be allowed for. The amount varies with different types of machines but $\frac{1}{2}$ in. or even less should be ample in most cases. Allow-ances must also be made for trims as they are necessary, punching, binding and bleeding (i.e. work running off the trimmed edge of the sheet).

Double cuts should be used only

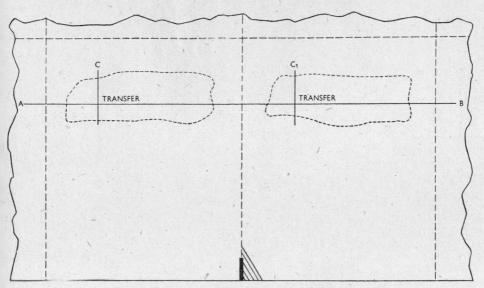

PATCHING UP A LETTER HEADING

Fig. 1. *The above letter heading is patched two on, and gripped at the foot. The detailed method of marking out the sheet is fully described in the text.*

when essential, and work should be carried out with a view to simplifying as far as possible the operations in the following-on departments. Where accuracy is not of marked importance, the use of newsprint or some similar absorbent patching base has material advantages.

The patching base should be at least as large as the sheet to be printed.

Example 1. A letter heading, two set, gripped at the foot (Fig. 1). The line (A B) is ruled to correspond with the longest straight line on the work, or to some other suitable point. A small trim may be allowed for at the foot of the sheet. Lines (c) and (c₁) pass through a suitable position or maybe points in the printed heading and the lines are ruled at right angles to (A B). The distance between (c) and (c₁) is exactly the width of the copy.

Pencil marks indicating the line (A B) may now be ruled on the edges of the transfers which should be stuck with a minimum of paste so that the lines on

the transfers or retransfers synchronize with those of the ruled base sheet. The short line on the gripper edge indicates the centre of the sheet and is placed centrally on the printing plate, unless placed out of centre for special reasons. Clamp allowance will depend on the type of machine.

In the case of such a simple job, an alternative method is to mark the plate by light contact of a metal point, and lay the matured transfers directly to position.

Example 2. These multiple diagrams (Fig. 2) should be studied carefully by the learner for they indicate general principles which can be applied to ruling out and patching of any shape of label.

About $\frac{1}{2}$ in. from the edge of the sheet a line would be ruled indicating gripper allowance. At right-angles to this, and either centrally or to the side of the sheet, another line is ruled. All other lines are measured from these two.

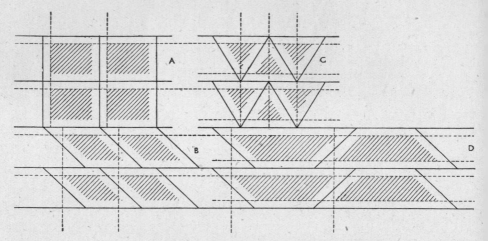

PATCHING LABELS OF VARIOUS SHAPES

Fig. 2. *The shaded areas indicate printed matter and the strong continuous lines are the guillotine cuts. The only lines which should appear on the patching base sheet are those which are broken. The printed image is patched to these lines. Schemes* (A) *and* (B) *are simple; schemes* (C) *and* (D) *are more complicated due to the interlocking of the labels.*

In the diagram, the printed area is indicated by shading; the cuts by continuous line; and all the actual lines required in the ruling scheme, by the broken lines. The broken lines are all that should appear on the ruled-out sheet.

Note that all lines are at 90 deg., whatever the shape of the design, and the work on the labels is positioned by three contact points with the ruled lines. Even Fig. 2D conforms to this rule, and if the simplicity of this ruling scheme

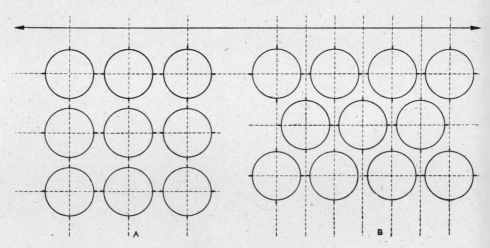

PATCHING CIRCULAR LABELS

Fig. 3. *Two methods of patching circular labels, both ruled out at 90 deg. The scheme shown on the left is square, while that on the right is staggered, as described in the text.*

appears to have been sacrificed, it is to provide greater accuracy in positioning the *long* sides of the work to the ruled lines. It is incidental that the short side of the work also synchronizes with a line.

Example 3. Two methods of patching circular labels are shown in Fig. 3. Both are ruled out at 90 deg. The first is a square, and if ticks are placed on the original label, both ruling out and patching are very simple.

The second "staggered" scheme requires a little careful thought. First decide on the allowance between each label. This amount plus the diameter of the label will give the vertical ruling through the centre of the first line of labels. The first horizontal line is easily found. The vertical lines for the alternate rows will be midway between those of the first line. Assuming the space between all labels to be the same, the position of the second horizontal line may be found by taking the distance from the centre of two labels on the first line and piercing this distance on the lower side of the

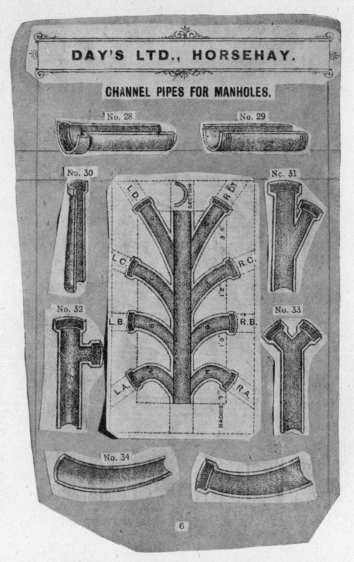

CATALOGUE PAGE OF PATCHED RETRANSFERS
Fig. 4. *The retransfers show light against the patching sheet. The few patching lines show clearly. The completed pages are imposed on a base sheet for retransferring to the machine plate.*

intermediate line and so on. These three points form the corners of an equilateral triangle.

Example 4. This is a contrasting type of work which requires very different treatment from the previous examples.

ORIGINALS FOR OFFSET AND DIRECT PRINTING

Two forms of the same original. That shown on the left is pre-pared for offset printing and that on the right for direct printing. This is an all-over pattern as used for book endpapers. Reference to illustrations in Chapter 15 shows the effect which is produced.

An average catalogue of this type (Fig. 4) would contain forty-eight pages. The printing area of each page is the same; the heading is common to each page and should be uniformly positioned; the folio numbers must also fall one over another. There ends the similarity of the pages. No two illustrations are alike in size or shape, but the pages should have a certain uniformity of colour or balance.

Also, a large amount of letterpress matter is incorporated, and the eye again plays an important part in obtain-ing position speedily. In addition, such small patches as folio and illustration numbers require a deftness in control which needs much practice. This control is rendered far more difficult as the transfer would be spoiled by a trace of paste on the surface.

Such work may conveniently be patched in separate pages and these then assembled on a suitable base sheet. This leads to a study of the imposition of bookwork which is dealt with in the letterpress section on pages 57 to 69.

It is important that the centre of the patched-up sheet should be indicated by a V cut in the gripper edge, and the edge of the printed sheet size should be indicated if it does not coincide with the edge of the base sheet. The position of work on the machine plate is important at all times, but increasingly so in the case of colour or register work.

PREPARING MACHINE PLATES

ZINC and aluminium plates are equally satisfactory for the purpose of lithographic printing, and as the former is the more widely used, comment will be restricted to zinc.

The zinc plate is grained mechanically to induce a water-retaining quality which is not native to the polished state of the metal. Also the roughened sur-face serves as an anchorage for both the image and non-image films.

Usually a medium grain is used for transferred work, a coarse grain for posters, and fine grain for half-tone.

The plate should be examined for physical deformities, and if satisfactory, it is well washed front and back, with clean running water to remove dust and superficial dirt. It is then sensitized or counter-etched. A common solution for this purpose is 4 oz. of alum, $\frac{1}{2}$ oz. of nitric acid, 80 oz. water. The nitric acid attacks the metal and breaks up the film of zinc oxide, while the alum deposits a film of water-insoluble basic aluminium sulphate. This aluminium salt is more sensitive to the image-forming materials than is the virgin metal.

The gripper edge of the plate is marked according to the clamp allowance for the particular machine and the middle of this line is also indicated. Corresponding cuts on the sheet are laid to synchronize to these three points.

Transferring is then done in a way to suit the paper which is being used. Self-adhesive papers are transferred to a dry surface; for other papers the plate surface is moistened with clean water, just sufficiently to cause the transfers to adhere to the surface during the first pull through the press.

Should any lines be broken they can now be repaired with drawing ink, or other additions may be made as required. Gum arabic solution is then applied to the whole surface of the plate, wiped down to a thin even film and quickly fanned dry.

Gum is hygroscopic, and a thin film is adsorbed on to the plate. When the excess gum is washed away with water, this adsorbed film remains and is moisture-attracting. As the image-forming materials have already contacted the plate, these parts attract waterproof ink and are not affected by the gum.

The image has now to be more firmly established by being charged with ink from a hand roller. This is a job calling for a high degree of skill.

Etching and Etches

"Etching a lithographic plate" is an expression which is not self-explanatory. Etching is normally associated with a biting action and the production of readily-visible results in a relatively short time. It will be recalled that lithographic stone is etched with a dilute solution of nitric acid; that normally a relief effect is not desired; and that the chief aim is to prepare the non-image sections of the stone so that the subsequent application of gum arabic solution will exert the maximum de-sensitizing effect.

A similar effect is achieved by different means and materials on metal plate. The purpose of etching a metal plate is to induce a water-attracting, but not a water-soluble, coating on the non-image portions of the plate, in contradistinction to the waterproof ink-attracting properties of the image portions. Solutions of acids such as phosphoric, gallic, chromic and tannic are used for this purpose; or acid phosphate salts such as ammonium dihydrogen phosphate, often in combination with neutral salts such as ammonium nitrate. Such solutions deposit chemically neutral salts on the non-image sections and these inhibit further image formation. Gum solution is then applied and the hygroscopic nature of the adherent film is thus increased. Gum is often added to the etch for control purposes.

Simple etches are effective and there appears to be no sufficient justification for the elaborate concoctions and decoctions which are too often used. A very simple but reasonably effective salt or white etch is 2 oz. ammonium dihydrogen phosphate (ammonium biphosphate), a slightly smaller quantity of ammonium nitrate, and 80 oz. cold water. This distributes readily on the plate and it works very clean. It should be moved round the plate for about three minutes, drained from the plate but not washed off, gum added, wiped thinly, and dried quickly. Gum may be added to the etch, in which case the quantity of water should be reduced, say 20 oz. thin gum and 40 oz. water.

A 2 per cent gummy solution of phosphoric acid is also a useful etch. (A stock solution may be made and reduced as required.) This may be moved round the plate for about one minute and then washed off before applying gum.

CHAPTER NINETEEN

PLATE-MAKING BY OFFSET DUPLICATION

ATMOSPHERIC EFFECTS. HUMIDITY CONTROL. IMPORTANCE OF PRECISION. TRAUNG HYDRAULIC PRESS. MULTI-TRANSFERRING MACHINE. CONSTRUCTIONAL DETAILS. PREPARING THE MACHINE. SETTING THE PLATE AND CYLINDER. TRANSFERRING.

PAPER is a hygroscopic material. It absorbs moisture from the atmosphere or releases moisture to the atmosphere until the moisture content of the paper and the relative humidity of the atmosphere are in equilibrium; that is, until the two are so balanced that neither gives nor takes from the other. Paper fibres are very sensitive to moisture changes, i.e. as moisture is absorbed the fibres swell; as moisture is given up the fibres contract. This effect on individual fibres is amplified in the collective fibres forming the sheet. The effect of atmospheric moisture in the printing industry is more far-reaching than is generally understood, but the present concern must be limited to the effect of atmospheric change on transferring register work. Register work covers a very wide range of lithographic productions and the subject will be dealt with in general terms.

Register Difficulties

Sheets of small size, say demy, are easily controlled by hand methods. If an error, say of $\frac{1}{3}$ of one per cent is made between the key and one of the colours, or between one colour and another, this error might reasonably be obscured by judicious positioning on the machine. A sheet twice this size would be much more difficult for the transferrer to manipulate, and assuming the margin of error is of the same percentage, the result may be quite unacceptable. Any further increases in sheet sizes markedly increase the difficulties both of the transferrer and the machine operator.

As the tendency is to use full sheets on large machines, and as humidity control has not yet been given the practical application which could reasonably be expected, it becomes necessary to devise means whereby plates can be made more consistently and with greater accuracy than when hand methods are used.

Where a large number of retransfers has to be pulled, the transfer paper is likely to be exposed to the atmosphere for a considerable time both during the pulling and patching or shining up, and possibly during a storing period. Small retransfers would not be expected to make difficulty due to the change in size of the individual unit, but such a multiplicity of patches needs the constant application of a high degree of skill for their satisfactory manipulation. While the probability of error in the size of small labels and the like is remote, the need for close control of the large patching base is urgent. Thus it is that the metal key gives such high efficiency.

Need for Precision

In the case of a badly-fitting plate, it is a serious matter to keep a single-colour machine standing while another plate is made. While it is often possible to change the order of printing and thus limit waste of time, this is not always the case. There is increasing

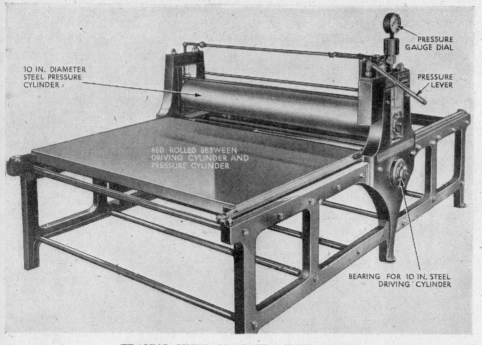

10 IN. DIAMETER
STEEL PRESSURE
CYLINDER

PRESSURE
GAUGE DIAL

PRESSURE
LEVER

BED ROLLED BETWEEN
DRIVING CYLINDER AND
PRESSURE CYLINDER

BEARING FOR 10 IN. STEEL
DRIVING CYLINDER

TRAUNG HYDRAULIC TRANSFER PRESS

Fig. 1. *This press has a roller in place of the traditional scraper. Controlled pressure is pre-set, applied by hydraulic means and indicated in lb. per sq. in. on the dial. This allows the transferring pressure to be constant for each forme. Pressure is distributed evenly over the whole area of the bed. This is essentially a power-driven press.*

urgency for perfectly-fitting plates in work for which two-colour machines are being used.

The development and wide use in America of the four-colour offset machine make it commercially imperative to produce *sets* of accurately-fitting plates with great regularity. The American solution to this problem is the Traung hydraulic transfer press, and this press gives very satisfactory results. Fig. 1 shows the general lines of the press, and the working procedure is broadly as follows:—

A metal sheet is provided as a mount for the key. Transfers are patched on this. The prepared or counter-etched machine plate is then placed on the press bed in the broadway direction and the job laid to accurate position. This in turn is covered by a thick fibre board. The desired amount of pressure is set by means of the short lever and is indicated in lb. per sq. in. on the dial. Forward and reverse motions are then controlled by press-button, while safety stops automatically limit the distance of the travel of the bed. Pressure is applied by the rolling motion of a cylinder and the action is very smooth and in great contrast to the friction of the usual scraper.

Despite these material advantages, the use of transfer paper and the need for depending on the human element for the positioning of the individual retransfers during the patching operation leave some room for error.

MULTI-TRANSFERRING MACHINE

IN the opinion of the writer the complete answer to this problem is the Multi-Transferring Machine. This unique machine (Fig. 2) is entirely British, and uses the offset principle for producing machine plates, by duplicating from a small original on metal plate. Transfer paper is not used with this machine, therefore the weaknesses which are inherent in transfer paper are entirely overcome. Work is carried out in a normal light and its progress can be seen by the operator at all stages. All operations are lithographic and within the scope of a good transferrer.

Register is such that two half-tone impressions of an image can be superimposed one over another without visible spread of the dot.

Any number of machine plates can be made, or any number of colour sets, with micrometric accuracy. Plates so prepared are sound in the image and clean in the non-image sections. Working properties are very good indeed— the work will outlast the grain, and plates are so easily, quickly and accurately made that there can be little reason for running them longer. Clean non-printing sections mean that the grain remains unimpaired when sent to the machine, and the probability of abusing the grain by unskilful preparatory treatment is overcome.

Constructional Points Explained

The machine itself is built on simple lines and is a particularly good engineering construction. The frame is massive and the three chief moving sections comprise: (1) a metal plate bed on which the original is clamped (Fig. 2 D); (2) a balanced segment which is covered with an offset blanket (E); (3) a cylinder to accommodate machine plates up to 64 by 44 in. (C). Movements of all parts are fully controlled and all controls are readily accessible.

The plate bed takes a design up to 20 in. square (Fig. 5). This bed can be revolved on an axis like a turntable, but it may be locked in any position, which

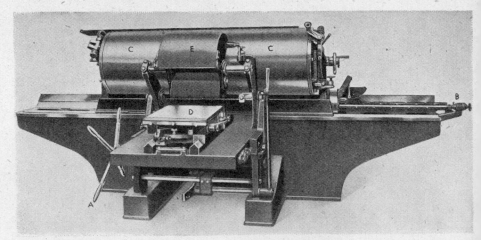

MULTI-TRANSFERRING MACHINE

Fig. 2. *General view of the Strachan & Henshaw Multi-Transferring Machine showing the massive frame, controls (A and B), original plate bed (D), offset segment (E), and machine plate cylinder (C). The letters in brackets refer also to the descriptive matter in the text.*

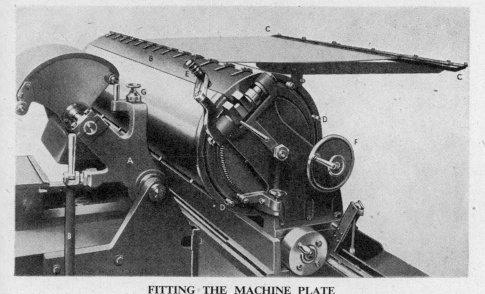

FITTING THE MACHINE PLATE

Fig. 3. *Side view showing how the machine plate is fitted. The revolving offset segment is on the left and part of the original plate is also visible. Note the magnifying eyepiece (E).*

position then becomes zero. From this position the bed can be turned to any 45 deg. point and locked by means of steel tongues (E) which are engaged by a steel jaw (D). This bed or table moves under the balanced segment and towards the cylinder, and movement is impelled by the four-point star wheel on the left (Fig. 2 A).

The offset segment revolves on a shaft, the bushes of which are housed in a framework which has slight movement both in the direction of the table and the cylinder (Fig. 3 A). This movement is actuated by the long vertical lever on the left. When this lever is in the upright position, the segment revolves clear both of the original plate and the cylinder. When the lever is drawn away from the cylinder, contact is made between the offset blanket and the original plate (Fig. 6 c). When pushed towards the cylinder, contact is made between the offset blanket and the machine plate on the cylinder. The

amount of pressure in both instances is applied mechanically and is constant. The segment is moved round by hand and stops determine the two printing positions.

The cylinder is seated by gravity in planed bearers (Fig. 6). Lateral movement is smooth and is done either by a small motor or by hand through a square threaded shaft. Usually, long movements are done electrically and final adjustments by hand. Despite the massiveness of the cylinder, peripheral movement is easy through the use of reducing gear, and an ample number of efficient and conveniently-placed locks and stops is provided to prevent inadvertent movement.

Preparing for a Job

Markings on the cylinder ends at $\frac{1}{2}$-in. intervals assist in fixing plates of various sizes in the desired position. Other controls will be noted as the method of operating the machine is outlined.

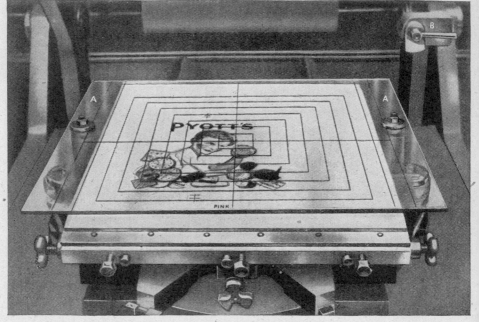

LOCKING THE ORIGINAL PLATE

Fig. 4. The original metal plate is locked to position on the bed and covered by the plate-glass key for setting. The plate bed top is moved by the adjusting screws until the register lines on metal plate synchronize with finely-etched lines on the glass key plate.

(a) *Setting the Original Plate.* The original plate should be of standard size, 18¾ by 16½ in., and it is necessary that the image be fitted with register lines. These should be placed centrally, or otherwise suitably disposed, be finely and accurately drawn, and not too near the work if this can be so arranged. Fixing the original plate on its table is a simple matter. One end is held by a clamping strip (Fig. 5 A), and the other in a straining bar (D).

The setting of the original to accurate position then follows. The two ball fittings of a ruled glass plate are placed into fixed sockets, one on each side of the table carriage (Fig. 5 C, C). The image on the metal plate is now visible through the ruled glass key plate (Fig. 4), and the table top is moved independently of the glass by means of six handscrews (Fig. 5 F), until the register lines on the original metal plate synchronize with those of the glass key plate. The table top is then locked to the carriage in this position.

A pencil line is then ruled across the original plate to indicate the edge of the design. By means of the star wheel on the left, the table is then moved inwards under the segment until it comes into contact with an adjustable stop not shown. The segment is then revolved until contact is made with the face of the stop which incorporates a hand grip (Figs. 4 and 6 B). This is placed on the right arm which carries the segment. The pencil line on the original plate is then made to synchronize with a deeply-scribed line on the segment. This, then, is the line of contact and the table stop is made secure.

(b) *Setting the Cylinder.* When the size of the machine plate has been decided, the steel gripper plate stretching across the cylinder (Fig. 3 B), is set to suit this size. Allowance for clamp room must then be made and this is measured from inside the jaws of the gripper plate and indicated by a pencil mark on the cylinder. The segment is then revolved until it comes into contact with the micrometer stop positioned on the right of the segment frame. The cylinder is then turned until the pencil line synchronizes with a scribed line on the right of the segment. This is to be the first printing position and it is marked by setting one of the stops in the groove round the end of the cylinder. The stops are loosened with a box spanner, placed between the powerful jaws in the engaged position and locked securely (Fig. 6 D).

Peripheral spacing distances are measured out and indicated by scribed lines on strips of metal $\frac{3}{4}$ in. wide and of suitable length. This metal strip is clipped round the end of the cylinder in a position which causes the first scribed line to synchronize with a fine line seen through the eye-piece of the magnifier (Fig. 3 E). The jaws are disengaged by a simple action, the cylinder moved round by turning the small wheel with tapering handle (F) until the next position is indicated through the eye-piece, and the next stop (D) is similarly fixed. This is repeated as many times as there are rows of labels or images in the peripheral direction.

Should an image be too narrow to come within the dimensions of the steel jaws, the similar jaws on the opposite end of the cylinder (Fig. 6 D) would be used for the control of alternate transfers.

(c) *Setting the Hexagonal Bar.* Lateral spacing of impressions is obtained

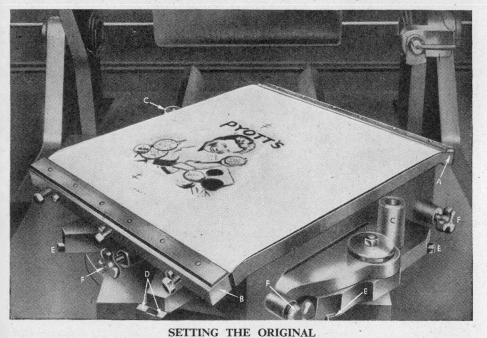

SETTING THE ORIGINAL

Fig. 5. *The original plate bed shown locked at a 45-deg. angle for transferring the image diagonally. The plate stretching bar and several adjusting screws can also be seen.*

READY FOR THE IMPRESSION

Fig. 6. *The offset blanket is in contact with the original plate and ready to receive the impression. The machine plate is in position to receive the image from the offset blanket.*

by movement of the cylinder behind the segment.

The system controlling this movement begins with a hexagonal bar positioned on the top of the machine bed, and carried on end brackets (Fig. 7). On each of the faces of this bar, stops may be mounted. Setting of these stops presents little difficulty and the distance between one stop and the next is the width of the label or image. The position of the first stop is worked out and the rest are set in juxtaposition, preferably by means of a metal gauge which can be suitably marked and retained for future use.

Each of the six faces of a bar can be used for a different job, for they are used quite independently. One setting of the stops serves for all the colours of one job, or for any number of jobs of the same width. Once a section or sections of the bar have been spaced for certain work, the setting can be retained for future use by lifting the bar out of the machine and substituting another. Much time is thus saved on repetition work, but a far greater advantage of retaining a set-up bar is that odd plates can be made for a colour set at any future time, and with a guaranteed accuracy.

To change from one job to another which is set on the same bar, simply requires the freely-revolving bar to be turned to expose the required face. Extending from the right side of the cylinder carriage is a sensitive gauge which is actuated by the stops on the hexagonal bar, through a pointer and a trigger (Figs. 3, 6 F and 7). As the trigger contacts the face of a stop, the pointer is moved. Reference to Fig. 7 will indicate clearly this system of control. The section drawing shows how the stops fit and are locked in position. Note the spacings of two different sets of stops. The trigger (c) is making contact with the stop (B) in such a manner that the pointer (D) is at zero. The spring plunger (E) pushes the bar so that it is under the control of micrometer (F).

The longer movements of the cylinder would be made on the electric motor, but the final position should be carefully approached by turning the flat, lower wheel (Fig. 6 G) in front of the trigger gauge, until the indicator registers zero.

(*d*) *The Micrometer Controls.* A set of plates for a colour job may be made to fit perfectly, and yet the later printed plates may be quite useless due to paper having changed size during the earlier printings. This exigency is provided for, and a new plate or plates can be made in which one label or a series of labels, or a row can be modified any number of thousandths of an inch and in any direction. Graduated modifications can be made for different labels in different parts of the sheet, and none of these movements affect the normal setting of the machine. Lateral movement is made on the micrometer which controls the hexagonal bar (Figs. 2 B and 7). The variation required is set on the micrometer and normal procedure is then followed in the transferring. Peripheral adjustment is made on the segment micrometer stop in a similar manner (Fig. 3 c). Diagonal movement is, of course, simply a combination of these two directions.

(*e*) *Fixing the Machine Plate on the Cylinder.* The settings are now complete, and the machine plate of the required size, suitably grained, well washed on both sides, counter-etched on the surface and quickly dried, is now fixed in position. This fixing operation is aided by two hinged supporting arms which swing out from the back of the machine (Fig. 3). The steel gripper plate (B) which runs the length of the cylinder, has been set for this size of plate, and the position of the gripper edge of the printed sheet has been indicated by a pencil mark on the cylinder.

The front edge of the plate is placed in the jaws of the gripper plate, and the detached straining bars are fixed to the back edge (Fig. 3 c, c). The cylinder is then turned until the straining bar falls into a recess in the cylinder, where it is pulled taut by the straining bar screws.

All is now ready for the transferring operations, and the cylinder is traversed to the first stop position with zero on the gauge and revolved to lock the stop jaws in the first peripheral stop.

Transferring Operations

This procedure is entirely lithographic and all the usual combined precautions when pulling retransfers and transferring must be carefully observed. Cleanliness is imperative if results are to be consistently satisfactory. The materials which are used, and their methods of control, both conform to standard practice. A good hand nap roller is the most important piece of equipment, and retransfer ink is best reduced with some press black, but the ink should be stiff.

In addition to checking all the machine settings very carefully before commencing any particular job, the condition of the offset blanket should be given the most careful attention at all times. The thickness of the blanket, the tension on the stretching bar, the physical condition of the rubber substance, and the mechanical excellence of the surface must all be attended to.

The image on the original plate is washed out, and charged with ink. By means of the star wheel, the carriage mounting the table is moved in under

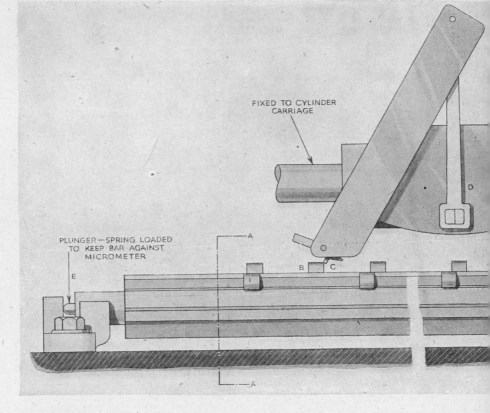

the segment and towards the cylinder until contact is made with a stop. The segment is then moved forward by hand until contact is made with the front lower stop which incorporates a hand grip. Outward movement of the long vertical handle brings the blanket into contact with the original plate and exerts a predetermined amount of pressure (Fig. 6 c). Return movement of the star wheel impresses the transfer on to the rubber offset blanket, and pressure is then manually released by returning the long lever to its central position.

A part turn of the handle-stop (Fig. 5) allows the projecting segment pin to pass this point as the segment is turned downwards by hand, and the pin finally contacts the micrometer stop with the ink-charged blanket facing the machine plate. Contact is made between the blanket and the machine plate by pushing the long lever towards the cylinder. Here again, the pressure between the blanket and the machine plate is constant and controlled. The lockjaw (Fig. 6 D) is released and the impression is transferred by turning the taper-handled wheel clockwise (Fig. 6 J). This revolves the cylinder and the first transfer is in position on the machine plate. Pressure is released and the segment returned to normal position, while the cylinder is left with the jaws locking the second stop.

Examination of the impression on the machine plate will indicate its quality. If it is satisfactory, no time should be lost in completing the whole job. Peripheral movement is continued until the row is completed, and then the cylinder

Fig. 7. *Method of spacing work laterally. The section drawing indicates how six different sets of stops are accommodated on the hexagonal bar, and the method of locking the stops by a countersunk screw. The stops are spaced by means of a metal gauge. A spring-loaded plunger on the left maintains the bar in firm contact with the micrometer on the opposite end. This micrometer may be used to adjust the hexagonal stop bar temporarily to compensate for paper variation, without affecting the normal set of the machine or any individual stop or group of stops. To change from one set of stops to another the bar is turned to bring uppermost the face which carries the required set of stops. The trigger is worked on a large leverage so that apparently large inaccuracies indicated on the window gauge at the end of arm D would be slight on the actual transfer. The stop bar is fitted to the frame while the gauge moves with the cylinder to which it is fixed.*

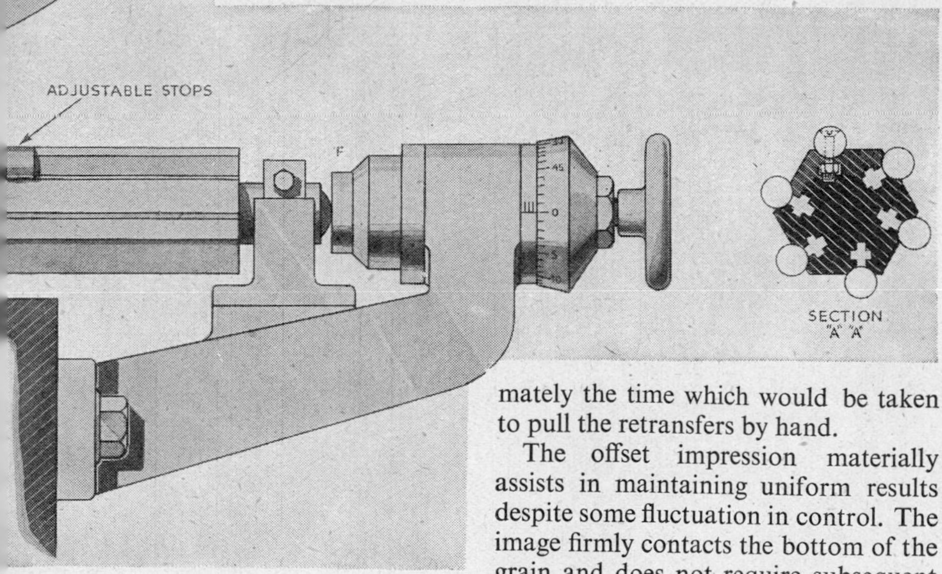

ADJUSTABLE STOPS

SECTION
"A" "A"

is returned to the control of the first peripheral stop and also moved laterally until the gauge pointer again registers zero. The usual order of transferring is therefore:—

3	6	9	12	15
2	5	8	11	14
1	4	7	10	13

GRIPPER

When the machine is set, the time taken to make such a plate is approximately the time which would be taken to pull the retransfers by hand.

The offset impression materially assists in maintaining uniform results despite some fluctuation in control. The image firmly contacts the bottom of the grain and does not require subsequent manipulation for this purpose. Solids are really firm and half-tones are clean.

Cleaning up the plate should be practically, if not entirely, unnecessary. Rolling up can also be dispensed with in a general way. The image can be dusted with french chalk, etched, gummed and dried quickly and sent to the machine or put into store. Two advantages of this are: (1) that the machine minder is given a grain which has not had local "attention"; (2) that the half-tone formation more nearly retains its correct colour values, due to a minimum of manipulation operations.

CHAPTER TWENTY

PHOTO-LITHOGRAPHY

SCIENTIFIC INVESTIGATION. LINE AND HALF-TONE NEGATIVES. COLOUR WORK.
MAKING THE IMAGE. COUNTER-ETCHING. INKING AND DEVELOPING. MODERN
TRENDS IN PLATE-MAKING. ADVANTAGES OF DEEP ETCH.

PHOTO-LITHOGRAPHY is a combination of photographic and lithographic methods for the purpose of producing printing images on lithographic surfaces. These images are then printed by the usual lithographic means. This may be said to be a modern way of image production in that it was not available in the early days of lithography. It is modern, too, in that photography is an active branch of scientific investigation, the findings of which can be adapted to lithographic photography. In addition, scientific and investigational work is constantly being carried out with the specific purpose of forwarding photo-lithographic interests and raising standards. This surging forward towards greater perfection is at once an incentive and a tonic to progressive craftsmen and a threat to those who would only ply an ancient craft in a more or less leisurely way.

Producing the Negative

Ordinary photographic methods are applied to produce a negative of the image which is required to be lithographically printed, but the equipment which is used is specially designed. Cameras have to provide images of suitable sizes for the printing machines; they are part of the unit. Large variations in size from copy to negative have to be provided for. The camera and copy board are usually in one unit and their relationship is easily and accurately adjusted for size variation and focusing.

Spring suspension of the camera frame is designed to reduce the effects of vibration. Illumination of the copy is by arc lights, and the lamps are often part of the camera unit with suitable adjustments for changing the area which is to be illuminated. A special process lens is used.

Wet plate, dry plate, film and paper all have their uses according to the kind of work being done. These are housed in the dark slide which is clipped to the back of the camera and easily detached for transport to and from the adjoining dark room.

For focusing purposes the dark slide is replaced by plate glass which is frosted except for a diagonal cross which assists in obtaining central positioning. When focus is sharp and of the correct size, lighting arranged, and suitable stop and aperture set, the focusing screen is changed for the dark slide in which is the sensitive photographic plate. This is then exposed and developed in the way best suited to the plate or film being used.

This procedure would produce a line negative from a line original such as a pen drawing in black. If the copy contained tonal values—say a photograph, pencil sketch or wash drawing—the result would be a continuous tone negative of the picture, unsuitable for producing a lithographic printing image.

When an ordinary photograph has to be reproduced by photo-lithography the picture has to be broken up into a

A   B   C
DIAGRAM OF A HALF-TONE SCREEN

Fig. 1. *Plate glass is covered with a resist, which is cut through with a diamond. The lines are then etched and filled with pigment. Plates A and B are cemented face to face to give the effect at C.*

dot formation. A special addition to the camera—known as a half-tone screen—is necessary for this purpose. This screen is made of two sheets of plate glass on which lines have been etched and filled in with opaque pigment (Fig. 1 A and B). These two plates are then cemented face to face with the lines at right angles. As the lines and spaces are of equal thickness the screen pattern is as shown in C. The screens most often used for photolithography have 133, 150, or 175 lines to the inch. Both finer and coarser screens also have their uses.

The screen is usually made in circular form and is readily inserted in and removed from the camera, for it is only required when reproducing continuous-tone copy. The screen is fitted on an adjusting frame immediately in front of the sensitized photographic plate. The distance at which the screen is set from the photographic plate, known as the screen distance, is critical, as it controls certain features of the resulting dot picture. Light, therefore, has to pass through the screen before it affects the photographic plate. The resulting effect is shown in diagrammatic form in Fig. 2. The smaller dots make the lighter sections of the picture, while the open circles show the effect of a completely "locked up" dot, thus producing a solid. A complete range of tonal effects can therefore be produced and the tonal effect can be seen if the diagram is placed at a distance and viewed with partly closed eyes.

The reader should also study Chapter 23 which deals fully with photographic reproduction methods.

Great skill in camera manipulation and control is required to obtain the best results, and a certain amount of hand work is usually necessary on the photographic plate. Treatment which approximates to the fine etching of the photo-engraver can be done on the photographic plate by dot reduction methods, so that the required tonal quality is produced on the printing plate without further manipulation.

The production of colour work is much more complicated than monochrome. If the copy holder contains a picture in full colour which has to be

HALF-TONE SCREEN EFFECT

Fig. 2. *The effect produced on a continuous tone picture when copied through the screen. The tonal effect can be seen if the diagram is viewed from a distance with partly closed eyes.*

P.T.G.—H

printed in four workings, these four printings are photographed individually and separated by suitably coloured light filters which are placed between the lens and the sensitive photographic plate. This plate, too, has to be of a special kind known as panchromatic, for ordinary photographic plates are only sensitive to a limited spectral range.

The exposure time has to be carefully adjusted for each colour, and the angles at which the screen is used have to be arranged to give the least mechanical pattern or moiré in the completed picture. It is usual to arrange the screen at 45 deg. for the most prominent colour and when single printings are being used. Common angles for colour work are as follows: yellow 15 deg., red 75 deg., blue 45 deg., and black 90 deg.

Making a Photo-litho Image

Making a photo-lithographic image is a very different matter from making a transferred image. The photo-litho image is formed by selectively hardening a light-sensitive film by exposure to arc lamps. The light-affected areas then attract printing ink, while the parts of the coating which were preserved from the action of light by the opaque parts of the negative are then removed by developing in water. The clear areas are made moisture-attracting by etching. These operations are known as metal printing or printing down.

This light-hardened base will continue to function as a printing image so long as it remains intact. It may be damaged by friction and by the action of acids or alkalis. Much can be done to resuscitate a wearing transferred image, but the crumbling foundations of this variety of photo-litho image do not lend themselves to such satisfactory repair.

A plate—say zinc—is grained by mechanical means in the usual way, but with a finer grain than is normal for a transferred image. Counter-etching is done with an acid solution to remove oxide and produce a clean metal surface. Dilute solutions of citric, acetic, or hydrochloric acids may be used, and the plate is then well washed with clean running water.

Alternatively, as the plate is taken from the graining machine it may be washed thoroughly, gummed and dried quickly to prevent oxidation. Or it may also be etched before gumming. When the plate is needed for printing down, all that is necessary before coating is to wash the surface with clean water.

Coating the Plate

The plate is then coated with a bichromated colloid solution which is whirled to drive off the moisture and assist in producing an even film. When dry, the film is sensitive to light.

Dried egg albumen is the most commonly used colloid for this purpose, but casein may also be used, and synthetic materials are now available. A good solution may be made from:—

Dried egg albumen	5 oz.
Ammonium bichromate, pure .	1-25 oz.
Liquid ammonia ·880 . .	approx. 1 oz.
Water to make	80 oz.

The speed of whirling will depend on the size of plate, the quality of grain, and specific gravity of the solution. The thinner the film, the more readily it is hardened, but it should be sufficiently thick to cover the peaks of the grain.

The plate is then placed in a vacuum printing frame, the photographic negative placed face down in the correct position, packed suitably and masked, the frame closed and the air extracted. This brings the zinc and the photographic plates into close contact and they are then subjected to the intense light of the arc lamps. Light passes through the transparent parts of the negative, but is held back by the opaque sections.

Apart from the thickness of the sensitive film, the time required for exposure is influenced by a number of things such as the intensity and spectral energy distribution of the printing light, the distance between the light source and the sensitive plate, the character of the negative, and the relative humidity of the atmosphere in the department.

Inking and Developing

On the completion of the exposure, the plate is removed from the printing frame and covered with a film of developing ink. This may be rolled on with a roller, but is more conveniently applied in liquid form with a soft rag. This waterproof ink is an aid to visibility.

The plate is now placed under running water and developed out with cotton wool or other suitable material. Soon the parts of the film which were preserved from the light by the opaque parts of the negative begin to wash away, while the light-affected parts of the plate corresponding to the open parts of the photographic negative, retain the ink and resist the developing. The plate is still lithographically clean and further work can be added by hand if needed.

Where more than one image is required, the frame would be opened after each exposure, the position of the negative changed, and the exposure repeated as many times as required. During such exposures the rest of the plate would be masked. The whole of the plate would then be developed at the same time.

Mechanical appliances ("step-and-repeat" machines) assist in making multiple exposures of photographic plates with extreme accuracy both in position and tonal quality on the printing surface.

Further treatment is simple. The plate may be etched, gummed and sent to the machine, or it may be rolled up before etching if any uncertainty exists.

MODERN TRENDS IN PLATE-MAKING

THERE is encouragement in reviewing the course of offset printing. The crudeness of early attempts has been overcome, and the remarkable development which has been recorded in recent years gives hope and expectation of a remarkable future for the craft.

This recorded progress emanates from many sources: a more general adoption of standards of greater precision; the tendency to measure rather than to guess; improvement in machinery and in the general standard of supplies; greater concentration of printing inks, together with improvements for their use for specialized purposes; and specific investigations of craft methods and processes. The future increase and intensification of technical education and instruction will establish these better standards more widely. Improvements will then be expected to show themselves in better quality of work, in higher production speeds, and a reduction in the spoilage of material.

Improvement in Technique

Early half-tone printing by offset left much to be desired. There were reasons for this. Even when half-tone negatives were suitable in range of contrast, dot formation was broken up as it was printed down to the grained plate; and, largely due to efforts to demonstrate what the new process could do, the printing was done on paper which still further degraded the result.

The justification for these things has now passed. Photographic technique has moved beyond its early tribulations and with a sufficiently high degree of skill, perfection can be closely approximated. These are indications of many healthy trends towards improved photo-lithographic methods of reproduction.

Essentials of Good Plates

The pre-requisite of good printing is good plates: plates which have clear general definition, sound dot formation, and durable printing qualities. To this end much thought is given to plate-making methods and the so-called deep - etch principle is extensively used.

The idea of deep etch is as old as the flat-bed machine; but its application on anything like a general scale is comparatively recent. The term deep etch is an unfortunate one, for it is misleading, and the process has consequently been misrepresented and misunderstood.

The theory was that a deeply etched plate would carry more ink after the manner of a gravure plate, and that this would give a correspondingly intense print on the paper and so overcome the flatness of offset printing. It is a matter of degree, and hope in this case outpaced reason. When the image is etched to the depth of two sheets of tissue paper, inking the image on the machine becomes difficult. Indeed, it is now generally realized that such an extreme depth has many disadvantages but that it does not possess any material advantages to set against them.

Vandyke Process

To review the subject very briefly: Dixon was granted a United States patent in 1854. In 1881, Goodwin was also granted a U.S. patent for a reversal process. This was modified in 1906 and is now widely known as the Vandyke process. Most present day methods of deep - etch plate making follow the general lines of the Vandyke of which the following is a general outline:—

A finely-grained zinc plate is counter-etched in the usual way, coated with a bichromated colloid and whirled until the coating is dry. This is then placed in the vacuum frame, a photographic *positive* (or a dense print on translucent paper) is placed in position, the frame closed and the exposure made without any masking. This has the effect of making a stencil in the places which are *not* to print finally. Development in water follows, but this may be hastened by warm water or very weak acid.

As the stencil is difficult to see at this stage, it may be stained with an aniline dye. The development must be continued until the lines are perfectly clear, for they are to form the final image. Counter-etch the exposed plate sections, wash and dry.

Examine the stencil for flaws and repair these with tinted gum solution and dry thoroughly. A strong image-forming and water-repelling ink is next rubbed into the clean sections, and the stencil is removed by soaking in water, or the action may be hastened by a weak acid or caustic solution.

When the stencil is completely removed, it should be treated in the same way as a freshly-transferred plate.

Explanations and Formulæ

Formula for the sensitized solution is not critical and the following recipe is typical :—

Fish glue	5 parts
Ammonium bichromate .	1 part
Water	20 parts

Ammonia should be added until the colour changes slightly.

A comparatively thick coating is used so that a surface hardening is obtained, and this assists the final removal of the temporary stencil. Any suitable counter-etch will serve and any aniline dye may be used, say 2 to 5 per cent methyl violet. Ink may be purchased, or any strong image-forming ink can be used. The following is a typical recipe :—

Litho chalk ink	.	.	6 parts
Litho drawing ink	.	.	2 parts
Copperplate ink	.	.	2 parts

Fuse these together and add 1 part of bitumen. Reduce or dissolve in turps and benzol. This might be turned to a deep-etch process by etching to some degree before inking in the image.

Necessary Precautions

This particular method is flexible, and although the materials need to be controlled their formulation is not critical. This is not the case with most deep-etch processes. Indeed, their success and the high and uniform standard of quality which they produce is largely dependent on the accurate formulation of solutions, close control of their application, and uniformity of the conditions under which they are used.

The British patent by Swan in 1904 mentions bichromated albumen, gum arabic, gelatine and casein. In addition to these colloids synthetic materials are now also quite frequently used.

Advantages of Deep Etch

It is generally agreed that superior results are obtained from deep-etched plates. The reasons given for this superiority are often confused. For example, it is usually said that the recessed image is preserved from the frictional wear of the printing operation. It is also held that there is no need for recess and that results are comparable.

The lasting properties of this type of image may be attributed to the direct application of the image-forming base to the freshly counter-etched surface. In preparation for this ink, a special lacquer base is often used as a binder. This has an extremely tenacious hold on the plate, makes a very durable and water-repelling base, and the finest dots are therefore well maintained.

From the commercial standpoint an advantage of deep-etch processes is that they lend themselves to control. For example, the content and specific gravity of a solution is known, the relative humidity of the atmosphere is checked and compensated for, the grain and the size of plate are standard, the speed of whirling is controlled, and the resulting film reacts in a known way. Again, the depth of etching is found to be most satisfactory when a certain concentration of acid is left on a plate for a certain definite time ; and so on through practically all the operations.

This type of image does not lend itself to satisfactory alterations on the printing plate; hence the greater need for preparatory care.

Recent Developments

From time to time a considerable number of patents have been granted for deep-etch processes in America, Britain and Germany. Most of these have now lapsed and deep-etch in some form is used very widely throughout the trade. This phase has served a useful purpose, but progress continues.

The principles on which two later patented processes are based, known respectively as the "Aller" and the "Alkuprint," are now claiming attention. Common features of both processes are that they have the image sections formed of different metal from the non-image sections. The image is formed on a smooth surface, thus assisting perfect dot formation. In contradistinction to the deep-etch system, the image base is *on* the surface and the thickness of the deposited copper is controllable.

These processes represent a fine achievement, and bring the indestructible lithographic plate materially nearer.

CHAPTER TWENTY-ONE

OFFSET MACHINES AND OFFSET PRINTING

DIRECT AND INDIRECT PRINTING. BEGINNING OF OFFSET. DIRECT ROTARY MACHINES. THE OFFSET PRINCIPLE. MACHINERY DESIGN. ROLLER AND INKING ARRANGEMENTS. AUTOMATIC FEEDERS. COLOUR OFFSET MACHINES. THE UNIT PRINCIPLE. SETTING A MACHINE. IMPRESSION CYLINDERS. OFFSET BLANKETS. LITHO INKS.

PRINTING consists essentially in charging a surface with a suitable ink and discharging this ink on to a desired stock. One class of printing (letterpress) makes use of a raised surface; ink is rolled on the elevations, and the stock, which is usually paper, is pressed into close contact with the surface. Due to the ink having a greater attraction for the paper than the material forming the printing surface, the ink is transferred to the paper. In another class of printing (gravure) an ink of low viscosity is flowed into shallow recesses from which it is extracted by the same forces of selective attraction. In this case the transfer of ink is accomplished under heavy pressure. The lithographic method uses a perfectly flat surface and the ink adheres to the image sections of the surface only. In this method, too, pressure is applied to the whole of the surface when a print is taken.

Direct and Indirect Methods

These processes are all known as *direct printing*, because the ink is transferred directly from the forme to the stock, and they lend themselves to the satisfactory production of an extremely wide range of printed work.

Certain materials are, however, not so suited to this direct method, as many early attempts to print metal sheets proved. The decorating of metal was,

therefore, done by what the isolated section of tin printers called the *indirect* or *transfer* method. The image was drawn to appear the right way on the stone; it was then printed on a specially prepared coated paper. The metal sheet was coated with copal varnish and, when tacky, the transfer was applied by running the metal sheet through the litho transfer press. When the paper was soaked off with water, the print appeared on the metal sheet, which was then fabricated as required.

About 1870, the direct flat-bed litho machine really came to its own after a period of great opposition. Transfers of the kind used for metal decoration were printed on these flat-bed machines.

Development of Flat-bed Machine

In 1875, R. Barclay was granted a patent for a modification of the flat-bed machine. The purpose of this modification was to enable metal sheets to be decorated in a more direct way than by the transfer method. Indeed, the print was put on the metal sheet by the printing machine. This was known to the tin-printer as the *direct* method of tin-printing as distinct from the *transfer* method. This mechanical modification of the flat-bed machine consisted in adding a second cylinder immediately above the normal one after the fashion of a mangle (Fig. 1). The lower cylinder was then covered with specially prepared card, and the print was made on this from the stone. The feedboard was also changed, and in the new form it consisted of a platform at the damper end which was arranged so as to present the flat metal sheet, first to lays and then to the contact point of the two cylinders. The sheet maintained its flat condition and emerged on a delivery tray or board over the inkers, with the printed image on the under side. Small wheels in the receiving board served to reduce the marking but did not prevent it.

Beginning of Offset

This was the beginning of offset printing. In the following year the method was put into commercial use. The offsetting medium has continually evolved, and even the present high achievement in offset blanket production (Fig. 2) is by no means final. Later, a change was made in the disposition of the extra cylinder which allowed both a face-up feed and delivery, as is shown in Fig. 3. The sheet is fed vertically downwards

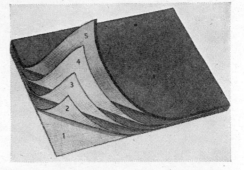

Fig. 2. *Offset blanket showing construction. Four plies of finely woven cotton fabric are cemented together with rubber and the surface coated with applications of rubber until the required thickness is obtained (see also the description given on page 248).*

into the grippers, and when the back end of the sheet clears the delivery board during the printing cycle of operations, the grippers release the sheet, which then flattens out and springs on to the tray. Many such machines are still in use, but they are not now manufactured.

Deep secrecy surrounded these machines, and for nearly thirty years the tin-printer carried on with his exclusive process while the litho printer struggled to get his prints on to hard paper. Individuals toyed with a variety of ideas and experiments, but the tin-printer

Fig. 1. *Diagram of a flat-bed offset machine patented by R. Barclay in 1875 and used for decorating metal sheets by the direct method.*

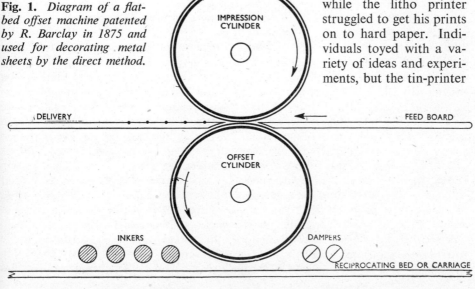

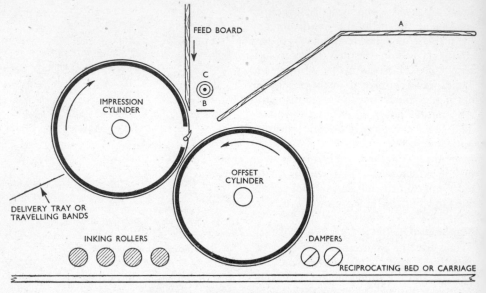

MODERN FLAT-BED TIN-PRINTER

Fig. 3. *A modern version of the flat-bed tin-printer showing the "hanging" impression cylinder. The sheets are taken from the board* (A) *and fed vertically down the feed board into the cylinder grippers. The freely revolving rubber wheel* (C) *controls the sheet as it passes;* (B) *is a plate to prevent foreign bodies falling on to the blanket.*

retained the exclusive commercial use of the offset method of printing.

Direct Rotary Machine

Towards the end of the nineteenth century the direct rotary litho machine was introduced to the trade in America and made possible by the use of thin metal printing plates. This overcame the clumsiness and the speed limitation of the flat-bed and was a marked forward step for the paper printer. But the tin-printer soon made use of this rotary motion, and in 1903 an extra cylinder was added to the direct rotary design, and the Mann Standard tin-printing rotary opened a new field of possibility when put into commercial production in 1904.

Developments still continued and when Rubel and the Harris brothers had their simultaneous inspirations to establish paper rotary offset machines, the early troubles of the offset principle had been overcome by thirty years of practical application in Great Britain. This does not detract from the remarkable work which has since been done by American printing engineers.

Principle of Offset

It will be seen that an offset print is not taken from the printing plate direct to the paper or stock, but is first made on an intermediate surface and transferred from there to the paper. The usual method is to have a special cylinder on which is stretched an offset blanket.

As the print is reversed on the offset blanket and again reversed when it is transferred on to the paper, it follows that the job which is to be printed offset appears the same on the machine plate as on the final print (Fig. 4). It should also be noted that offset printing is

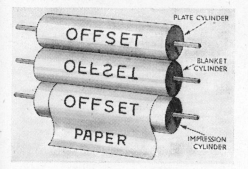

Fig. 4. *Illustrating the principle of off-set printing, as described in the text.*

done by both rotary and flat-bed machines, and, therefore, the term offset is not synonymous with rotary, despite the decline of flat-beds (Figs. 5 and 6).

It will also be appreciated that the term "direct method" as used by the first offset tin-printers was quite clear to them, but is now confusing due to the wider subsequent application of the offset process. As this was a specialized printing group, very largely isolated

from other trade contacts, the terms which they used were their own concern; but it should be clearly understood that *all* metal sheet printing is *offset* printing; that the principle is the same as used now for printing on paper; and that litho-offset machines have developed from earlier tin-printing machines.

For all practical purposes offset printing is exclusively a lithographic process, the notable exception being the specialized letterpress machines for the printing of thin metal collapsible tubes of such types as are used for tooth-paste, shaving-cream and the like.

Offset Machine Improvements

The importance of the first rotary offset paper printing machines of the American period tends to be dwarfed by modern developments. Indeed, the printers' engineer has made almost phenomenal progress during the present century. The first machines had few of the modern refinements which are

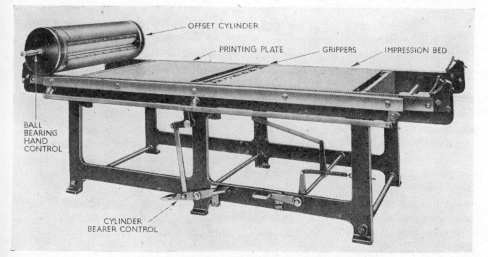

OFFSET PROOFING PRESS
Fig. 5. *The press has one bed for the metal plate and one for the sheet to be printed. The cylinder is covered with an offset blanket. The plate is inked by hand and the paper laid to gauges. The cylinder is rolled over the plate and takes ink on the blanket on the first revolution, and on the second revolution the ink is transferred to the sheet.*
P.T.G.—H*

FLAT-BED OFFSET MACHINE

Fig. 6. *The large cylinder is covered with an offset blanket; the sheet is fed into a half-size steel impression cylinder, and delivered by means of the half-size top cylinder to the tapes and thence by fliers to the delivery board which is shown above the inking system.*

now taken for granted. They were not built with any intention of frequent dismantling, and presumably the bearings were intended to last the lifetime of the machine.

Automatic control was a later development, and starting and stopping the early machines, lifting and lowering rollers and putting cylinders into and out of contact manually was a matter calling for sustained agility.

Automatic Feed

In the first machines long runs were not specially catered for. Small feed and delivery trays kept the minder constantly on the move. Built-out feed and delivery have greatly added to convenience and efficiency (Fig. 7). Inking power has been given careful attention, automatic washing-up devices have become standard equipment. Automatic sheet feeders are almost the rule rather than the exception, and in the highest development the sheet itself controls the contact of the cylinders, the actuating of the inking rollers, the continuity of ink and water supply from the fountains.

Different opinions exist among the machine makers as to whether bearers of a machine should run in contact or with a small clearance. American, and the British Crabtree machines are examples using contact bearers between plate and blanket cylinders; most other makers arrange for a clearance.

Machine Construction Problems

Offset machines offer many problems to the machine designer, and it is interesting to note how the different makers have overcome some of these difficulties. The direct rotary machines, the Mann Standard tin-printer and the Mann two-revolution machines all have ink slabs on the opposite side of the plate cylinder. This large surface is very effective in ridding the ink of the accumulated water and thus keeping the ink fresh. As these large cylinders were not conducive to high speeds, the size of the cylinder has been reduced as much as possible. This practice in turn involves other problems, such as maintaining or increasing the efficiency of the inking system at increasing machine speeds.

The elaborate inking system on a modern offset machine is a source of amazement to most letterpress printers.

Fig. 8 shows clearly the roller and inking arrangements. This inking system also breaks up the ink before it reaches the printing plate, thus allowing the maximum concentration of ink to be carried; for the amount of ink which can be transferred without deformation by the offset blanket is more limited in offset work than in the direct method.

The need for the utmost concentration of offset inks is clear, and ink manufacturers have not only produced remarkable results, but continue to make progress. The engineers, too, have taken up the matter of making maximum use of available inks, and the Schlesinger, or Progress inking device (Fig. 9) is notable in this respect. It consists of a self-contained system of rollers which takes the ink from the ink fountain vibrator and thoroughly breaks it down by shearing action before passing it on to the usual roller system. The ink then requires a minimum addition of thinning agents and this results in reduction or elimination of scum, and maximum intensity of the print.

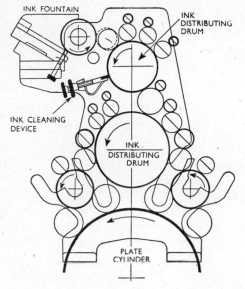

Fig. 8. *Inking system of a rotary offset machine showing mechanical ink-cleaning device.*

This device is exclusive to Waite & Saville litho-offset machines, and Ratcliff tin-printing machines.

To obtain lithographic printing of good and uniform standard, continuous production over fairly long periods is necessary. Only thus can the balance

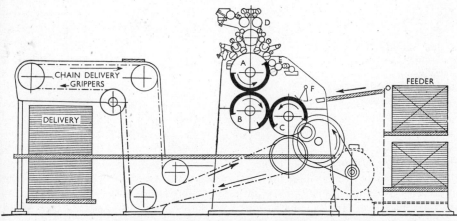

ROTARY OFFSET MACHINE—BASIC DIAGRAM

Fig. 7. *Diagram of Mann Fast Three rotary offset.* (A) *Plate cylinder;* (B) *blanket cylinder;* (C) *impression cylinder;* (D) *inking system;* (E) *damping rollers;* (F) *swing grippers.*

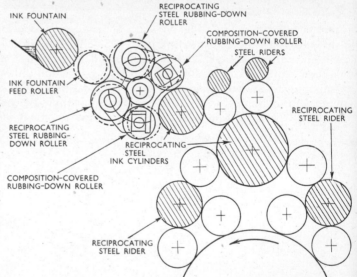

Fig. 9. *The Progress inking device: a series of rubber and oscillating metal rollers which accept ink from the ink-fountain vibrator roller and break it down by shearing action before passing it to the distributing rollers. The diagram on the right shows the arrangement of the rubber and metal rollers and their action in breaking down the ink.*

INK FOUNTAIN

RECIPROCATING STEEL RUBBING-DOWN ROLLER

COMPOSITION-COVERED RUBBING-DOWN ROLLER

STEEL RIDERS

INK FOUNTAIN FEED ROLLER

RECIPROCATING STEEL RIDER

RECIPROCATING STEEL RUBBING-DOWN ROLLER

RECIPROCATING STEEL INK CYLINDERS

COMPOSITION-COVERED RUBBING-DOWN ROLLER

RECIPROCATING STEEL RIDER

between water and ink be maintained. Probably the most useful single contribution to this end is the automatic feeder. This is not new but it has not received the universal application which might be expected. The latest principle is known as stream feed (Fig. 10).

Separation of the sheet from the pile is done at the back edge, and as the sheet moves to the control of the forwarding wheels the next is separated and started on its journey. A stream of overlapping sheets is thus started down the feed-board with a distance of about

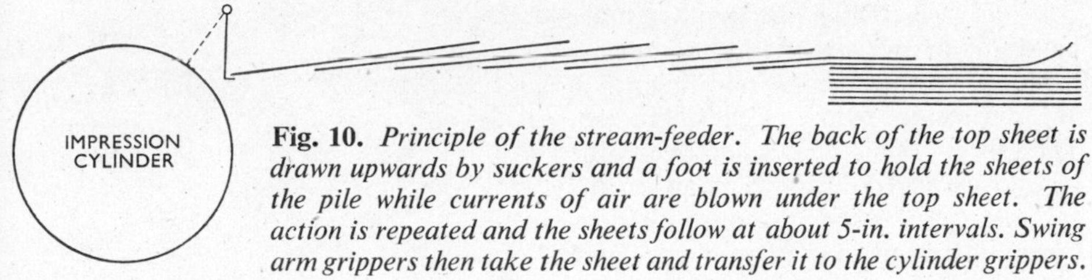

Fig. 10. *Principle of the stream-feeder. The back of the top sheet is drawn upwards by suckers and a foot is inserted to hold the sheets of the pile while currents of air are blown under the top sheet. The action is repeated and the sheets follow at about 5-in. intervals. Swing arm grippers then take the sheet and transfer it to the cylinder grippers.*

IMPRESSION CYLINDER

5 in. between the *front* edges of each sheet. When the machine is printing, the sheets move forward continuously and slowly, for a sheet has but 5 in. (approximately) to travel for each revolution of the cylinder. High speed and close register are automatically attained.

A swing-feed device then takes the sheet from the stationary lays and transfers it at speed to the impression cylinder grippers, thus overcoming an old source of register trouble. Automatic feeders are further described on pages 143 to 145 of Chapter 11.

TWO- THREE- AND FOUR-COLOUR OFFSET

THE first British offset machine made by George Mann was a modification of the successful tin-printer. After many experiments, the impression cylinder was reduced to half the size of that of the tin-printing machine and at the same time the feed and delivery boards were changed.

The next demand was for a machine to print two colours at the same time. Ingenuity again modified the single-colour machine and the arrangement shown in Fig. 11 resulted. The ink slab on the plate cylinder A was replaced by

a second plate. Two sets of rollers were so arranged that each of the rollers inked one plate.

A second blanket was added to the cylinder B so that each plate prints a single colour on to its own blanket. The sheet is fed to the impression cylinder C which holds the sheet while the impression is taken from both blankets. Delivery is assisted by the added transfer cylinder H. The impression cylinder C is also covered with an offset blanket and by easy adjustments the sheet can be printed front and back simultaneously.

Fig. 11. *Two-colour offset machine. It is explained on this and the following pages. The inking system is shown at* E 1, E 2, *and the damping system at* F 1, F 2.

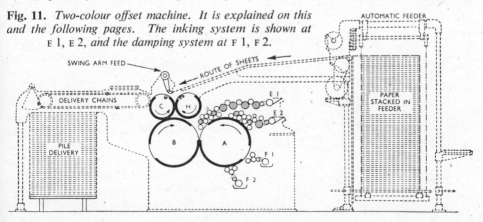

In order to do this the small cylinder makes its first revolution in the printing position without a sheet and thus takes an impression from the first blanket. The sheet then passes between the second blanket and the blanket on the cylinder c and is printed on both sides during the single revolution of the small cylinder, and immediately passed to the delivery grippers. This means that one image is reversed twice before reaching the paper, so that the image which is delivered on the under side of the sheet must appear on the plate as for direct printing, i.e. reversed.

This machine can therefore print two colours on the front of the sheet, or the same or different colours on the front and back of the sheet.

The single-revolution type of machine —having cylinders of equal diameter— has come into general use, and the dispositions of the cylinders, in order to obtain two colours, are very varied. All makers claim certain advantages.

The Crabtree Ensign machine is de-

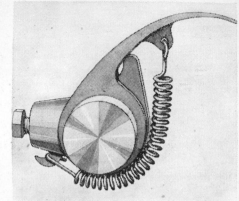

Fig. 13. *Spring gripper showing a section through the gripper bar. All the grippers are normally actuated simultaneously, but each can be opened individually without affecting the other. Tension is applied by the spring.*

servedly popular. The disposition of the cylinders is shown in Fig. 12. The open front provides a high degree of accessibility, and both feed and delivery are at the end away from the plate. Only the blanket or offset cylinder is adjustable, and this is moved relative to either the plate or blanket by means of a double eccentric without disturbing other settings. Contact cylinder bearers, helical gears, eccentric settings to dampers and rollers, individually sprung grippers (Fig. 13), are other features, while the performance is of a high standard from whatever angle approach is made. In the two-colour version of this machine (Figs. 14 and 15), a second unit is added horizontally above the first and both units are accessible for operation from the floor level.

Fig. 12. *Crabtree Ensign single-colour offset machine. The sheet is fed face down; its path through the machine and to the delivery chain is indicated by arrows.*

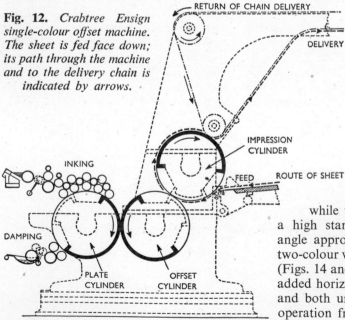

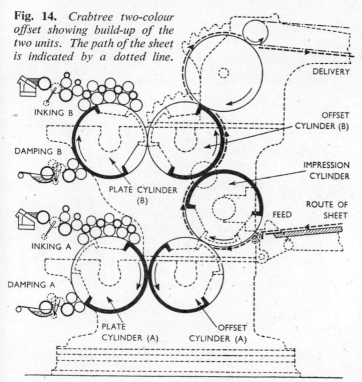

Fig. 14. *Crabtree two-colour offset showing build-up of the two units. The path of the sheet is indicated by a dotted line.*

INKING B

DAMPING B

PLATE CYLINDER (B)

INKING A

DAMPING A

PLATE CYLINDER (A)

OFFSET CYLINDER (A)

DELIVERY

OFFSET CYLINDER (B)

IMPRESSION CYLINDER

ROUTE OF SHEET

FEED

A three-colour Ensign machine is also made. This has a third horizontal unit which is reached by a stage. Feed and delivery are practically as in the single - colour. This is a useful machine for certain kinds of work, but it has not the wide application of the two-colour.

Unit Principle

About 1929 a strong move was made by American offset machine designers to set a new standard. The unit principle was unanimously accepted

CRABTREE ENSIGN TWO-COLOUR ROTARY OFFSET MACHINE

Fig. 15. *This illustration should be compared with the above basic diagram, Fig. 14. The Elless stream feeder is in the centre, and delivery on the right. This disposition provides the maximum accessibility to the plate cylinder, damping and inking systems.*

(Fig. 17). By this method a four-colour machine consists of four single-colour units arranged in sequence. It should, however, be clearly understood that two-, three- or four-colour machines must be built as such, and that the additions of units later is not usually practical. It is highly probable that the addition of such units will soon become feasible.

The Harris four-colour offset machine which is illustrated in Fig. 17 was first in operation in 1931. This firm now fits the British H.T.B. stream feeder as standard equipment—a splen-

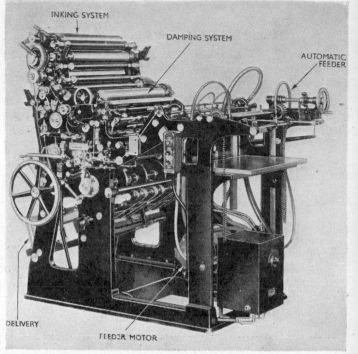

SINGLE-COLOUR ROTARY OFFSET MACHINE

Fig. 16. *Harris-Seybold-Potter offset machine with automatic feeder and built-in delivery. The motor is fitted inside the frame making a compact unit of high speed and efficiency.*

did combination. The path of the sheet through the machine is indicated by the thick line. From the first blanket or impression cylinder the sheet is taken by the grippers of the large-diameter transfer cylinder to the second unit,

and so on through the cycle of units.

The Hoe and Miehle companies also build offsets on the unit principle. The Miehle machine transfers the sheet from one impression cylinder to the next by a series of three transfer

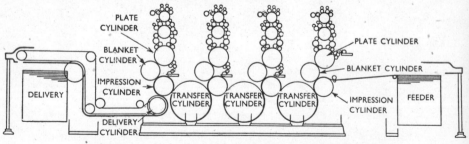

HARRIS FOUR-COLOUR ROTARY OFFSET MACHINE

Fig. 17. *One colour is printed by each unit. The sheet is transferred from one unit to the next by grippers on the large transfer cylinders, and delivered by chain grippers.*

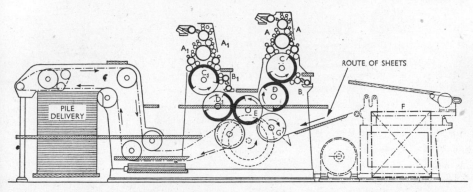

MANN FAST FIVE ROTARY OFFSET: BASIC DIAGRAM

Fig. 18. *The sheet is fed into cylinder* G, *transferred to cylinder* E, *where it is held while the impression is taken from blankets* D *and* D 1. (A A 1) *Inking system;* (B B 1) *damping systems;* (C C 1) *plate cylinders. Inking systems are similar to detailed diagram Fig. 8, page 235.*

cylinders, all of which have a common diameter with the machine cylinders. The Hoe unit machine carries the sheet from one impression cylinder to the next by controlled chain mechanism. The sheet is picked up at the feed end of the machine and held in one set of grippers until printing is completed by the whole of the units, when it is transferred to the delivery mechanism.

In addition to the two-revolution machine a single-revolution arrangement is also now used in the British Mann types known as Fast Three (Fig. 20) and Fast Five (Figs. 18 and 19), which are one- and two-colour offset

MANN FAST FIVE ROTARY OFFSET MACHINE

Fig. 19. *The two units are similar but not identical in construction. Note build-out for extended pile delivery. No feeder is shown but any type of auto feeder can be fitted.*

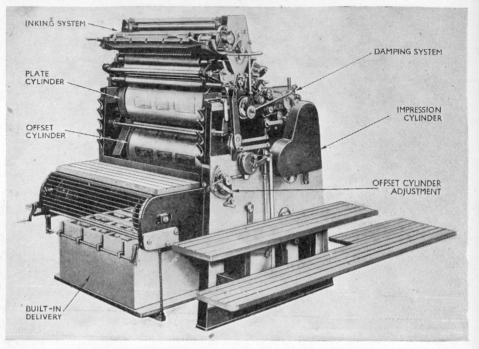

MANN FAST THREE ROTARY OFFSET MACHINE

Fig. 20. *The inking system is above the plate cylinder and the offset cylinder below. The impression cylinder is not visible, and the compact delivery is low set.*

machines respectively. The vertical type of construction is followed. Cylinder sizes are small for the printing area, and to increase the time allowed for feeding the sheet, a device is introduced into the feed cylinder to accelerate the back of the sheet once the front edge is taken by the grippers.

Single-colour machines are built on similar general lines by Furnival, Ratcliff and Waite & Saville in Great Britain and Marinoni-Voirin in France.

HINTS ON OFFSET PRINTING

OFFSET printing machinery is precision built. When this simple fact is more generally realized the craft will have made a corresponding step forward, for trade machinery will then be nearer to obtaining the skilled treatment which it needs to give best service. Cylinders, for example, are ground to within one thousandth of an inch tolerance. The plate cylinder is ground to take a plate of a certain number of thousandths in thickness; the blanket cylinder is similarly ground; the amount of overpressure between blanket and plate to give the best result is known; and machines are made so that cylinders bear a definite relationship one to another.

Thus far there is *no guessing*. Clearly then, what an offset printer should do when setting up the machine or preparing to run a job, is to make accurate

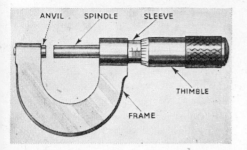

Fig. 21. *Micrometer showing the simple construction and the various parts.*

measurements; transfer these measurements to the machine; and at least the machine will then have a chance to run. The measuring instrument is the micrometer (Fig. 21). It is very simple to use, and is by far the most important tool of the offset printer. It makes the difference between *knowing* and *guessing*.

The anvil and the sleeve of the micrometer are fixed, and the spindle turns with the thimble on a fine thread. The object to be measured is placed between the anvil and spindle; the thimble is then screwed to firm but light contact, and the reading on the gauge indicates the thickness in thousandth parts of an inch.

Two scales can be seen in the diagram. On the sleeve is a long horizontal datum line which is crossed by a set of long lines. When the spindle makes contact with the anvil the edge of the scale on the thimble closes up to the first long line and registers zero.

Progress in the design of the offset machine has been indicated. Precision in machine manufacture has similarly improved. Also, modern machines are expected to run much faster than the earlier types. It should be understood, therefore, that a degree of error which would cause little trouble in an old, large-geared, slow-moving type of machine, would be quite unacceptable in a modern machine running at high speed.

Unfortunately for all concerned, the apprentice, the craftsman, the employer, the craft, the machine manufacturer, and the trade generally, have no standard on which to evaluate machinery obsolescence. Therefore, new machinery tends to be acquired by a process of infiltration; and it is easier to transfer old standards to the management of new machines than it is to raise old standards of manipulation in anticipation of new machinery at an uncertain date. This is but one of many vicious concentric circles, and it behoves the craftsman to be deliberate in his attempts to keep abreast of the fast-moving times.

The reader should follow out this thought for himself, making full use of the following hints, outlines and general principles as a guide to procedure.

General Principles

The first thing to learn about a new or fresh offset machine is the correct way to stop it. Other things may then follow in less rigid sequence.

A machine should not be run on power until careful inspection indicates that all is clear. Remove all tools and rags, and pull the wheel *by hand* one complete revolution. A complete cycle may be from one to seven cylinder revolutions, according to the type of delivery.

Oiling should be done regularly and with suitable grade of oil or oils and grease. Heavy bearings require heavy lubricant while the comparatively slow-moving automatic feeder requires a lighter oil. Oil should be put in the cups or oil-holes, and not run down the machine frame. Oil on the floor or in the well of the machine is unsightly, unnecessary and wasteful. Oil on the machine stands is dangerous, particularly to those who are not so nimble as in their earlier youth. Be careful to see that only oil goes into the oilcan.

Cylinders and bearers should be kept free from rust and deposit by wiping with a paraffin rag. A trace of oil is an advantage to the plate cylinder and essential to bearers, but the use of abrasives should be strictly prohibited.

Setting a Machine

Setting a machine should be a very infrequent operation, but when it is done the greatest care should be exercised. Take a plate of full size for the machine and of correct calliper. If such a plate is not available make up a thinner plate with paper underpacking so that plate plus paper make the correct thickness. Tissue is one thousandth of an inch, and other stock is readily measured with the micrometer.

Remove riders and oscillators and set inkers with firm but not heavy pressure. Metal feelers are useful for testing the fit of the spindles in the roller cups. Nap rollers should be set a little heavier than composition rollers, but they should not fall over the back edge of the plate or kick at the front edge when the machine is running. Set the inkers circumferentially to the oscillating rollers in their fixed cups, and move the machine until the inkers are off the plate, and test inkers to oscillator setting again. If contact is not retained in this position there will be trouble with water. Test the ink fountain vibrator and set if required.

If this setting is done correctly there will be no difficulty in inking either solids or half-tones, and all that remains to be done is to set all plates to this same surface level. This is one of the essential applications of the micrometer.

Dampers should then be set to the same plate. Probably these are more important than the inkers, and not least important is the ink fountain vibrator.

Dampers have completely changed from the built-up affairs of early days,

to a single molleton (cotton fabric) covering a rubber or composition base. Making, materials, setting, cleaning, maintenance, and fountain solution, make a long and important sequence which may be summarized thus: retain the shape of the base; keep both the material and the brass roller clean; set with light, even pressure both to plate and brass roller; and use either clean water in the fountain or retain a solution at a pH of 4·6, which represents a slightly acid condition.

If the cylinders are now placed in the printing position the gap between the plate and the blanket cylinder will indicate the amount of packing with which the blanket cylinder has to be dressed. This gap should be over-packed to ·003 in. to allow for pressure, roughly the thickness of a piece of printing paper.

Blanket Standards

Blankets are made in two standard thicknesses, ·065 in. and ·075 in. As rubber tends to change its thickness in certain circumstances it is good practice to carry a small amount of floating packing under the blanket, so that compensation for such changes can be made without interfering with the machine settings. It will now be seen by the bearer height whether one or two blankets are required. The practice of makers varies in this respect. One blanket is ample from the standpoint of the quality of the print, but the resilience provided by two blankets is kinder to the machine on the occasions when other things than sheets of paper find their way between the cylinders.

The gripper edge of the blanket is marked on the back, and it should be squared up from this edge. Be quite sure that both the clamp and the stretching bar are in the centre; or if not, file a centre mark on each and measure from the centre of the blanket.

Stretching the blanket is a simple operation which is frequently carried out with a ritual which is as elaborate as it is unnecessary. The blanket should be sufficiently tight to prevent creep, which would cause doubling of the impression, and sufficiently slack to retain some resilience. The more the blanket is forced round the stretching bar the thinner it becomes on the printing surface. When the pressure is set, draw up the blanket with a firm pull, run the machine with pressure on, to massage the blanket for a few revolutions, and then draw it up again. Tension should not be drumtight but should be even, except where necessary to cut out an end section due to the ratchet. Naturally, there is greater resistance on a large blanket than on a small one.

To Set a Machine without Bearers. Fix blanket(s) and all packing except the overpressure sheet. Take off pressure and insert strips of paper between the printing plate and the blanket. Bring up the blanket cylinder evenly by the adjusting nuts until the strips can be extracted only with a firm pull. Apply more pressure to make up for the thickness of the setting paper. Run a thin film of ink solid on the plate and pack the blanket in low places with tissue until a bare, even result is obtained. Insert a sheet of ·003 in. under the blanket to give overpressure, fasten lock nuts and test on the cleaned blanket.

To Set a Machine requiring Bearer Clearance. Put the cylinders in printing position, adjust the blanket and plate cylinder bearers to the clearance required and test the distance of the gap between the plate and the cut-out for the blanket. Put on the blanket(s) and packing, level up as previously described, and insert the overpressure sheet.

To Set a Machine having Bearer Contact. Put the machine in printing position and see that the pressure arm is fully extended and in contact with the stop. Take off pressure on each side sufficiently to part the bearers, meantime retain clearance between the bearers of blanket and impression cylinders. Balance the two bearers by using feelers of known thickness, add pressure equal to the thickness of the feeler so as to obtain bearer contact, and in addition add a small amount, say three thousandths of an inch, to ensure firm pressure. Test should be made for play in the bushes, and this should be compensated for.

Impression Cylinders

A certain amount of pressure is required to transfer printing ink from one surface to another. Different kinds of paper require different amounts of pressure to obtain satisfactory transference of the ink. The amount of pressure required for any particular paper is soon found by experience, but the rule should be to use the minimum of pressure which will give the required result. Smooth paper takes an impression with less pressure than rougher paper.

Paper varies in thickness, and this also has to be taken into account when setting the impression cylinder. Say a smooth paper requires three thousandths of an inch of pressure to obtain good results and the thickness of the paper is three thousandths of an inch, and a rougher paper requires seven thousandths of an inch of pressure and this is also the thickness of the paper. Then the same setting of the machine is correct for both papers, and the impression cylinder will just be in contact with the blanket when in the printing position. By experience of the printing quality of the paper, and measurement of the thickness of the paper by the micrometer, guesswork is again avoided. While pressure between the impression and blanket cylinders is important, it is not so critical as the

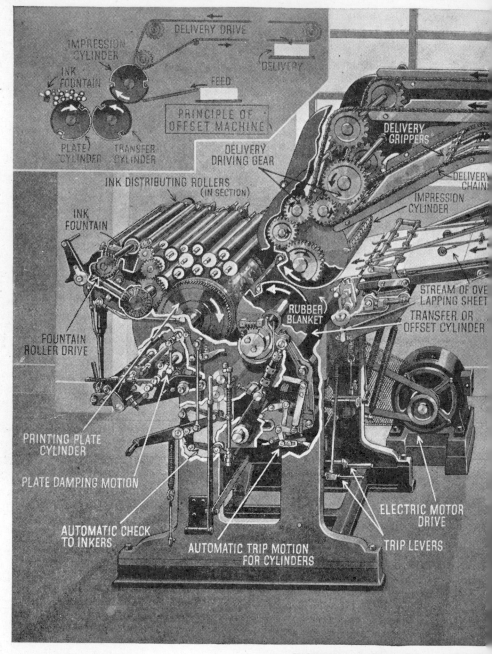

WORKING PARTS OF A LITHO

Detailed drawing showing the working parts of a Crabtree rotary offset machine. The inset shows the relative positions of the cylinders, feed and delivery. Plate and impression cylinders are in fixed bushes, and the offset cylinder is housed in a double eccentric bush by which this cylinder is adjusted both to the plate and the impression cylinders. The

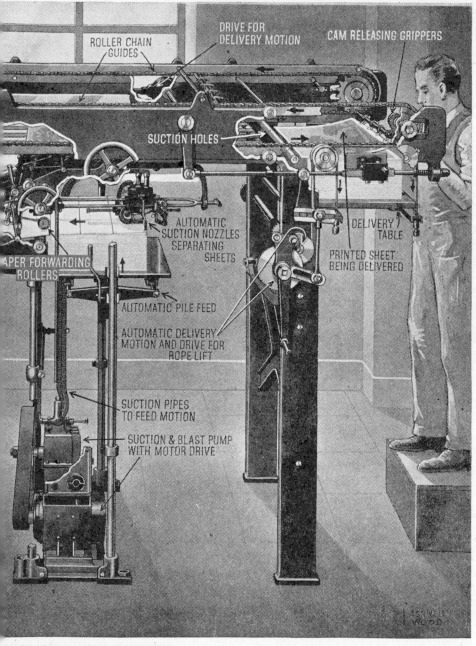

ROLLER CHAIN GUIDES

DRIVE FOR DELIVERY MOTION

CAM RELEASING GRIPPERS

SUCTION HOLES

AUTOMATIC SUCTION NOZZLES SEPARATING SHEETS

PAPER FORWARDING ROLLERS

DELIVERY TABLE

PRINTED SHEET BEING DELIVERED

AUTOMATIC PILE FEED

AUTOMATIC DELIVERY MOTION AND DRIVE FOR ROPE LIFT

SUCTION PIPES TO FEED MOTION

SUCTION & BLAST PUMP WITH MOTOR DRIVE

ROTARY OFFSET MACHINE

feeder is of the stream type, and the sheets overlap about five inches. A generous pile is provided for, and this rises automatically so that the top sheet is always in position to be taken by the suction nozzles. Separation and forwarding movements are from the back edge of the sheet in this type of feeder. The pile delivery similarly descends under control.

balance between the plate and the blanket.

The practice of manufacturers varies with regard to the impression cylinder. Some cylinders are bare, some have a metal shell under which the packing is inserted, while others have a blanket either of the offset type or of rexine or similar cloth. One advantage of the covered cylinder is that pressure can be modified by changing the packing under this blanket rather than by altering machine settings. Slight alterations are quite justifiable and that is the purpose of the small clearance which may be left between the bearers of the impression and the blanket cylinders.

Setting the Impression Cylinder. Where the impression cylinder is not dressed, it has to be brought to such juxtaposition with the blanket that the print is satisfactorily transferred to the paper. To do this, move the cylinders to printing contact, insert *cut* strips of paper between the offset blanket and the impression cylinder, and bring the cylinders together by the impression-cylinder adjustment until the strips are evenly and fairly firmly gripped.

Where the bearers of plate and blanket cylinders are running in contact, those of blanket and impression may also be set solid. But this is not necessary, and a clearance of two or three thousandths of an inch is a convenience for making slight adjustments due to different stock thicknesses or printability. Normally, then, this clearance will be allowed, and blanket plus packing sheets will then be added to an amount sufficient to give the required pressure.

Rubber Blanket Coating

The rubber which forms the surface of the offset blanket may be soft, medium or hard, according to the mix and the vulcanizing. A medium rubber hardness has been assumed in suggesting ·003 in. as the required overpressure. But a soft surface would work with slightly less pressure, while a hard surface may require slightly more. Rubber is coloured with various pigments. The colour is not necessarily an indication of the quality or the degree of hardness.

Cream, green, red, brown or grey blankets (these are the usual colours), all may have either a hard or a soft finish. The relative amount of rubber to base is also a source of misunderstanding. Early ideas catered for a high amount of resilience and elasticity and therefore thick rubber. This is old history. A modern blanket has a cotton base woven as fine as a 120 half-tone screen. Special treatment takes the stretch out of this, and four plies are cemented together by spreading layers of rubber (Fig. 2). The surface is then laid on in a large number of amazingly thin deposits to make a final aggregate of about ·020 to ·025 in., which is about the thickness of a plate.

Treatment of Blanket. The blanket should not be washed more than is necessary. When making ready, pull a few waste sheets to clear the blanket until the correct position is obtained, and then wash the blanket before beginning the run. New blankets have a preserving coating which should be removed before starting to print. Water and solvent will usually remove this, but some prefer to add fine pumice powder to hasten the removal.

When washing a blanket aim at removing the ink, and do not spread ink over the whole surface in a thin layer. It is good practice to pass the water sponge over the blanket before the washing solution. Water removes the gum or fountain deposit and fibres which have accumulated from the stock. Many good blanket-washing solutions are available. Ordinary paraffin is acceptable, if not ideal. Turpentine must not be used, and petrol must be free from lead. Otherwise there is probably more in the manner of using than in the solution which is used. Wash quickly; keep the solution from penetrating under the edges of the blanket; wipe quickly with a second rag. Dust with french chalk if desired but do not use sulphur. Keep all these materials from the gears and the bearers.

Mixing Lithographic Inks

The formulation of printing ink is a highly-specialized job. It is work which calls for the constant use of new materials, both to assist working properties and concentration. The printer knows little or nothing of these materials. Ink is usually supplied to the printer in stiffer consistency than would normally be used on the machine. It is then the printer's responsibility to suit the ink to the machine and the stock to be printed, and to adjust the drying time as may be necessary. Ink will usually work if given the chance. Try it. Add nothing without good reason, and then add the least which will give the required result.

Much offset printing trouble is due to incorrect ink mixing. Paraffin is *not* a good general ink reducer and makes far more trouble than it overcomes.

Lithographic varnishes, raw and boiled linseed oils, and wax varnish will do practically all that is called for in reducing inks to workable consistency.

Driers should be used sparingly, measured carefully as a poundage or percentage, and added to the ink when it is about to be used; paste drier is best for colour work. It dries with a matt finish and allows subsequent printings to key, and it dries throughout the film. Cobalt drier is much more powerful, but dries with a surface skin which is glossy and does not lift other ink well. As drying inks are severe on the plate and do not work well, drying by pene-

tration of the stock should be used.

For further information in regard to litho inks the reader should refer to Chapter 29.

In earlier days of lithographic printing there may have been some justification for a spacious vest pocket, but printers should realize that this day has gone. Present aims should be towards methodical simplification, and away from chaotic complication. The consistent use of the micrometer is an example of the former. When plates are measured and built up as and when needed, the surface of the plate retains its correct relationship with dampers, inkers and blanket. The grain is retained over a maximum period; the image is subjected to the least wear; the print is on the blanket right away; and the attention of the minder can be given to other matters which now appear of little importance in their isolation.

Two Types of Craftsmen

The alternative method is unfortunately better known. No micrometer—just hope! The plate is thin and does not roll up firmly. It is easy to blame the plate-making department, but meantime the image is not improving by its friction and water treatment. It may be found at first that the print does not appear on the blanket. Obviously (?) more pressure is required.

Immediately this is done the machine is incorrectly set: the impression is still bad. After much struggling the rollers are set lower, and the result *appears* to be better. The damping is not too good either, so this calls for further adjustment. What a sorry story! What a way to treat a precision machine!

The best type of craftsman looks and always thinks at least one stage ahead of current production. He foresees trouble before stepping into it, and he chooses to step round it instead.

CHAPTER TWENTY-TWO

ENGRAVING AND RELIEF STAMPING

HAND ENGRAVING. MAKING THE TRACING. MARKING THE DESIGN. ENSURING REGISTER. PUNCHING THE LETTERING. SUNK WORK. ORNAMENTAL ENGRAVING. RULING MACHINE AND PANTOGRAPH. HAND AND MACHINE STAMPING. GOLD AND SILVER STAMPING. DIE-STAMPING DIFFICULTIES AND THEIR REMEDIES.

THE word engraving covers a wide field of activities, such as block making, nameplate engraving, and jewellers' engraving, and it should be made clear that we are describing in this chapter only the preparation of dies for relief stamping and embossing by engraving and etching.

In this province hand engraving still holds pride of place, despite the development in recent years of machines which will handle limited classes of work quite successfully. To give the reader an insight into the methods adopted, we will assume that a design for a two-colour letter heading has been accepted by the client and passed to the engraver to engrave dies for relief stamping.

To introduce each of the normal types of engraving, we will further assume that in addition to usual hand-cut work, the heading includes some punched and machine-engraved lettering, a view of a factory and a badge which has to be sunk, i.e. modelled in high relief.

Making the Tracing

The engraver first makes a tracing on gelatine of the key working, using a pointed steel tool called a dry-point. Into the scratched lines of his tracing he places powdered graphite, wiping away the surplus powder (Fig. 1). Next he selects two mild steel die blanks $\frac{5}{8}$ in. thick and large enough to overlap the design by about $\frac{1}{4}$ in. all round. The surface of these blanks would have been previously ground on a surface grinder and then highly polished. The engraver proceeds to burnish this polished surface, using a diagonal movement of his burnisher, and then coats the surface with a very thin film of wax or plasticine (Fig. 2). He lays his gelatine tracing face downwards on the die blank and by burnishing the back of the gelatine transfers the graphite from his tracing to the waxed surface of the steel.

Accurate Alignment

With his dry-point he next scratches parallel lines top and bottom of all lettering, and then marks his design on to the steel by scratching lightly over the graphite outline. When this has been completed he removes the waxed coating bearing the graphite outline which is no longer required. His guide lines at top and bottom of the lines of lettering help him to keep lettering in alignment, but as a further aid he scratches vertical lines between each letter. In this connection it should be borne in mind that the engraver often works from a rough sketch, and the correction of faulty spacing or alignment is part of his work.

ENGRAVING A LETTER HEADING

Fig. 1. *Making a tracing on gelatine with a steel-pointed tool. Powdered graphite is afterwards placed into the scratched lines of the tracing, the surplus being wiped away.*

This completes the preliminary work and the engraver is now in a position to commence the engraving proper (Fig. 3). The die is rested on a sandbag, a small leather bag filled with silver sand and whiting. All cuts are made from right to left, the die being turned in whichever direction is necessary to allow the graver to follow the outline of the work. Throughout the actual cutting operation the engraver watches his work through a magnifying glass which is held in position on an adjustable stand.

The heavy lines, usually the down strokes of the lettering, are cut first, a graver with a rather wide cutting edge known as a scorper being used for this purpose. The lines are entered and re-entered with the graver until they are of the correct width and depth. The fine lines are cut next with a pointed graver known as a lozenge, and finally the work is finished up with a squared graver. A certain amount of burr is thrown up by the graver, and this is subsequently removed with emery cloth.

The die for the second working is cut in exactly the same way, but to ensure register the design is applied to the metal in a slightly different manner. The completed key die is coated with a plasticine film and a sheet of gelatine pressed into close contact with it. The gelatine when removed bears a plasticine outline of the key working which is then rubbed down on the second die blank. It is then a fairly straightforward operation to dry-point the outline of the second colour on to the steel in exact register with the first colour.

TRANSFERRING THE GELATINE TRACING

Fig. 2. *The gelatine tracing is placed face downwards on the die blank, and the graphite is transferred to the waxed surface of the steel by burnishing the back of the gelatine.*

RE-ENTERING WITH THE GRAVER

Fig. 3. *The engraver is about to re-enter with his graver, one of the lines of his engraving. All cuts are made from right to left, the die being turned in any direction to suit the engraver.*

The dies are next passed over to a die-sinker for the addition of the punched lettering, usually the smallest lettering on the die—telephones, telegrams, directors' names, etc. (Fig. 4). The die-sinker marks out carefully with lines scratched on the surface of the die the position in which this lettering is to appear. He is equipped with sets of punches, comprising the alphabet and numerals in various sizes and styles. They consist of pieces of hardened tool steel about 3 in. long with letters or numerals engraved in relief at one end.

Each punch is held in position over the die and by tapping smartly with a light hammer the letters are impressed into the steel one at a time. It is, of course, essential that the punches be held absolutely vertical while being used, and it will be appreciated that this operation calls for a very high degree of skill; as does also the correct placing of the letters to ensure alignment.

The die-sinker is also responsible for work which has to be sunk, in this particular instance the badge. For this part of the work he lays down a gelatine tracing in a similar manner to the lettering engraver, and then with hammer and

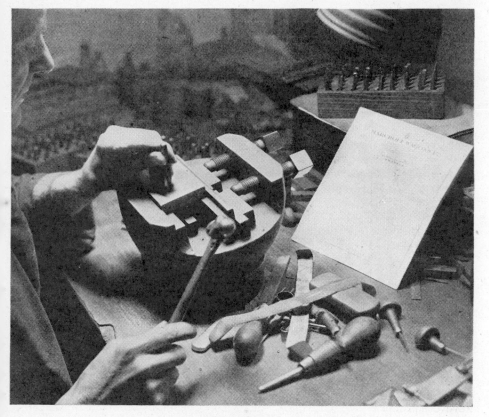

DIE SINKING

Fig. 4. *Very small lettering such as the telephone number and telegraphic address in a letter heading is inserted in the die by means of steel punches, which are hardened steel tools about three inches in length, with the character engraved in relief on one end.*

chisel proceeds to chisel out the whole of the design in silhouette, working only to the shallowest level. By a combination of chiselling and cutting with a graver he then works down to the deeper portions of the die.

A skilled die-sinker makes considerable use of the burrs thrown up by his chisel and gravers. As he has to obtain all the effects of light and shade by modelling, the finished effect is really a piece of sculpture in reverse.

The ornamental work, in this case the view of the factory, has now to be engraved and for this purpose the die will be passed over to another engraver who specializes in this class of work. The latter makes a very careful gelatine tracing of the portion of the design for which he is responsible, and then lays an acid-resisting wax ground on the die. To do this he has to warm the steel until it is hot enough to melt the ground, and after covering the surface with the wax, it is smoothed out into a level film by the use of a rubber roller. When the ground has become cold he rubs down his gelatine tracing in a similar manner to the lettering engraver.

Etching the Plate

The next operation is to scratch away the ground along the lines of his design with a dry-point, and then apply acid to bite into the steel which has been exposed. When the work has been etched to the desired depth, the acid is removed, blotting paper being used to absorb the last remnants.

It may be that some parts of the design have to be more lightly etched than others. In this case the engraver will remove the acid as soon as these parts have been sufficiently etched, and will then apply a stopping medium (usually Brunswick black) to cover these parts. The acid is applied once again, to give sufficient depth to the rest of the work.

To give it strength and contrast the engraver will often apply small quantities of acid to selected parts of the design to etch them a little deeper; and after the acid has been removed a certain amount of hand cutting with a graver is generally necessary to give added sparkle to the reproduction. It will be appreciated that a skilled craftsman can produce very beautiful effects by a combination of etching, stopping away, re-etching and hand cutting.

Ruling Machine

The ornamental engraver also makes use of what is known in the trade as a ruling machine for laying tints, giving a somewhat similar effect to the blockmaker's mechanical tints (Fig. 5). This machine makes use of a diamond point which scratches parallel lines across the ground which the engraver has laid previously upon the die. By means of a ratchet, the lines can be placed close together or far apart, according to whether a heavy or light effect is required.

Very heavy tints approaching a solid can be obtained by making two close rulings at right angles to each other. This is known as sable ruling. The lines are ruled right across the design, overlapping it by about $\frac{1}{4}$ in. all round; and before etching the engraver paints out with Brunswick black along the outlines and at any other points where he does not want the tint to appear. By etching the different parts of his work for varying periods, a wide variety of effects can be obtained, including vignettes, graduated tints and the appearance of light and shade on the object reproduced.

Engraving Machines

As mentioned previously, machines which will handle certain classes of work, chiefly lettering, have been introduced in recent years. Model C Universal engraving machine (Fig. 6) is an

American product which works from enlarged master plates on the pantograph principle. The master plates are supplied in a very wide range of styles. The die blank is coated with an acid resist and clamped to the bed of the machine. Using a pointer at the end of a perpendicular arm of the machine, the operator traces the letters required from the selected master plates.

The movements of the pointer are reproduced on a smaller scale by a diamond point which thus scratches a reduced facsimile of the lettering on the acid-resisting ground. The lettering is then etched to the required depth with acid. Special master plates can, of course, be cut for any work suitable for etching, but as the plates have to be cut on a very greatly enlarged scale, they are naturally expensive. The cost is justified only when the design is to be reproduced frequently, as in the case of certain badges.

The machine is suitable for small lettering which does not have to be deeply engraved, but, as an etched line is never as clean as a cut line, a certain raggedness is noticeable in the case of larger or heavier lettering where the acid has to be left on the steel for a long period. For this reason machine-engraved lettering is usually bitten rather lightly and then recut by hand.

ENGRAVER'S RULING MACHINE

Fig. 5. *By means of a diamond point this machine rules parallel lines either close together or far apart which are subsequently etched into the surface of the die or copper plate. The ruling machine is used for the production of tints, shadows, or other work of an ornamental nature.*

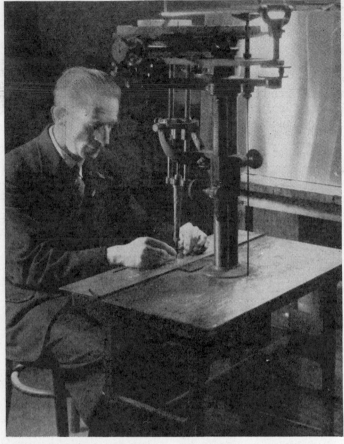

MODEL C UNIVERSAL ENGRAVING MACHINE

Fig. 6. *The engraving machine works from enlarged master plates from which the design is reduced on the pantograph principle. The diamond point is raised or lowered by means of a pedal.*

cherry red, and then plunging them into cold water. To avoid distortion, dies are lowered into the water end on, and as smoothly as possible. This hardening process has one disadvantage. If any alterations to the existing dies are required the latter have to be softened before they can be touched with a graver. It may therefore be as well at this stage to describe the softening process.

The dies are put into a steel box containing powdered charcoal. Further charcoal is added until the box is full. The lid is then closed and sealed with fire-clay. The box is placed in an enclosed furnace (called a muffle) and heated until cherry red, after which the heat is turned off and the box left to cool. It is essential to exclude all air from the dies during the softening process; otherwise the surface of the die would be scaled or damaged by burning.

After the engraving has been completed the dies are case-hardened to prevent wear in the stamping operation. This is done by heating them in a bath of molten cyanide until the dies are a

RELIEF STAMPING

ALTHOUGH hand stamping is an extremely slow process it is still used very widely for short runs from small dies. The die is stuck by means of gutta-percha to the chuck, which is a rectangular piece of steel fitting exactly into a recess in the bed of the press. The dab which corresponds to the platen of a printing press is removed, and a piece of force card about $\frac{1}{8}$ in. thick is

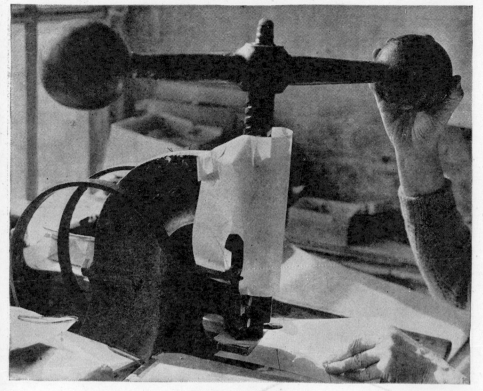

HAND STAMPING

Fig. 7. *Showing the press being swung. The dab descends, squeezing the paper between the force and the die. Thus an impression of the engraving is obtained on the force card.*

stuck to it with gum. The dab is then replaced in the press where it is secured to the end of the plunger by a taper pin.

The weighted arm at the top of the press is swung round causing the plunger to descend and forcing the dab with its force card in position in close contact with the die (Fig. 7). An impression of the engraving is thus obtained on the force card. The dab is removed once again and with the aid of a sharp knife the operator cuts away the force card around the impression, leaving it only where it is required to press the paper into the engraving. This is shown in Fig. 8. A piece of rubber-coated cloth is next stuck over the surface of the dab which is then replaced in the press.

Pins are inserted in the feed-board in correct position to act as lay edges for the paper to be stamped, and if the stamping is plain (i.e. no ink being used) the job can now be run off. This is done by taking sheets, one at a time, from a pile at the left of the press, feeding them in between the die and the force, and swinging the press so that the paper is impressed into the engraving by the force. After each impression the sheet is removed and placed in a pile at the right of the press.

For black or colour stamping the preparatory work is exactly as outlined above, but before each impression the die has to be charged with ink. This is done by removing from the press the

CUTTING THE FORCE FOR MACHINE STAMPING

Fig. 8. *With a sharp knife the operator cuts away the force card around the impression, leaving only the part which is required to press the paper into the engraving.*

chuck on which the die is mounted, brushing ink into the engraving (Fig. 9), and then removing surplus ink from the face of the die by wiping it face downwards across a sheet of wiping paper. After this the die is replaced in the press and the impression taken.

Gough presses work on a similar principle to ordinary hand presses, but the inking and wiping are accomplished by mechanical means, thus obviating the necessity for removing the die before each impression.

For gold and silver stamping the procedure is the same as for colour stamping except that an additional working is involved. This is known as burnishing, and is accomplished by running the

sheets through the press a second time without any ink. A piece of very thin copper foil is stuck over the surface of the die, and the original impression, which in metallic inks is very crude, is pressed into close contact with the copper foil lining the recesses of the engraving. This imparts a very fine finish and brings out the details of the engraving.

Machine Stamping

Waite and Saville die-stamping machines are used almost exclusively in Great Britain and indeed throughout the world. In the Standard machine, which was the original model, the die is secured face upwards to the bed of the machine which travels backwards and forwards in a horizontal plane. Starting from its extreme backward position the die first passes beneath an inking roller which floods it with ink, and then, as it moves forward, passes under the wiping pad which removes all surplus ink from the face of the die, leaving it only in the recesses of the engraving.

This wiping pad consists of a steel bed over which are stretched two thicknesses of blanket. Wipe-off paper is threaded through the machine from a coil at the top and passes over the surface of the wiping pad before being rewound on another roll. Thus, as the bed of the machine comes forward, the surface of the die is pressed against the wipe-off paper at the point where it passes over the blanket and after each impression a clean surface of wipe is drawn over the pad. At its extreme forward position the bed comes to rest immediately over a massive plunger which is forced upwards by a toggle action, thereby raising the bed vertically towards the dab on which the force is mounted.

Sheets are fed in from a pile on the feed-board which is situated on the left of the machine. As the plunger rises, the force presses the paper into the recesses of the engraving. The plunger then descends so that the die-stamped sheet can be withdrawn and placed on the board fitted at the right of the machine.

The Inverted machine (Fig. 10) works on somewhat similar lines, but in order to economize ink and wipe-off paper a scraper blade has been fitted to scrape surplus ink from the face of the die before it is wiped. To facilitate this the die is held face downwards in a carrier which moves between the back and the front of the machine.

After being inked at the backward position of the carrier the die passes over the scraper blade, which is fitted in such a way that the surplus ink runs down the blade and then back to the ink duct. The face-downwards position necessitates, of course, a transposition of the positions of the wiping mechanism and the dab, which are situated below

HAND STAMPING

Fig. 9. *The ink is brushed into the die, and the surplus ink removed from the face by wiping downwards across a sheet of wiping paper.*

MACHINE STAMPING

Fig. 10. *Feeding the Inverted machine, to which an ink scraper is fitted. With this model the paper is fed in face upwards.*

the die instead of above it as in the Standard machine; but this has the advantage of enabling the sheets to be fed face upwards instead of downwards.

Economical Operation

The Inverted machine shows a saving of approximately 75 per cent in ink consumption and from 25 to 50 per cent in wipe-off paper as compared with the Standard machine; but despite this the latter is by no means obsolete. It has distinct advantages for certain classes of work, such as stamping from exceptionally heavy dies, or dies with surface hollows as a result of alterations.

The procedure adopted for setting up dies in both types of machine which have been described is as follows:—

The die is locked into the die-box by means of set screws. A piece of force card large enough to cover the die is gummed on one side and placed gummed side uppermost on top of the die. The machine is allowed to make one impression which squeezes the force card into close contact with the dab, to which it adheres. Approximately equal quantities of ink and varnish are put into the ink duct, which is then allowed to run until the two are thoroughly mixed. The inking roller is adjusted so that it makes contact with the die at the right position to fill the engraving without covering the edges of the steel with ink.

The wiping mechanism is set by means of ratchets so that sufficient, and only just sufficient, length of wipe-off paper is let out at each impression to wipe the die clean.

Pressure is adjusted by means of a hand wheel until just sufficient impression is obtained. It is usual to increase the impression on lightly-engraved areas, such as small lettering, by sticking pieces of gummed tape on the force at these points underneath the force cloth. Brass guides against which the sheets are laid are set so that the stamping falls in the correct position.

A paper mask with an opening just sufficiently large to allow the die and force to meet is pasted over the feed plate; or, in the case of the Inverted machine, on a special holder provided for the purpose.

As die-stamped work takes some time to dry, the stamped sheets are placed in trays with raised edges which can be stacked one on top of another without anything coming into contact with the wet ink. Work is usually dry enough to be knocked up and packed the day after it has been stamped.

Gold and Silver Stamping

The preparatory work is exactly similar to that involved in colour stamping, but as metallic inks are water colours (that is, their base is a mixture of water and gum instead of varnish) it is necessary to use a rubber inking roller, or alternatively to cover the ordinary composition roller with rubber tubing. The work has to be burnished after stamping, and this is done by running it through the machine a second time with copper foil impressed into the engraving in the same way as was described in the case of hand stamping.

When stamping in gold or silver on the Inverted machine only a small quantity of ink should be placed in the duct at any one time. This allows further quantities of fresh ink to be added, as the original supply loses brilliance through being constantly scraped from the die and being returned to the duct.

Die-stamping Difficulties

Feathering is the name given to a ragged, fuzzy impression, one of the commonest defects encountered. It is usually caused by shallow engraving and is accentuated by the use of a paper with a rough surface. The remedy is to deepen the engraving and to use, if possible, a smooth-surface paper.

Flicking is encountered chiefly when stamping rather heavily engraved dies on an Inverted machine. Wisps of ink, looking almost like hairs, appear round the heavier lettering. The trouble arises when the varnish is too tacky, and it usually disappears if a "shorter" varnish is used. It is, however, advisable to avoid stamping from dies with exceptionally heavy engraving when using an Inverted machine.

Cracking. Unless elastic inks and varnish are used die-stamping will crack if the paper is folded across the stamping after it is dry. Unfortunately, elastic varnish takes so long to dry that it is impractical to use it for all classes of work, and in most stamping houses a compromise is reached by using a proportion of elastic varnish when mixing the ink. It is very necessary to do so in cases where one working superimposes another; otherwise the first stamping will crumble away in places.

Spurting. Another very common fault is caused by ink running from a heavily-cut part of the engraving into the etched lines of shading or surface-engraved ornamental work, giving a very blotched and ragged effect. The trouble can be eliminated entirely if, when the die is engraved, the etched lines are stopped just before they reach any deeply-engraved work.

Faulty Register. One of the most frequent causes of bad register is inaccurate cutting of the paper. It is absolutely essential to see that the two edges to which one is laying are at right-angles to each other before starting any register job. Another difficulty which is encountered fairly frequently is caused through the use of excessive pressure in the first working. As a result the paper is expanded very slightly and it is then found that the second working will not fit. This trouble can be avoided if the minimum pressure necessary is used.

CHAPTER TWENTY-THREE

PROCESS ENGRAVING

HALF-TONE AND LINE BLOCKS. ORIGINALS AND DUPLICATES. ELECTROS, STEREOS AND PLASTIC CASTS. PREPARING THE NEGATIVE. PRINTING ON METAL. ETCHING. LINE COLOUR WORK. COLOUR HALF-TONES. THREE- AND FOUR-COLOUR BLOCKS. FINE ETCHING FOR COLOUR. USE OF TRANSFERS. COLLOTYPE PROCESS.

PROCESS engraving is sometimes understood to describe only the methods of producing printing surfaces by means of photographic manipulation, but it actually includes rather more than this. There are ways of reproduction by process in which the camera is quite unnecessary, such as transferring from hand-engraved copper plates, or from designs drawn on starch paper or even upon the metal itself. A knowledge of the principal kinds of process blocks or process plates is essential, and also of the means by which they are usually produced and the class of copy most suitable for each method.

The learner often finds it difficult to distinguish between the main varieties of printing blocks used on letterpress machines for although, broadly speaking, there are only two sorts, viz. *originals* and *duplicates*, there are in fact several kinds of each.

Production of Originals

Original blocks, produced by means of an etching process, are of two kinds, viz. *line* blocks and *half-tone* blocks. The chief difference between line and half-tone is that the line process requires an original in which the printing and non-printing areas are predetermined by the artist's drawing, and no interpretation is needed in their reproduction; whereas the half-tone process has to carry out its own interpretation of light and dark parts by the use of an optical instrument known as the half-tone screen. The illustrations in this book provide examples of line and half-tone blocks.

Half-tone Screen

The screen—a cross-line grating—is interposed between the lens and the sensitized photographic plate, and it automatically breaks up the graduated tones of the picture into dots of varying sizes. The resulting negative consists of large dots in the lighter parts and small dots in the shadows. In this the skill of the operator is paramount, for whether the negative is for the letterpress or the litho process it must have clear glass in those parts which are subsequently to appear in the printed reproduction, and be quite opaque in those parts where no impression is required.

In fact, the basic success of all photo-process work resides with the camera operator, for no amount of manipulation afterwards will replace what is lacking in the negative; and the nearer such a negative approaches the condition of being a photographic stencil the simpler are the ensuing operations and the more certain their achievement.

Besides the two kinds of original blocks, line and half-tone, which have to be handled by the letterpress printer, there are three kinds of duplicates, viz. electros, stereos, and plastic casts. But first let us learn to recognize the original blocks.

The *line block*, or zinco as it is familiarly called, is easily identified by the fact that it is usually of zinc (although it can be of copper for specially fine work). The lines which form the printing surface stand up in bold relief, while the non-printing parts are etched down, the larger non-printing areas being cut away by a routing machine. This ensures that they do not come into contact with the inking rollers or touch the paper sheet while printing is in progress.

The *half-tone block* has a smooth and level surface all over from the lightest parts to the darkest areas, and its detail can be seen only by tilting the block against a source of illumination. Half-tone blocks are usually of copper, but when used for newspapers are nearly always made on zinc, this being more amenable to underlaying or "bumping up" in the darker parts, and it costs less than copper.

Electros and *stereos* are moulded and can be obtained only from an existing block (line or half-tone) or from a forme of type.

A *plastic duplicate* is obtained by taking a mould with a thermo setting powder, of which there are several kinds. A heated hydraulic press is utilized, and when the mould is set, it can be used as a matrix from which one or a number of plastic casts can be retaken. Electros and stereos are heavy plates, but the plastic duplicate has the advantage of possessing very little weight.

There is little or no difference in the printing quality of an original plate, an electro, a stereo, or a plastic cast, although it is claimed for the last named that, being less susceptible to variations of temperature, it has a greater affinity for printing ink. On the other hand, repairs and alterations are more easily effected with original plates and electros, or with stereos, by means of soldering and hand engraving.

Identifying the Block

It is essential that the learner should be able to discriminate between the five kinds of blocks already mentioned, and the suitability of each for the many different types of original from which blocks are made.

Line blocks or *zincos* (short for zincograph) and newspaper half-tones of 50 or 65 screen are made on zinc of about 16 gauge thickness (Birmingham wire gauge).

Half-tones, 75 screen and upwards for catalogues and magazines and book illustrations, are usually made on copper, also about 16 gauge (thickness of a new penny). On the Continent fine-screen half-tones are frequently made on zinc.

Electrotypes (electros, for short) are thicker plates, and consist of a shell of copper backed up with soft metal to a thickness of one-sixth of an inch or 12 point. Electros are sometimes nickel or chromium faced when specially heavy wear on the plate is involved.

Stereotypes (or stereos) are also of 12-point thickness and of white metal throughout; they have no shell but the printing surface is often nickelled for extra wearing quality.

Plastic duplicates may be transparent or opaque, pale in colour or nearly black, according to the variety of thermoplastic powder used, but are easily identified by their extremely

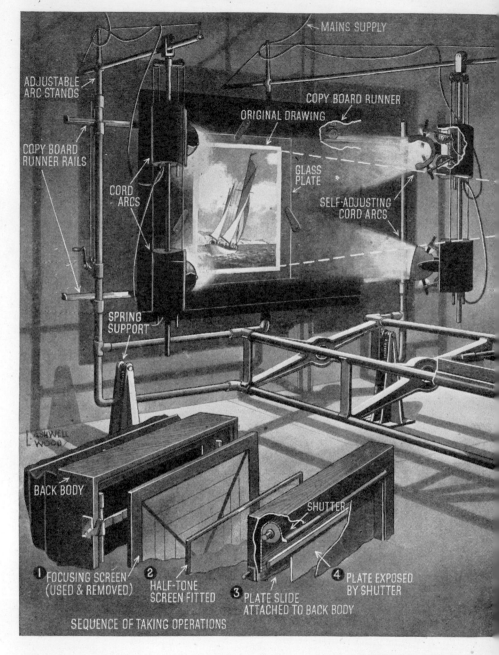

WORKING PARTS OF

Fig. 1. *The copy board and arc lamps are suspended on an iron frame which hangs on spring supports to avoid vibration. The copy board has runners for lateral movement. The arcs are paired, with pulley cords for self-centring, and can be splayed or brought together by the adjustable stand arms to suit the size of the original. The white dotted lines show the path*

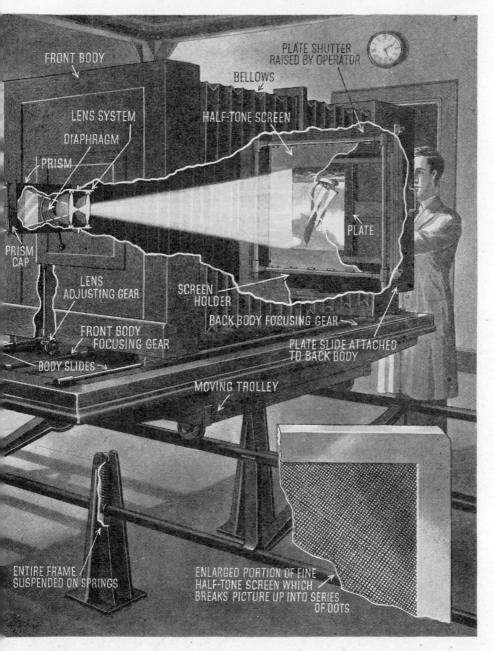

FRONT BODY

PLATE SHUTTER
RAISED BY OPERATOR

BELLOWS

LENS SYSTEM

HALF-TONE SCREEN

DIAPHRAGM

PRISM

PLATE

PRISM
CAP

LENS
ADJUSTING GEAR

SCREEN
HOLDER

BACK BODY FOCUSING GEAR

FRONT BODY
FOCUSING GEAR

PLATE SLIDE ATTACHED
TO BACK BODY

BODY SLIDES

MOVING TROLLEY

ENTIRE FRAME
SUSPENDED ON SPRINGS

ENLARGED PORTION OF FINE
HALF-TONE SCREEN WHICH
BREAKS PICTURE UP INTO SERIES
OF DOTS

A PROCESS CAMERA

of the reflected light, from copy to lens system, being reversed by the prism; it passes through the lens diaphragm, and on to the half-tone screen where the image is broken up into dots on the sensitive plate. The drawing also shows construction of back body of the camera, with screen gear and plate slide with roller shutter. An enlargement of the screen is also shown.

P.T.G.—I*

light weight. Their thickness is usually about half-way between 16 gauge and 12 point, but it is preferable they should be 12 point so that they may be interchangeable with metal stereos for mounting on the same base. Plastic plates, which are made of thermo setting material, are also in use.

Character of Copy

The most suitable copy for line work consists of line drawings or prints, proofs from type, transfers from copper plates, drawings done on starch paper, lithographic transfers, and artists' work drawn direct on zinc.

Copy suitable for half-tone consists of wash drawings, oil and water-colour paintings, photographs, including monochrome and colour work from flat surfaces; also fabrics and similar materials which can be successfully reproduced direct from the object.

Preparing the Negative

The first operation in the making of a line block is to take a photograph of the original on a photographic plate. This is called making a line negative, and it can be done either by the wet-

Fig. 2. *Right-angled mirror for correcting the reversal. It contains an optically flat piece of glass, silvered on its surface.*

plate or dry-plate method, using a process camera (Fig. 1). The image becomes reversed when passing through the lens so the photographic result is backward or reversed left to right. To overcome this, the negative film is stripped off the glass and turned over on another glass so that it reassumes the position of the copy.

Alternatively, an optical prism (Fig. 1) or a right-angled mirror (Fig. 2) is used in the camera to correct the reversal and bring the image right way round. Another way for line work only is to place the sensitive plate in the camera with its glass towards the lens (this is not possible with half-tone because of the screen adjustment).

Printing on Metal

A piece of metal, usually zinc, of 16 gauge, is chemically cleaned and coated with a sensitive emulsion of albumen and ammonium bichromate, evenly flowed and dried on a whirler (Fig. 3). The line negative is placed in contact with this coated metal in a process printing frame.

Heavy pressure forces the metal into thorough contact with the line negative, and the frame with negative and coated metal is exposed to the printing light, either sunlight or electric arc lamp (Fig. 1).

The light passes through the transparent parts of the negative and affects the bichromated albumen so as to render it insoluble. The dark opaque parts of the negative keep the light from the emulsion so that it is not affected in those masked parts, which remain perfectly soluble.

The frame having been opened in subdued light, to prevent further light action on the sensitive emulsion, the printed sheet of metal is removed from the printing frame and coated with etching ink. After this ink has been evenly and smoothly distributed over the entire surface with a composition roller, the plate is developed by immersion in water. This slowly dissolves the soluble albumen which washes off, taking its covering of ink with it. The insoluble (light-hardened) parts of the image, with their ink top, adhere to the metal and eventually become the acid-resist of the plate.

The metal plate now has on it a reproduction of the original copy and is called a zinc print. The image on the metal is now backward or reversed in position; that is, it is left to right.

The dried zinc print is covered with a bituminous powder, and this is dusted off leaving a

METAL PRINTING

Fig. 3. Coating a copper plate with a sensitized emulsion. A contact print will be made of this from the "screen negative." Note the centrifugal whirler attached to the plate by means of a suction bulb, enabling the plate to be dried face downwards over a gas ring.

"topping layer" adhering to the greasy image. When heated to a proper temperature this powder melts and becomes the acid-resisting top which protects the image, while the bare parts of the metal are etched (Fig. 5).

The modern practice is to use a vacuum frame for printing down. This frame has several advantages over the older type of screw frame (Fig. 4).

The printing frame has a flat base on which lies a blanket of rubber. This blanket is attached on one corner to a motor suction pump by means of a tube. The glass in the frame may be hinged, or it may be entirely separated as shown in Fig. 4 on page 268, so that when the negative and metal are placed in contact the glass is brought down on the negative and the metal. The motor is then started up, the air between glass and metal being sucked out, thus causing a vacuum which results in perfect contact of metal and negative without

VACUUM PRINTING FRAME AND PUMP

Fig. 4. *The cover glass is raised to show the rubber bed on which the sensitized metal is laid with negative on top. The cover comes down and is fastened by lever hooks, making it airtight.*

resist. As the acid eats the metal away sideways as well as downwards there is always the danger that it will underbite the image. This is called undercutting and is prevented only by careful handling on the part of the etcher after the first stage or bite. Electric etching is now in use in many process houses (Fig. 6).

When the plate has been etched to the proper depth without injury in the first bath, the acid is washed off, the plate dried and the sides of the image, now in slight relief, are dusted with another resinous powder called dragon's blood. This latter is melted by heat and forms a resist on the sides of the parts now standing in relief, thereby protecting them against undercutting during the next acid bite. This procedure is repeated for each bite until the plate has reached sufficient depth. The resist is then cleaned off, the top lightly rolled and the plate given a finishing bath to remove all roughness.

In order to get greater depth in the larger areas, as well as to remove excess metal, the plate is routed. This is done on a routing machine with a high-speed milling tool which cuts the waste metal clean away (Fig. 8).

The plate is now inked with a roller and printing ink, and proofs are taken

pressure. This minimizes any danger of breakage of negatives.

Another advantage is that a number of prints from other negatives can be made at the same time, and if necessary with different gauge metals. A further great advantage of this frame is that when making line and tone combination prints, the metal being face up, the second negative can be more easily registered to the first print.

Etching

The plate is placed in a rocking tray or splash-etching machine with a solution of nitric acid, which attacks the metal except where protected by the

LINE ETCHERS WORKING ON A HOT PLATE

Fig. 5. *In line etching the art is to protect the "sides" of lines from under-biting during etching. This is done by rolling and dusting the plates with dragon's blood which, when heated, runs slightly and forms a protective shoulder round the lines of the design.*

ELECTRIC ETCHING

Fig. 6. *The plates are hung on the copper bars. This method is the reverse of the copper-plating process in which copper is deposited on the mould. In electric etching the copper in the exposed portions of the plate is disintegrated by the electric current.*

FINE ETCHING AS A CRAFT

Fig. 7. *After giving an initial rough etch the fine etcher protects parts of the plate with a resist which will prevent these parts from becoming further lightened in subsequent etching baths, or alternatively he can apply etching solution by means of a brush to lighten certain parts of the plate locally without affecting the rest of the plate.*

from the inked plate by hand press. The plate is then mounted to bring it up to type height ready for the printing machine. In cases where the etched plate is not to be printed from, but only required as an original from which moulds may be taken for electrotyping, stereotyping or plastic duplicates, it need not be fully routed, but should preferably retain its surround or waste metal areas, for use as a strengthening support during moulding.

The Half-tone Plate

A half-tone is made in a similar manner, but as the copy is composed of tones instead of lines it has to be translated in the camera. For this purpose a screen is used. This consists of two sheets of plate glass covered with ruled black lines, and cemented together with the lines at right angles to each other, the intersections thus making a mesh or grating. This is brought up close to the sensitive photographic plate by a mechanism in the camera (Figs. 1 and 9).

On exposure to the original, this screen, under the necessary conditions, translates the half-tones into dots of varying sizes, large in the highest lights and smallest in the shadows, while the dots in the intervening tones vary in size according to the intensity of light reflected from each part of the copy.

The difference between an ordinary photographic negative and a screen-process negative is important and may be defined as follows: an ordinary photographic negative is a continuous record of even character but uneven density, and a screen negative is a record of uneven character and even density. Stripping the film or otherwise rectifying the reversal left to right applies in half-tone in exactly the same way as in line work.

The metal, usually copper, is covered with a coating of bichromated fish glue, dried and placed in contact with the half-tone negative in a printing frame in the same manner as line work and exposed to light, but the print is developed without rolling up or covering with etching ink. The glue itself forms a top consisting of dots and solids, which act as an acid-resist without the use of topping powder. After development, the image, now called a copper print, is heated (burned in) until the glue becomes a hard enamel capable of resisting the etching solution.

The etching solution is perchloride of iron, which dissolves the metal away between the dots, leaving the dots standing in relief where protected by the glue top.

An alternative to the fish glue top is a solution of shellac

called a cold enamel, of which there are two or three kinds sold ready prepared. These cold-printing solutions are usually recommended for zinc work, as they do not require burning in, and thus they avoid the danger of a high temperature injuring the zinc, a metal easily made brittle by excessive heat.

Fine etching is a term applied to local treatment of the half-tone plate whereby certain parts are staged or protected with an acid-resisting varnish, such as bitumen in benzol, shellac in methylated spirit, or lithographic ink thinned with turpentine. This is prepared by the

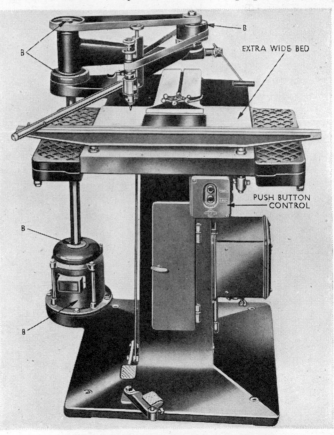

BALL-BEARING ROUTING MACHINE

Fig. 8. *The lever arm carrying the cutter moves upon a frontal support which is raised or lowered by means of the pedal which is shown.* B *Shows where ball-bearings are fitted.*

Fig. 9. *Enlargement of a ruled half-tone screen showing the usual 1 : 1 proportion of black line to white space.*

worker, who usually has his own favourite formula. The covering is applied with a sable brush and requires considerable artistic skill to avoid crudities. When the varnish is dry the plate is re-immersed in the etching bath to lighten the unprotected areas, by reducing the sizes of the dots.

Fine etching may also be done without re-immersion by applying the etching fluid locally to certain parts of the plate with a brush, and sponging off as soon as the dots have been sufficiently reduced. By these means fine tones are preserved and detail is emphasized or a poor original improved (Fig. 7).

Line Colour Work

From ordinary black-and-white reproduction to colour blockmaking is not such a wide step as might be imagined, for very little additional apparatus is needed. Let us take line work as an example and assume that we have a coloured drawing consisting of a black outline filled in with flat colour tints, this being a typical coloured original as handed to the blockmaker.

The first step is to separate the key outline from the colours, and if these are of a mixed quality it is rarely possible to do this photographically. The more straightforward method is to make a key tracing. From this tracing a negative is made to the required size and a zinc plate is etched. Using the same negative, bichromate prints are made on bright zinc, and these are slightly etched in a very dilute one per cent nitric acid bath, which dulls the metal surface on all parts not covered by the ink-albumen image.

The plate is then cleaned with a non-greasy solvent, leaving the design in bright outline on a matt ground ready for the artist to paint in the colour portions with lithographic ink. This is repeated using a print for each colour as required. If the coloured areas are not all solid, that is to say if there are some parts of lighter tone, these are outlined with gum and an inked film is used (Ben Day tinting medium) by which a tint of dots or lines may be laid on the metal. The gum is then removed by water and the plate is ready for the etcher (see Colour Section).

Colour Half-tone

Under this category are included all fully coloured originals, such as watercolours, oil paintings and also natural colour photographs taken direct from the object, such as flowers, furniture, textiles, carpets and manufactured articles of every description. Most of these can be handled in the photo-engraver's studio, but for outdoor scenes, art gallery work, motor-cars and other large objects it is necessary to use a triple-shot colour camera, or a camera with a sliding back to make three exposures in quick succession through the tricolour filters, blue-violet, green and red. By this means negative records are obtained which are used for the yellow, red and blue printings respectively (see Colour Section).

In colour half-tone work the skill of the photographic operator is most important, and many safeguards and

PRIMARY PIGMENT COLOURS AND COLOUR GRADATION

The three primary pigment colours: yellow, red and blue, may be used in combination to form a wide variety of shades. Where the three colours completely overlap, as in the centre of the top diagram, the result is black. While a fair black result is possible by the three-colour process, a greatly improved effect is obtainable by the addition of a black printing, as shown in the example of four-colour work in this Section. The three-colour process is widely used, and has played an important part in the development of Publicity printing.

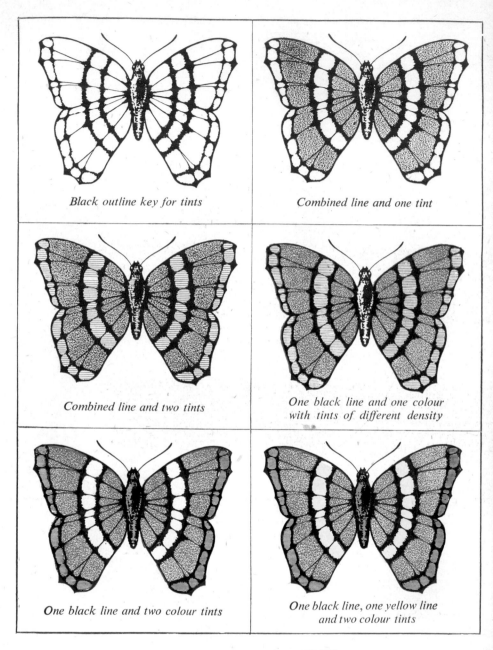

Black outline key for tints

Combined line and one tint

Combined line and two tints

One black line and one colour
with tints of different density

One black line and two colour tints

One black line, one yellow line
and two colour tints

USE OF MECHANICAL TINTS

Effective variations of tone are obtained by the use of mechanical tints, both in black and white and in colour. The above illustrations show two of the many mechanical tints available. Line colour work lends itself to a great variety of purposes. From an ordinary black and white original the blockmaker can produce colour blocks by the use of mechanical tints, provided that a general colour guide is supplied to indicate the nature of the tints.

FOUR-COLOUR LINE AND TINT WORK

An example of line work printed in black, yellow, red and blue. Note the effect of the superimposing of various tints, such as the yellow and blue, resulting in a pleasing green shade, and the purple obtained by means of the red and blue. By the combined use of tints and solids in line colour work attractive effects may be obtained, even when printed on a paper of which the finish is unsuitable for half-tone work with a fine screen.

"DUPLEX" HALF-TONE WORK

An extra colour, overprinted on an ordinary black and white half-tone illustration, greatly enhances the pictorial effect. The plate for the colour tint is made by the blockmaker from an ordinary monochrome photograph. The colour of ink used for the tint is selected to suit the subject, as in the above sunset effect, printed with the red used in this Section.

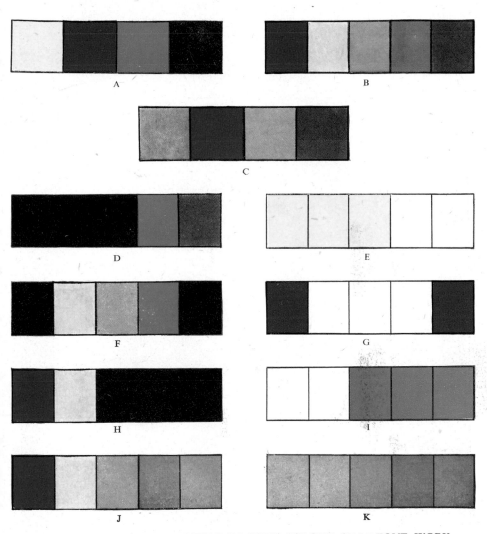

FUNCTION OF LIGHT FILTERS IN FOUR-COLOUR HALF-TONE WORK

(A) *Printing colours: yellow, crimson, blue and black.* (B) *Order of the colours in the spectrum.* (C) *Filter colours: amber, red, green and violet.* (D) *Yellow negative, showing violet filter absorption.* (E) *Positive printing plate, yellow.* (F) *Red negative, showing green filter absorption.* (G) *Positive printing plate, red.* (H) *Blue negative, showing red filter absorption.* (I) *Positive printing plate, blue.* (J) *Black negative, showing amber filter absorption.* (K) *Positive printing plate, black.*

COLOUR ISOLATION AND DIFFUSION

Each of the two panels contains the same amount of red. In the squares it is isolated and in the screen diffused. (From a study by Mr. F. Birren in the "American Printer.")

FOUR-COLOUR HALF-TONE WORK,

A good example of the infinite variation in colour obtainable from four printings (black, yellow, red and blue) in half-tone. The illustration on the right-hand page shows the

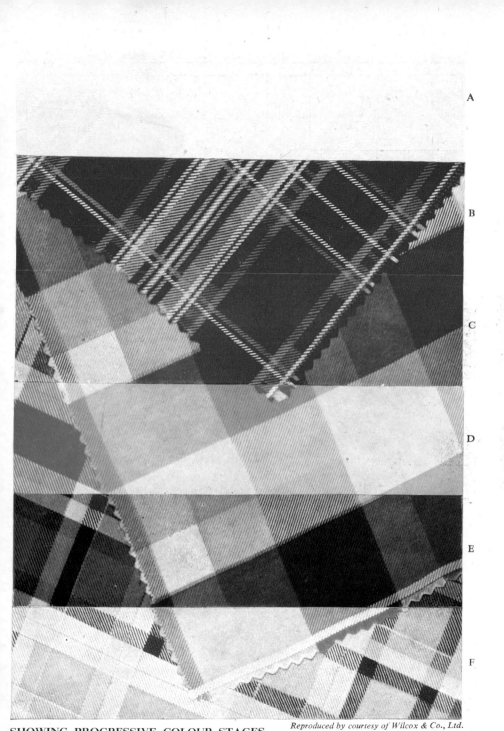

SHOWING PROGRESSIVE COLOUR STAGES

Reproduced by courtesy of Wilcox & Co., Ltd.

progressive stages of each colour block, as well as the combined effects as the colours over-lap. (A) *Yellow.* (B) *Red.* (C) *Red on yellow.* (D) *Blue.* (E) *Blue on red and yellow.* (F) *Black.*

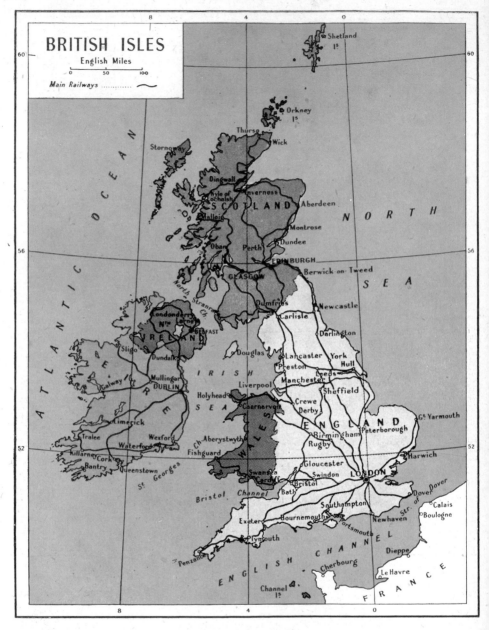

LETTERPRESS MAP PRINTING IN COLOUR

A politically-coloured map of the British Isles printed from line blocks in black, yellow, red and blue. Although most map printing in colour is carried out by offset litho, increasing use of letterpress blocks is being made for map work. The black key for this further example of line colour work was made from a geographical draughtsman's black and white drawing. The colour blocks were produced from the draughtsman's rough colour guide.

tests have to be incorporated in the process. Exposures and development of the three negatives must be very exact as to time and temperature so as to maintain equal density of the tonal range in each negative.

To prevent any dominance of one colour upsetting the balance, one such safeguard is to introduce a neutral graded tone-strip in the margin of the view, and to compare the result in all three plates. With colour work done direct, at the engraver's premises, it is usual, with suitable originals, to incorporate the half-tone screen with the colour exposures and thus save one set of operations, viz. the necessity of making a set of continuous-tone positives from the colour negatives, as with the indirect method. Time is also saved.

With certain coloured originals, which have a medium range of colour tones, it is possible to obtain by two-colour half-tone a pleasing result imitating the three-colour process to some extent. The filters used for the purpose are a modification of the standard tricolour set, and they are chosen by the operator according to the prevailing colours appearing in the original. The printing inks are generally paired so as to be complementary to each other, viz. red and green, orange and blue, yellow and mauve, any such pairs giving a black impression where the solids overlap, as well as a fair range of colour tones in between.

If the colour drawings are, however, specially made to suit the two-colour process, and the range of colour tones is

HAND ENGRAVING ON A HALF-TONE BLOCK
The engraver tools portions of a block that are to appear dead white. He also touches up any blemishes which may appear on the block, and trims the edges.

50   55

60   65

75   85

100   120

HALF-TONE SCREENS

Screens 50-65 are suitable for news stock and cheap printing papers. Screens 75-120 are used for machine-finished, super-calendered and imitation art papers. 100 screen is used for the half-tones in the text of this book, and 150 screen for the Colour Section half-tones.

not too extensive, a very good result is obtained by complete colour separation; retouching and deep etching, or hand engraving parts away on each plate is necessary to ensure clean colours and increased brilliance in the final reproduction.

Three-colour and Four-colour Half-tone

This process, the most scientific of all photo-engraving procedure, is based upon the theory that white light consists of three primary sensations: red, green and blue. If three exposures be made on panchromatic plates using each of these colours as filters, a set of negatives recording together all the light reflected from the original is obtained (see Colour Section).

Positives of these records placed in a triple-projection lantern together with the filters through which they were taken, and superimposed, will *additively* produce all the colours of the original up to pure white. Alternatively, if made into half-tone blocks and printed in the complementary inks, yellow, magenta, and blue-green, they will *subtract* the reflected light from white paper in the opposite

(Top) Diagram showing half-tone print on metal, indicating the size of the dots at the commencement of etching. (Below) Half-tone plate in its final stage with the reduced size of black dots after etching, showing the reduced size of high-light dots and the opening-up of the tones near the shadows.

way, to give all colours and varying tones down to solid black.

A fourth working in black is frequently used with the three-colour process. The original is given a full exposure through a yellow filter, using a panchromatic plate (or perhaps an infra-red plate), the idea being to obtain maximum density in all the colour areas with transparency in the black parts only. The block for the black printing acts as a key outline and helps to compensate for any lack of registration in the colour printings, besides covering up garishness in the reproduction.

The Direct Method

The original, such as a water-colour drawing, together with a pair of register marks, a neutral graded strip and a colour chart are fastened on the copy board. The colour chart consists of three patches of the standard three-colour printing inks, yellow, magenta, and blue-green. This chart is used for identifying the three colour-separation negatives.

To ensure that there is no alteration in the definition of the image it is better to focus through one of the filters, the K3 yellow (fourth printer) filter being the most suitable. The stop and screen distance remain constant for the three colour exposures, but the angles of the screen ruling are not the same for each negative. Cross line screens are supplied ruled at suitable angles to avoid moiré or pattern, which appears if the dots cross each other at acute angles, or alternatively a circular screen, fixed in a holder, may be used; this permits of the screen being rotated to the desired angles for each colour.

Sometimes a large rectangular screen ruled at 45 deg. is employed for all the negatives, but this necessitates a copy board that can be rotated; thus the original, instead of the screen, is turned

to the correct angle. For three-colour work the angles are generally spaced 30 deg. apart, i.e. yellow printer 75 deg., magenta 15 deg., and blue printer 45 deg. For four-colour reproduction the angles are: yellow printer 90 deg., magenta 15 deg., blue 75 deg., black 45 deg. It should be noted that the strong colours are spaced 30 deg. apart and the lighter colour, yellow, 15 deg. from the red and blue. When the negatives are dry they should be checked to ensure that they register before printing on the metal.

When dealing with ordinary halftone work a good original can be tackled without much fine etching; but in colour reproduction, owing to the inherent drawbacks of filter separation, and the lack of inks of the correct shades, the personal element cannot be omitted, and the skill of the colour etcher is an indispensable factor in endeavouring to obtain facsimile results.

Fine Etching for Colour

Staging of the plate, by covering up certain parts to hold extra colour while allowing other parts to continue etching, is effected as in black-and-white work. Some dots are thus caused to retain their full area, while others are reduced in size, thereby carrying more or less colour in the final printing.

Colour etching is a very delicate operation requiring considerable experience, but a colour chart showing the proportionate size of the dots in each plate, which will produce any colour mixture, is available. One of these, by the technical staff of the School of Photo-Engraving, Bolt Court, London, is a very effective guide in colour reproduction, and an indispensable help in carrying out revisions after first proofing. It is also useful for "dot etching on the negative," a method lately adopted in photo-litho work where the size of the dots cannot be altered once the image is on the metal. Many firms have their own colour charts.

With the indirect method, where a set of positives has to be made from the colour-separation negatives, the colour correction may be done by dye-retouching or pencil work on these positives. Skill and judgment are needed in deciding how much tone can be added to a positive to carry the right amount of ink when printed in the corresponding colour.

Sometimes it is desired to make one or more colour printings to work with another block, which may be a line or half-tone. The usual practice is to have proofs made in transfer ink on India or Scotch retransfer paper, using a hand press for pulling the proofs. Or it may be that a letterpress block is required from a hand-engraved intaglio copper plate, in which case a copper plate press is used.

Another example would be that of a design, already laid down on stone for lithographic printing, which is required for letterpress printing. In this case the transfer would be pulled on the litho press.

Alternatively, the artist draws his design direct upon the retransfer paper which may be of smooth or grained texture, using in the first place a pen or brush, and in the latter case litho crayon.

A transfer being obtained, whether proofed or drawn, the next step is to have it slightly damped by sponging the reverse side of the sheet, or by laying it between moist blotting paper. The zinc plate is chemically cleaned and the

PLATE BEVELLING

The finished plate has a flange cut round it through which pins are driven for fixing the plate to the mounting material (wood or metal). The etched plate is held down by a wide clamp on the sliding bed which conveys it past a high-speed cutting wheel.

damped transfer laid thereon, using a soft roller or squeegee to avoid air bells. The whole is pulled through a hand press to establish close contact; it is then allowed to stand awhile for evaporation of moisture.

The back is then thoroughly wetted until the paper can be readily peeled off, the whole of the work having adhered to the metal. The transfer can then be rolled with lithographic ink and powdered with bitumen as for relief etching, or the surface can be rendered matt in a weak bath, and cleaned off leaving the bright image for the artist to paint in the parts required.

COLLOTYPE

COLLOTYPE is a photographic method of producing a printing surface in gelatine, by which a picture in tones may be reproduced without the use of the half-tone screen.

Although it cannot be generally considered as a suitable method for very long runs, beautiful work can be done by its means. The process is sometimes used for the reproduction of objects of art and with lithography as a reinforcing medium for coloured subjects.

The absence of the ruled screen gives collotype its great advantage in subjects requiring the finest detail, the half-tone interpretation being achieved by a natural reticulation (wrinkling of surface, producing crossed-line appearance) of the gelatine film which is almost invisible.

Describing the collotype process, Mr. L. P. Clerc in the Ilford Manual of Process Work, 1940, says: "The process of printing from bichromated gelatine, carrying greasy inks, was devised, about 1860, by Poitevin, who called it photolithography, and the process was introduced industrially in 1867, under the name of *phototypie* by du Motay and Maréchal, who substituted planed and polished copper plates for the lithographic stone which Poitevin employed.

"Shortly afterwards, Albert substituted a glass plate for the supports previously used. Numerous improvements: a silicate underlayer, oven heating, a supplementary exposure through the back, and the use of glycerine for wetting, were successively introduced by various workers.

"Under ordinary practical conditions a thick glass plate, which has been carefully ground flat and grained, is coated with a layer of silicate to ensure adhesion of the sensitive layer, covered with bichromated gelatine, and dried in the oven. The gelatine reticulates and hardens during this heating operation, becoming much harder and more sensitive at the centre of each of the granulations than at the edges.

"In this condition the glass plate is exposed to light under a reversed negative, and then exposed liberally for a few seconds through the back to make the gelatine adhere more firmly to the support by diminishing its swelling; excess bichromate is removed by prolonged washing.

"After drying, the gelatine is impregnated with a mixture of water and glycerine, which causes the gelatine to

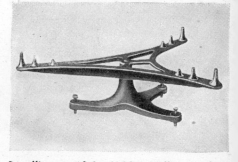

Levelling stand for holding collotype plates while they are being coated with emulsion.

swell in places which were protected from the action of light by density in the negative; the plate is then placed in position in the printing press. The greasy inks adhere only to the dry part of the gelatine and the distribution of sensitivity within each granulation in the reticulated gelatine is responsible for converting the full tone image of the negative into an irregular grain half-toned image."

In modern collotype printing a sheet of glass, not less than $\frac{5}{8}$ in. thick and larger than the picture, is used, the surface being finely ground by means of wet emery powder. Usually two plates are placed one above the other with emery and water between. The plates are rotated until a fine and uniformly-ground surface is produced, when they are washed clean and dried. The plates are then given a coating of albumen and waterglass, then dried and heated.

Oven in which the collotype plate is slowly dried by means of a gas heater below the oven.

Each plate is now coated with a solution of gelatine and potassium bichromate, the glass being placed on the levelling screws of a drying oven containing hot water or steam pipes which will permit the plate to be dried by heat. Drying is by evaporation from the liquid gelatine—the film does not set in the first instance.

The choice of gelatine is important and so are the conditions of drying—temperature and rate. The plate must be allowed to cool slowly after heating.

The plate is now exposed to light under a suitable negative. Collotype plates printed under negatives having strong contrasts are seldom satisfactory. After exposure, the negative is removed and the exposed plate plunged into cold water and washed until free from the remaining potassium bichromate, when the film will be colourless. The

Filtering container by which the solution is kept at the correct temperature for coating the plate. It can be heated by means of gas or spirit burners placed underneath.

plate, after development, is dried. When it is to be printed, which may be by hand on the press or by power at the machine, the plate is made level and is covered with a mixture of water, glycerine and ammonia.

This solution is absorbed, and the film now swells and in time becomes damp in different degrees according to the exposure received.

The press employed for hand printing is practically the same as a scraper litho press, but is generally made with better adjustments, and there is provided an iron bedplate with sliding plates and screws for clamping. A power machine is similar in character to a litho machine, but the rolling and damping arrangements are different.

In collotype printing it is not easy to maintain the uniform moisture conditions which control gradation. Many experiments have been made to overcome the difficulty, while retaining the advantages of collotype: the ease of plate preparation and the cheapness.

In one successful process a finely-grained zinc plate is thinly coated with bichromated gelatine and printed under a screen negative which may have been made with a very fine ruling, say, 400 lines per inch. After exposure the plate is washed out and printed damp. Here the gradation depends on dot area, and the conditions for successful printing are more easily maintained (Aquatone).

In one application of the collotype principle a celluloid film base is used.

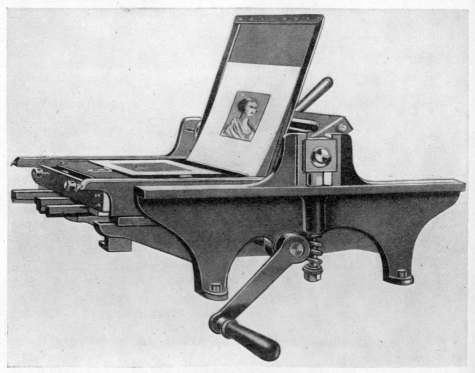

COLLOTYPE PROOF PRESS

The bed is shown with collotype plate clamped down. The proof just taken is leaning against the tympan, and the impression lever in the background is at the "off" position. Pressure is adjustable by means of the spring and nut on each side.

CHAPTER TWENTY-FOUR

SETTING UP A SMALL PROCESS PLANT

CAPITAL OUTLAY. LABOUR COSTS. STUDIO EQUIPMENT. LAYOUT PLAN. THE DARK ROOM. CAMERA WORK. LIGHTING ARRANGEMENTS. SUPPLY OF MATERIALS.

THE question is frequently raised as to whether the setting up of a process plant, independently or perhaps in conjunction with a newspaper or printing establishment, is a feasible and worth-while proposition. Let us therefore look at the possibilities from a number of different angles, e.g. capital outlay; labour required for working; space available; amount already being spent in the buying of blocks from commercial photo-engravers; and any scope for expanding the use of such products in one's own business.

Taking the last-named item as a basis for argument it will be well to remember that labour represents at least half of the cost of the photo-engraver's product. Evidence of this can be found in a brochure, published by the Federation of Master Process Engravers, entitled "Process Engravings and their Cost," which gives the following figures as revealed by the balance sheets of a representative process firm established for a number of years:—

				Per cent
Salaries and wages	..	..	..	54·6
Materials	..	..	..	9·5
Rent, rates and taxes, electric light, power and gas		..	..	5·0
Discount	..	..	..	7·3
Income tax and insurances		..	..	2·2
All other expenses	..	..	..	11·1
Depreciation	..	..	..	1·5
Procuring business, travellers, advertising, etc.		..	..	7·5
Net profit	..	..	..	1·3
				100

The brochure also states: "Details may vary slightly in different firms but the essential difference in the calculation lies in salaries and wages, which in no case can be less than 50 per cent and in most cases is considerably more."

The percentage of profit may appear small, but since the value of a process business is turned over on average three times within a year, the total profit available brings in 4 per cent on the annual turnover.

It may be suspected that these figures are special pleading, but as an employing photo-engraver, the present writer is able to confirm them as a result of twenty years' experience, and their inclusion in this volume may be useful to some others as food for thought, or as an example wherewith to check working balance sheets where a photo-engraving department has started.

Minimum Process Plant

The smallest conceivable process plant would be that of a provincial newspaper making its own engravings, say a full page of illustrations every week, costing about £25 if purchased from an engraving firm. From the foregoing list of percentages we know that half of this, viz. £12 10s., represents wages of the staff, so we can only budget for say one man and an assistant. Not a very safe position, for if the man should fall ill then the help of an engraving firm would again be required; but such an arrangement has been successful in cases where the proprietors have been able to obtain the services of an all-round worker.

Assuming that it is possible to engage a man with a complete knowledge of all the operations of process engraving, and also a lad from one of the technical schools who has some knowledge of photographic work, and is willing to be bound as an apprentice, here is the nucleus for running a small process plant.

A news plant of small dimensions could be installed for about £1,500 capital outlay. This limited amount is assuming that the work will be of one kind only, viz. zinc half-tones of coarse screen, unmounted plates, such as would be used in a local newspaper. If copper is introduced and a variety of screen rulings, together with a mounting department using woodworking machinery, the cost of plant would be approximately doubled, and further labour would be necessary.

Essential Equipment

Keeping ourselves to the local newspaper department, however, let us consider the chief items of engraving plant and the smallest space needed for working it in a healthy manner, using either wet-plate or dry-plate methods.

Studio Equipment. Process camera taking 15 × 12 plates; half-tone screen, 50 lines per inch; lens and prism; spring stand and copy board; pair of arc lamps; dark room with safelights; retouching desk; work benches; dipping baths; flat troughs; 2 slate sinks 6 × 3 × 1 ft.; and a drying cupboard.

Metal Printing. Treadle guillotine for metal; whirler and stove; arc lamp and table; sink 6 × 3 × 1 ft.; 2 printing frames 15 × 12 in.; working bench; flat troughs.

Etching and Finishing. Etching machine and rocking bath; burning-in stove; 6-ft. sink; hot plate; dusting box; work bench; cooling slab; cleaning trough; routing machine; metal shoot plane; tooling bench; hand press for proofs.

Other essential items would have to be provided: dishes for developing and intensifying; inking slabs; hand rollers; brushes for varnishing and powdering and for etching and cleaning off; also an engraver's sandbag and engraving tools, ruling pens, spirit and turps cans.

The equipment would also include steel rule and T-square for lining-up; magnifiers; scales; weights and measuring glasses; basins and funnels for glue; hammers and punches for corrections.

Layout for small Process Plant

The floor space required for comfortable working would be 600-700 sq. ft., which could be arranged as shown in Fig. 1.

In studying Fig. 1 there are certain points to be observed, viz. all drainage is on the darker side of the premises only, and the work which requires most light, such as etching and engraving, is all on the other side. Although the camera stand is only 15 ft. long there should be double the distance available as shown, in case of an outsize job requiring excessive reduction.

The copy board position, at right-angles to the windows, is very important in order to avoid bright reflections when photographing glossy surfaced copies, or prints pressed under glass for flatness.

All sinks should be made of slate about 1 in. in thickness, of slabs bolted together, seated in flexible bitumen. The inside measurements should be 6 × 3 × 1 ft.

The Dark Room. Although the plan gives 15 × 6 ft. this should be taken as a minimum size, and a little extra would be of great advantage, especially

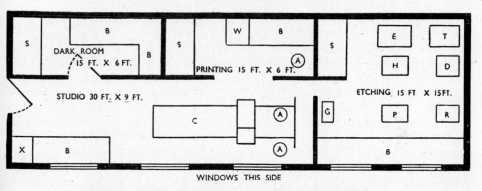

LAYOUT FOR A SMALL PROCESS DEPARTMENT

Fig. 1. *The floor space is between 600 and 700 sq. ft.* (A) *Arc lamps;* (B) *work benches;* (C) *camera;* (D) *dusting box;* (E) *etching machine;* (G) *guillotine;* (H) *hotplate;* (P) *proof press;* (R) *router;* (S) *slate sinks 6 ft.× 3 ft.× 1 ft.;* (T) *trough;* (W) *whirler;* (X) *retouching desk.*

when working wet collodion, where the fumes of ether may cause discomfort. In any case good ventilation and equable temperature are important with either wet- or dry-plate methods and a constant 65 deg. F. is best. It is also advisable that the tank for the water supply should be inside the building where it is not subject to extremes of summer heat or winter cold. Certain developers are affected by change of temperature. *Hydrokinone* is the most popular for dry-plate work, but if too warm it will fog and if too cold it will refuse to act.

The safelight should be of ample proportions and it is well if it can be fitted with three alternative safelights: orange for wet collodion and bromide work, ruby for rapid dry-plates, green for panchromatic plates.

Modern practice tends to dispense with a door to the dark room and substitute instead a light-trapped entrance, but this means more space and there are drawbacks in a small studio, owing to the possible entry of dust from other parts of the shop.

Fixing baths of the upright dipping variety with cover are best, and if facility for draining the fixed plate into

the bath is provided it will obviate waste and help the recovery of silver. Hyposulphite of soda should not be splashed about because it may cause spots in the negatives, and it will eat its way through a brick wall.

A camera for photo-mechanical reproduction work normally consists of three upright frames of mahogany separated by two substantial bellows. These frames are supported upon a rigid base and are moved by rack and pinion or central screw for focusing, the whole mounted upon a carriage which travels along a runway. The carriage is made with a turntable movement enabling the camera to be used either sideways with mirror or prism for reversing left to right as in letterpress and collotype, or facing the copy without reversal as in photo-litho offset (see pages 264 and 265).

The runway, constructed as a unit together with copy board, is either suspended from above by four ropes or hung by coiled springs to a floor stand; this is to counteract possible vibration from machinery or traffic in the vicinity affecting the building, which would cause lack of sharpness in the negatives.

Vibration is a drawback specially to

be guarded against because, although an inexperienced photographer might hardly notice it when reproducing views, portraits or ordinary objects, if asked to copy a lace curtain would find himself faced with an impossible task, for the mesh of the fabric would disappear even in slight vibration and show nothing but a smooth tone. For this reason it is also advisable that the arc lamps used for lighting the original should not be attached to the copy board but supported independently, for they may require attention during an exposure, and can then be adjusted without risk of jarring the camera.

Lighting the Camera. The question of a main supply of electricity is important and if this is lacking, as it may be in country districts, then the provision of a generating set of between 8 and 10 h.p. is envisaged with storage batteries strong enough to run two 15-ampere arc lamps for the camera and one 30-ampere arc for printing down. This would involve further considerable capital outlay.

Illuminating the Copy Board

Three different varieties of electric light are at present in use for illuminating the copy board—arc lamps, mercury vapour lamps and gas-filled (half-watt) incandescent lamps. For operating the wet collodion process the arc lamp is indispensable, but if using dry-plates gas-filled incandescent lamps are quite suitable, requiring little or no attention. Four lamps of 1,000 watts, two on each side of the copy, would be needed giving approximately 8,000 candle power.

Arc lamps for ordinary black-and-white line and half-tone work may be of the enclosed kind using solid carbons rich in ultra-violet; but if colour work is contemplated the arcs should be of the open kind with white-flame cored

carbons, giving a more extended spectrum. In either case the current required for each lamp would be 10 to 15 amperes.

Mercury vapour lamps, formerly not very popular owing to the narrow spectrum emitted, have been lately much improved by the incorporating of fluorescent material within the tubes. This approximates a daylight effect, but they are more suitable for the etching room, where they are not subjected to repeated switching on and off.

Where a main supply of electricity is available the current is usually alternating 200 to 230 volts, but failing such supply, and having to install a generating set with a dynamo and storage cells, it is usual to provide for direct or continuous current at say 50 volts and a battery of 26 accumulator cells.

It is obvious that the laying down of a process plant is not such a simple affair as may appear at first sight; and it is not so much the initial outlay, but the upkeep, which demands the most careful consideration.

Expensive and highly-skilled labour must be kept steadily employed, otherwise the loss through waiting time will very soon eat up any profit which may have appeared possible at the outset.

While the foregoing plan gives a fair indication of how much is involved in starting a small plant for zinc only, and capable of being run by one journeyman with an assistant, it allows room for accommodating two or three journeymen to cater for commercial blockmaking: say operator and metalprinter, etcher and one apprentice. In order to cover the wages for such increase of staff, however, the turnover necessary would have to be expanded from the original weekly production of £25 up to an average of about £50 of process work. More outlay would be required for screens and for mounting

LINE ETCHING DEPARTMENT

In the foreground a gas stove is shown upon which the zinc plates are heated after they have been powdered with dragon's blood. Etchers on the left are shown washing off, drying and examining their plates, while those on the right are using the mechanical rocking baths in which their plates are being etched. Sinks occupy the middle of the room.

PROCESS ARTISTS AT WORK

A typical artist's bench similar to those used by the fine etchers. North-lighted windows should be arranged, and artificial lighting should be well designed so as to avoid shadows.

PROCESS PROOFING DEPARTMENT

*In the foreground hand proof presses for unmounted plates being inked by hand. In the
background two platen machines for proofing from mounted blocks or for colour proofs.*

machinery, bringing the capital up by another 50 per cent.

It is sometimes assumed that half-tone blockmaking and photo-litho can be worked together in one process department, but this idea will prove unwarranted for several reasons. Firstly, the sheets of metal to be handled in photo-litho are very much larger, necessitating bigger sinks; a power whirler with drying fitment; a graining machine for plate preparation; an acid vat; a very large vacuum printing-frame; and possibly a much larger camera with lens, screens and arc lamps in proportion. All these would more than double the capital outlay.

Litho and Letterpress Screens

It must also be borne in mind that the class of screen-negative required for photo-litho is quite different from that used in letterpress work, for the latter requires a flat gradation with large high-light dots which are fined down in the etching process, whereas the photo-litho process requires a steeper gradation with small dots in the high-lights, dots of a size comparable with the

letterpress plate *after* its final etching.

In a large establishment the two processes can be worked more or less in conjunction, but only by keeping their departments well defined. In this connection an interesting division in photo-litho is made by trade union procedure, between the process side and the printers' side. All work done from the original copy, viz. negative making, coating the metal, printing-down and developing to the inking stage, is the care of the members of the Society of Litho Artists, Designers, Engravers and Process Workers; and the finished plate bearing the image is taken over by members of the Society of Lithographic Printers, who have full jurisdiction from that stage to the final printed product.

The supply of metals, chemicals and all sundries for the various processes has become a specialized branch of the reproduction craft, a high technical knowledge being required for its servicing, so that with the exception of dry-plates the large manufacturers do not undertake to deal with the many minor queries of the small buyer.

CHAPTER TWENTY-FIVE

GRAVURE PROCESSES AND THEIR DEVELOPMENT

NEGATIVES AND POSITIVES. RETOUCHING. COLOUR GRAVURE. USE OF LIGHT-FILTERS. PLANNING AND LAYOUT. CARBON TISSUE TREATMENT. PLATE AND CYLINDER COPPER DEPOSITING. LAYING THE TISSUE. ETCHING AND ENGRAVING. PRINTING METHODS. INK AND PAPER. RECENT GRAVURE PROCESSES. SECURITY PRINTING.

IT will be as well, at the outset, to understand clearly the implications of the three headings under which all printing processes are listed. They are: relief, planographic and intaglio.

Relief printing, as its name implies, is that in which the printing surface stands in relief, that is, above the surrounding non-printing area; identified in this category is letterpress from type, plate, half-tone and line blocks, wood and lino cuts.

Planographic is the term used to describe a printing surface on the same level as the plate, which by special treatment based on the antipathy of grease and water, accepts the ink while the area around resists it. Lithography, pantone and collotype are outstanding examples of the planographic method.

Intaglio and Photogravure

Photogravure is an intaglio process, and, like all such processes, the design to be printed is below the surface. The steel and copper engravings of earlier days, the artist's aquatints, line etchings and dry points are examples of intaglio work.

The distinction between the three main groups tends to become less clear as time passes and new developments

emerge. The Pantone and Renck plates described as planographic are usually printed in letterpress ink upon letterpress machines, and the plates are in slight relief. Modern photo-lithography, using the offset deep-etch technique, prints from a slightly intaglio image; while intaglio half-tone is a modified half-tone image etched into a cylinder instead of being etched in relief. A more recent intaglio method makes use of an intaglio half-tone image which varies in depth with depth of tone, just as in gravure. In relief printing the dots in a half-tone block, which fashion the printing image, vary in size according to the degree of light and shade required, whereas in photogravure variation of tones is effected by differences in depth of the ink-filled cavities or cells in the copper cylinder.

Wearing Properties Compared

It is interesting to compare the wearing properties of minute raised dots, subjected to the continuous wear of modern machinery, or those of a surface image whose clearness depends upon retaining firmness of outline, with those of these etched cavities lying snugly concealed beneath the level of the plate itself. Such a comparison will show that in photogravure printing the initial qualities of the original to be reproduced are likely to be maintained much longer, and deterioration is less, except in the extreme high-lights.

In the photogravure process the velvety solids, subtle gradations of tone and sparkling high-lights are entirely controlled by the depth of the etched cavities, the depth being determined by the variation in tones of the original from which the print is reproduced.

First Rotary Intaglio

Rotary intaglio was first used in the production of printed calico and wall-paper as long ago as 1785, when the engraved copper cylinders were attached to a primitive type of printing machine, a thin film of ink being applied which filled the etched cells. The residue was scraped away with a thin knife or blade. This blade was the forerunner of the modern doctor.

For some years the process, which had been invented and developed by the Rembrandt Intaglio Printing Company, was a closely guarded secret; but a secret widely shared cannot hold out for long, and the technical experts in the trade ultimately laid it bare.

The distinguishing feature of the photogravure process is carbon tissue, a gelatined paper which is sensitized so that the image can be printed upon it from the positives, and by means of which the copper is etched. The tissue is usually coloured, enabling a careful watch to be kept throughout the various stages in the preparation of the resist. The carbon tissue is a pigmented gelatine-coated paper, sensitized before use.

The reason for referring to the tissue at this stage is the necessity of emphasizing the fact that the natural basis of gravure is actually photographic. The type or pictures to be reproduced are exposed directly to this sensitized resist, which is printed, developed and laid on the cylinder without the intervention of any mechanical aids.

It is true that upon this film there has also been imposed a very fine ruled screen; but this, in photogravure, is a positive screen, and its effect is to crisscross the design with very fine lines which form the walls of the cells during etching, and break up each tone into rectangular cavities of a uniform size, without affecting their depth.

A complete photogravure plant is composed of a number of departments, each engaged upon one specialized branch of the process. As a general rule there is very little overlapping, and the worker therefore should make a special study of that section of gravure in which his future is to be spent.

Nevertheless, some knowledge of the methods leading up to, and subsequent to, his individual part of the process is essential. He who would make his mark in the photogravure process must be "jack" of all its specialized departments, and a master of one of them.

Gravure Plant

Gravure plant consists of a photographic studio; a retouching department; a planning room; a section where carbon printing, developing and laying are done; and an etching, cylinder depositing, grinding and polishing department. The editorial and artists' departments and the machine rooms are placed conveniently near to them.

The progress of a job from one extremity of the building to the other begins in the editorial or art department, which, receiving the original from the customer, passes it on to the studio. There, negatives are made to the correct size, document prints made from them and returned to the compositor, who in turn makes from them a dummy copy or layout.

From the retouched negatives, positives are made, and on receipt of the completed dummy or layout, the planning department plans the job, sending it, when completed, to the printing room where the image from the positives is printed upon the carbon tissue, developed and laid on the copper, and ultimately etched. The etched plate or cylinder is then put on the printing machine.

The production of negative and positive, layout, imposition and planning, and ultimately machining, are in some respects merely variations of established systems in process-engraving, and they can be easily followed in their basic relationship to any one of them; but the preparation of plate or cylinder for intaglio printing is a specialized process and it bears no relation to the other methods.

On the complete understanding of this rests the foundation of the workers' position in photogravure.

Unlike half-tone and photo-litho, a *continuous* tone negative is required for gravure, no mechanical screen being used in making it or in copying it for the positives.

The original to be reproduced is fixed to the copy board and photographed direct. The camera is usually one with an interchangeable lens, so that it can be used for enlarging, reducing or copying (Fig. 1).

In process work the negative has to be copied or re-photographed in order to make a positive; and it must be remembered that as the positive has to be reversed it has to go through yet one more copying process. When this diapositive is being made the negative must be placed in front of the camera with the film side out.

To make the negative, after fixing the

PHOTOGRAPHIC COPYING UNIT

Fig. 1. *The photographer, or as he is termed in the trade, the operator, is shown withdrawing the dark slide in the negative carrier at the back of the camera. The illustration on pages 264 and 265 gives a clear picture of a process camera and its construction.*

original in position on the board, and the correct focus and the amount of exposure necessary having been ascertained, the plate or film is placed in the slide and the photograph taken.

This, in a few words, is the actual procedure; but much more than this is involved. Originals cannot always be relied upon to be the best for reproduction purposes; a press photograph may have to be copied, consisting of a picture of men and women clad in white under an equatorial sun, all hard whites and heavy blacks, with few if any intervening tones; or it may be a beautifully retouched example of a studio portrait. Such divergencies may often be all together on a made-up page.

Importance of Standardization

Whatever the limitations of the originals, the result must conform to a rigid standard of uniform quality, in which all the positives are correctly balanced and within the standard range of densities. This standardization is a very important feature in gravure, for reasons which will become obvious as we trace the course of development in the process. The cylinder prepared for etching will perhaps contain thirty-two pages of pictures, and unless each separate positive is within the standard range of photographic densities the etcher has not the slightest chance of producing a satisfactory result.

It is to avoid such a contretemps that the skill of the camera operator is needed; by varying the exposure and development he can improve on a poor original. He can do even more by reduction, with a weak solution of potassium ferricyanide and hypo.

A good type of negative is one with a fairly long scale of gradation in which the shadows are barely covered and the high-lights not unduly closed in. When a perfect rendering of high-lights and shadows can be sacrificed to some extent, the negative should be developed longer to give increased contrast; if the interest is in the lower tones development can be curtailed. Normal subjects require normal treatment; flat subjects should have their contrast increased.

There is little agreement even among experts as to what constitutes a perfect negative and positive, and diagrammatic graphs illustrative of degrees of density will be meaningless to learners. Broadly speaking they should be free from technical defects, neutral in colour, and the image sharp and in conformity with prearranged printing and etching requirements. Various authorities have established several scientific principles governing the ideal in both negative and positive; in fact, a device for the checking and measurement of densities is used in many studios, but these are technicalities that must wait upon experience.

Matching Guides

In most firms it is the practice to select, as a guide for operators, a standard negative and positive conforming to the firm's particular requirements, taking into consideration the class of work, type of material used, and local and general conditions. To this guide everything is matched. The guide is fixed in the illuminated glass frame over the operator's sink or on a special matching table. It must be remembered, however, that the standard of these guides varies considerably in different gravure firms.

Retouching

It has been demonstrated how the skill of the operator can influence the final result, but the limitations of the methods at his command are self-evident. No amount of intensification can put back details irretrievably lost in the photography, such as the folds in the drapery of a white dress; the outline of a figure; or spots and blemishes in a much used original. No reduction can bring out some important detail which is hidden beneath a large area of dense shadow.

The negative must be passed on to the retoucher, the defects made good, and returned to the studio for the positive to be made. This in turn is sent back to the retouching department for improvement.

Retouching is an essential and important process in the production of a high quality reproduction, and one that necessitates a close study, inasmuch as over-retouching can have a somewhat startling effect on the finished print.

Every negative, and a large proportion of positives, can be improved by skilful retouching. The assistance of the retoucher, however, should be directed primarily to the negative, as the work on the negative will have the most important bearing on the finished result.

Work on the positive should be reduced to an absolute minimum; in fact the retoucher's aim should be to complete his corrective work on the negative, leaving nothing else to be done on the positive but the filling in of small spots and other blemishes (Fig. 2).

Spots and pinholes are the inevitable result of a dust-laden atmosphere in the studio; and although the operator should wipe the negative very carefully before making the transparency, it is not

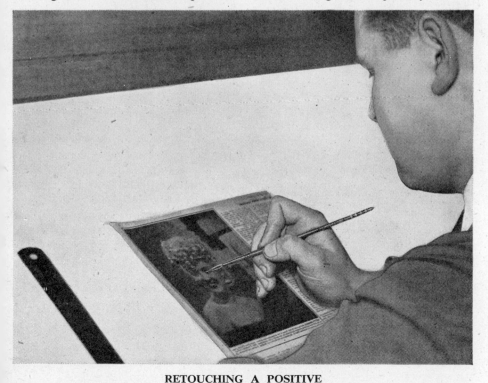

RETOUCHING A POSITIVE

Fig. 2. *A gravure retoucher at work on a positive. With the aid of neutral dyes suitably diluted, and a brush, he is strengthening weaknesses in the photographic tones.*

always possible to avoid last-second settlements of dust particles.

In both negative and positive such blemishes as holes in the original, and scratches and defects in the photographic plate itself, should be carefully spotted out, making quite certain that the spotting medium used is no stronger than the area in which the blemish appears.

All retouching must be invisible, unostentatious, and in keeping with the photographic quality and texture of the print. At one time work on the negative was done with a soft pencil or lead, aided by a soft leather or papier mâché stump, rubbed occasionally on a block of graphite, or dipped in the dust from the lead shavings of the pencil.

PROCESS LENS AND PRISM

The lens used in photogravure is the same as that used in process work. In fact, the same type of camera is suitable for process engraving, photo-litho or photogravure reproduction.

Positive retouching at that time was carried out on the back of the plate upon which a rapidly drying spirit matt-varnish had first been evenly poured. This gave a surface for pencil and stump; in addition, certain areas could be neatly scraped away in order to enhance the brightness of the high-lights, or to reduce the strength of particular tones.

Today the retoucher uses chemical methods—ferricyanide-hypo applied with a brush or cotton wool for local reduction, and dye for local strengthening. The modern retoucher uses a neutral-coloured grey or red (neo-coccine) liquid dye, diluted with water to the strength which his retouching requires, and applied with a fine sable brush.

A fine wash of this dye will reproduce in facsimile the shade and regularity of a photographic tone, and it must be firmly impressed upon the retoucher that the replacing of missing tones is his chief object. Slight local reduction is carried out with Frictol or similar abrasive.

A negative with too little density in its high-lights can be assisted by the application of one or two skilfully placed strengthening washes; and a mass of blurred detail can be separated by reinforcing certain objects at the expense of the remainder.

After being corrected, the negative is painted round with an opaque paint, the border, or limit of the image being ruled, or if it is necessary, vignetted. In the case of the latter the hard edge of the opaque is broken gently and softly into the picture by an aerograph.

If lines of overprinting type occur in the job, they must also be painted out to ensure that they appear perfectly white on the positive. Boxes and decorative designs with ruled white areas are similarly treated.

Artistic Effects

On the positive, gaps in a broken line can be made up and weaknesses in a faint outline, or the blacks of a figure restored; but the retoucher will find that it is the middle tones which will need his attention most. The beauty of cloud formations can be enhanced, the middle tones of a landscape supported, and other weaknesses made good by subtle washes of dye; but all such retouching must form an integral part of the surrounding area, and it must be borne in mind that no additions on the positive should be stronger than the heaviest photographic tone. At this stage, too, dirt and black spots are easily removed with a sharp scraper nib.

Bearing all these points in mind, the general principles of the retoucher's work can be laid down. Firstly, the retoucher looks for spots, scratches and other blemishes, then for weaknesses in the tonal rendering, and finally for missing detail.

So far we have been dealing with reproductions in one colour, or monochrome, but colour-gravure has become an outstanding feature of the process today. Recent improvements in web printing having hastened its development, it is now safe to say that the colour process at its best is capable of producing a facsimile reproduction from practically any kind of original.

The conditions governing the making of a good set of tricolour separations are precisely those which apply to the making of good monochrome negatives, with the exception that panchromatic plates must be used and each of them exposed through one of the colour filters (Fig. 3).

To appreciate the importance of panchromatic plates and films it is necessary to appreciate the difference between the three types of sensitive material available. The oldest material, the "ordinary" type of emulsion, is sensitive only to the violet and blue end of the visible spectrum. Later, by the addition of eosin or erythrosine to the emulsion, the sensitivity was extended to the yellow-green and yellow, producing the ortho- or iso-chromatic emulsions which, among other uses, may be used with advantage in the copying of originals on yellowed or faded paper.

The modern panchromatic emulsions are sensitized with special dyes to the whole visible spectrum; the sensitivity is not, however, equal over the whole range, and it is necessary to use filters

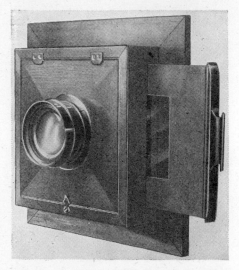

Fig. 3. *A colour filter for colour photogravure is shown in its holder, in position behind the camera lens.*

to obtain the optimum results. All photographic plates are sensitive beyond the visible spectrum at the violet end, but only a limited amount of ultra-violet is normally useful, as most is absorbed by the glass of the lens.

In the case of colour the inclusion of ultra-violet is objectionable, but, since it is absorbed by all the light-filters normally used, this is of little consequence. Panchromatic emulsions are also sensitive into the infra-red, but again the filters attend to this. Where it is desired to use the infra-red end of the spectrum special infra-red emulsions are available for this purpose.

Light-filters

Panchromatic plates are almost exclusively used for colour separation, although some firms use ordinary plates for the yellow printer. Film may be used instead of glass where the register is not important, but unless the temperature and humidity can be closely controlled the use of film cannot be generally recommended.

Light-filters for process work consist of thin sheets of dyed gelatine, used either in this form or as optical flats in which the gelatine is cemented between sheets of optically worked plate glass. Where optical flats are used behind the lens it is usual to focus up with a dummy filter supplied by the filter makers, so as to compensate for the slight optical effect due to the thickness of the filters. Tricolour filters are designed to transmit a colour representing one-third of the spectrum; the print from the filtered negative is printed in a colour complementary to the colour of the filter used. The blue filter negative is the yellow printer; the green filter negative is the red printer; while the red filter negative is the blue printer. Where a gamma or similar filter is used this is only for correction purposes and is intended to be a key or fourth printer.

In other words, the filters separate the light proceeding from the original into its red, green and blue components; and, with the use of panchromatic material, red, green and blue filters, each transmitting approximately one-third of the spectrum, are inserted between or in front or behind the lens when the exposure is made. Correct registration of the three or four colours being a primary requisite, small crosses or register marks are pasted or drawn on the original, which ensures their being on each separate plate in an exactly identical position. A colour chart, placed on the margin of the original, but within photographic range and containing a square or circle of the three colours, magenta, blue-green, yellow, which are actually going to be used in the printing, is also included as an additional means of identification of the colours.

Ensuring Standardization

This enables the yellow printing plate to be instantly recognized by the fact that it will be the one colour represented on the chart that will be shown on the plate as a clear patch, and similarly in the case of the red and blue. Each plate will show clearly a very light tone of the two other colours, its own colour being indicated by an almost clear patch. A further precaution ensuring the standardization and balance of the three negatives is taken by photographing with the original a scale or wedge of neutral greys, consisting of a series of graded stepped-up photographic tones, ranging between the solid and the high-light, and made on glossy bromide paper.

By ascertaining that each of these strips exactly corresponds in density the operator is sure of a similarly faithful rendering in the tones of his separations.

The camera must have a first-class

apochromatic lens, i.e. fully corrected for colour; portrait or rectilinear lenses do not focus all colours in the same plane.

With the original mounted on the copy board, register marks, colour chart, and tone wedge in position, the operator makes the three or four exposures through the red, green, blue and perhaps gamma filters.

The surface of the filters must on no account be damaged, and to this end they are usually mounted in a cardboard holder, unless they are cemented between glass (optical flats).

Although the order of exposure is of little consequence it is advisable to mount the filters, red, green and blue, in that order, a longer exposure to artificial light being necessary through the blue, which makes the yellow plate.

The necessity for correct exposure and correctly timed development is obvious. The exposure factors for each of the filters used are readily obtained from the plate manufacturers' tables, which give the factors for the usual illuminants, including daylight. Where a key or fourth printer is to be used, and it usually is in commercial work, the key is generally printed from the text cylinder.

Colour originals for reproduction vary considerably; they may be oil or water colours; colour transparencies such as Dufay or Kodachrome; or even hand-coloured photo-prints. Some fashion originals are made up from actual fabric with the addition of a certain amount of art work; while others may be unassembled composites consisting of colour transparencies with separate art work and type. The colour transparencies are often miniatures requiring a high degree of enlargement, and the making of such colour sets requires absolute rigidity in apparatus and great care in manipulation.

Photographic colour originals have come much to the front in recent years, and both colour transparencies and prints from the one-shot cameras are popular. Improved colour separation from transparencies may be obtained by the use of the special filters developed by the makers for these dye images.

Whatever original is supplied, the colour separation is of necessity a compromise; the almost ideal filters are never matched by printing inks of anything like such an ideal response. The filters, good as they are, overlap their wavebands. Certain shades of green will be found to be showing a modicum of tone on the red plate; purple shadows, too, will be over strong on the yellow plate. To explain the chemical reactions of paints and inks in photographic reproduction would involve an extremely technical analysis without shedding any light upon the process of photogravure. It is admitted, however, that variations in tonal rendering of colour separations exist and, in spite of all possible developments, these variations may still continue to exist.

Colour Correction

Colour retouching or correction is a matter of skill and experience, allied to a knowledge of the process and a familiarity with tone values. The retoucher should have an artistic sense including an all-round experience of colour.

The retoucher has to know just exactly how much of a certain blue added to a specified yellow will be sufficient to make the precise shade of green in the original. It is his job to know and to retouch the negatives and later the positives, in accordance with that knowledge.

One of the biggest drawbacks to gravure up to recent times was that the extent to which the colour correction was successful could only be measured after the cylinder or plate had been etched and printed. Although a certain amount of work could be done on the etched cylinder it was somewhat limited in scope, and even fine-etching, which meant a re-etching of certain weaknesses, was not without difficulty.

Recent Improvements

But recent advances in colour photographic technique have largely eliminated this drawback, and it is possible today to make a set of transparencies from the retouched colour negatives under similarly controlled conditions; from these a carbro print and colour progressives can be sent to the printer for comparison with the original. By this method deficiencies in the colour corrections can be made good, and modifications or intensifications carried out before the printing stage is reached.

The general outline of the process is as follows: three negatives of the subject are made on colour sensitive plates through tricolour filters. Bromide prints are made from these, and from the prints images are made, in blue, red and yellow, each being developed on to a piece of clear celluloid. These are then transferred and superimposed in register on to a gelatine-coated paper. This process is identical with carbro.

An interesting method of colour correction by photographic means, designed to reduce colour retouching, makes use of correction masks. These masks are very lightly printed positives, and are bound up in contact with the negative before making the final positives through a camera. In the original system the masks were made from the key, and, by binding up with each colour in turn, were intended to correct for the use of a fourth printer. The method has, however, been taken further, and

an elaborate technique developed by using masks especially made to correct the deficiencies in the violet and green.

Yet another system taken from colour photographic technique is one that no student of modern colour-gravure can afford to ignore.

In this new method, separation negatives are printed upon sheets of gelatine, coloured blue-green, magenta and yellow, thus making coloured relief positives. Added to the ordinary colouring pigment is a silver halides emulsion.

The three relief positives are temporarily placed one over the other, in register, and the combined result viewed in an illuminated glass frame. If the colour rendering is satisfactory, they are dissembled and the colour image on each transformed into a black deposit by immersion in a developing mixture, converting the silver halides into black metallic silver. The black and white positives are then printed directly on to the carbon tissue.

The advantages of this process are apparent. During the viewing, one is enabled by the imposition of the three-coloured reliefs to see exactly what the finished result will be, and if divergencies between them and the original exist, the reliefs can be returned for further treatment.

With the advance of natural colour photography much of the earlier crudities of colour separation will disappear.

Two-colour Gravure

Attractive results can be obtained by two-colour combinations, and today periodicals, magazines, and much advertising matter make increasing use of two-colour gravure.

A brown key printing with an orange or red tint is a much favoured example of this, while other pleasing blendings can be expressed in blue and red, or black and green. Generally, in photographing the original, it will be found that the filter should be roughly complementary to the printing colour, a blue filter being used for the orange or red printer, and an orange or red filter for the blue or green printer.

Usually originals are designed in the desired two colours, but it is quite possible to make a two-colour set from a black and white original without resorting to filters.

A single negative is made and retouched, and from it, two positives, the second one being reduced to a ghost by the aid of ferricyanide. On this ghost the retoucher, with the aid of dyes, can build his second colour; and some extremely fine results can be achieved by a skilful and artistic colour retoucher.

Planning and Layout

Planning is a distinct and specialized department of gravure, and demands the most meticulous and accurate care and attention.

When the negatives are made, document prints are taken from them. These are sent with pulls of all type matter to the customer or the editorial department, where they are trimmed to the required size and pasted in exact position on to a sheet of paper which is afterwards returned to the planning department, folded in the form of a precise duplicate, or dummy, of the finished job.

From this dummy the planner makes a tracing, marking out the dimensions of each page, making due allowance for trimming and folding, and indicating the limits of type matter and pictures.

A piece of clean glass is placed on the glass-topped mounting table, which is built in the shape of a box, enclosed at back and sides, with a whitewashed interior illuminated by lamps. The retouched negatives, squared, and with

the edges painted out with opaque paint, are then fixed in position under the paper guide, lightly stuck down with adhesive paper and, when satisfactorily placed, doubly secured by pasting orange or black paper around the edges.

As the guide sheet will have been drawn the right way round it will be necessary to turn it over to check the mounting. When this has been done, the negative, or in the case of a composite page of pictures the page, is returned to the photographic studio and a positive made from it. The procedure when the positive has been made and retouched is very similar. A very much larger sheet of glass will be required, if for instance eight, sixteen or more pages are to be mounted in position.

It is absolutely essential first to make sure that the mounting glass has been polished clean; any mark or scratch will show alarmingly in the subsequent printing operation. A scratch scarcely visible to the naked eye will stand out clearly under powerful arc lights.

In mounting the positives the drawn out sheet is placed on the table and the mounting glass on top of it. With the position of the picture clearly indicated and visible through the illuminated glass it is quite a simple matter to fix the positives in their correct place and stick them down.

Today type matter is often pulled on transparent colourless Cellophane or type tissue, and becomes the positive for mounting in conjunction with the illustrations.

Many firms, however, photograph their type, and from the negative make line films or strippers for planning on the tone positives.

In certain gravure firms, type and pictures are mounted, and later, etched, together; in others they are treated

Portion of a photogravure screen greatly enlarged. The blank squares will form the cells on the resist, all equal in size, and the cross-lines the protecting walls.

separately. The reason for this difference in treatment will be made clear when the process of etching is described.

Planning a single-colour job is a fairly straightforward operation; it is with two- and three-colour work that the real problems arise.

The full success of colour-gravure depends as much upon perfect registration as upon the colour rendering itself, and the operator planning a colour set has to make certain that in mounting the positives they are in absolutely exact register.

Register Marks

Each one will bear upon it, photographed from the original, the register marks already referred to, and consisting of two small black lines crossing at right-angles, on the clear glass at the edge of the plate. To test them one glass is placed over another, making sure that the crosses on the top plate cover the corresponding crosses underneath. When a number of illustrations in colour are together it is more than ever necessary to mount them accurately.

The mounting glass being satisfactory, the yellow positives are put into position and fastened down by adhesive tape or gummed paper; the reds are similarly mounted and placed on top.

As in monochrome planning, immediately upon the glass-topped table and under the set of yellow positives is the sheet of paper on which the layout has been drawn, containing master register marks, so that, looking through, the operator can guide his top glass into position.

To assist in getting correct imposition, planners use a register glass, which is an instrument with a small lens through which they are able to see only the portion of the glass in the vicinity of the registering crosses. By this means optical errors of judgment are eliminated.

Carbon Tissue Treatment

When the positives, both pictures and type, have been mounted and every detail of density, quality, position and registration carefully checked, they are transferred to the carbon printing department.

It has been stated previously that the distinguishing feature of gravure is the gelatined, pigment paper upon which the positives are printed, and which becomes the basic resist for etching. This pigment paper is merely a paper coated evenly with a gelatine emulsion mixed with an insoluble pigment.

Gelatine, a complex organic substance, absorbs water and aqueous solutions, and swells during absorption. The pigment serves two purposes: it provides a visible image during and after development, and it limits the amount of light penetrating the film.

Carbon tissue is supplied in rolls 12 ft. long and in various widths, and can be cut to any required size. When it leaves the manufacturer it contains about 10 per cent water, and this must not be allowed to evaporate, or the tissue will become brittle and will seriously affect, if not ruin, the subsequent etching. It should be kept stored in an air-conditioned atmosphere.

The paper has next to be made sensitive to light; accordingly it is immersed in a bath containing a solution of distilled water, and potassium or potassium-ammonium bichromate.

The solution in the bath must be allowed to soak into the tissue evenly, and the worker who manipulates it should wear rubber gloves for two reasons: firstly, because bichromate is highly injurious to the skin; and secondly, no grease from the hands must be allowed to mar the paper.

When the tissue is thoroughly saturated, it is placed face downward on a sheet of glass or a ferrotype plate, which, in preparation, has been carefully cleaned; it is next squeegeed and all the superfluous solution dried off, and put in a drying oven or cupboard.

Drying is a gradual process; the paper should be peeled off the glass before it curls and detaches itself, a sign that it has been too long in the oven.

It will be plain that the nature of this gelatine-coated paper renders it extremely susceptible to atmospheric conditions, and that changes in the temperature of the room in which it is used will have an important effect. But in modern gravure printing works the humidity of the printing and etching departments is controlled and regulated strictly in accordance with the prerequisite conditions, and many of the troubles which worried the early craftsmen have been eliminated.

When the tissue is dry it is ready for screening. The cross-lined screen used in photogravure differs from those used in the production of half-tones, inasmuch as, being no part of the design,

its function is merely to create on the metal a fine barrier of lines which, forming the walls of the cells, are impervious to the etch.

The screens used today are actually original engraved positives with opaque squares on a transparent ground, and they are printed direct on to the carbon tissue, thus ensuring a sharpness of outline incomparably superior to the best screen copy. They vary between 150 and 175 lines to the inch for pictorial matter and up to 400 lines to the inch for postage stamps and similar special purposes.

The screen is placed on the bed of a vacuum printing frame and the sheet of tissue in contact over it. The frame is then locked up, and air pumped out until an absolutely air-tight contact between the screen and tissue is established. The arc lights are switched on and the exposure is then made.

Screen Exposure

For the screen exposure it is essential that only one light is used; it is kept stationary, otherwise the movement would cause mottles and a thickening of the lines of the squares. The distance of the light from the screen should not be less than the diagonal measurement of the screen.

We have now a sheet of sensitized paper with a screen printed upon it. The next part of the process is more or less a repetition, except that type or pictures have now to be printed upon the screened tissue. The glass upon which the positives are mounted is put into the pneumatic frame, the tissue again placed in contact, and exposed, but this time to a uniform diffused lighting consisting of four arcs moving in a vertical motion. Mercury vapour lamps, placed about 1 ft. apart and 18 in. from the frame, are often used; these distribute the light uniformly.

The actinic value of artificial light varies within wide limits, and in the exposure of positives this can lead to a similarly wide margin of error if the exposure is made by time. An actinometer will be found useful in controlling the exposure. This is a miniature printing frame with a width of graduated and numbered tones, and by exposing a piece of ordinary photographic printing-out paper at the same time as the positives, one can decide the point at which the correct exposure is attained. Another method, even more accurate, is by the use of an integrating photo-electric meter.

Plate and Cylinder Copper Depositing

In the early days of gravure the cylinders from which the image was printed were tubes made of copper about $\frac{1}{2}$ in. in thickness, but these were superseded; today they have bases of steel and cast iron which, with a copper deposit, are either built up to a maximum size and etched a number of times (each successive etching being ground off until the minimum size has been reached) or, alternatively, they are "skin-deposited."

This latter method consists of the building up of a layer of copper on a chemical or mechanical coating which ensures the non-adherence of this layer to the base copper of the cylinder. It is made of just sufficient thickness to be submitted to one etching operation and afterwards stripped off completely.

The base copper on which the shell is to be deposited is ground and polished, all imperfections, scratches, holes or marks being removed. The cylinder is then chemically cleaned, treated with a silvering solution and a separating solution, and then placed as quickly as possible in an electro-copper depositing bath, where it is rapidly rotated. The cylinder may be totally immersed in the solution, but more usually only one-third is actually in the bath. The bath consists of copper sulphate, sulphuric acid and probably an additional agent to promote smoothness and hardness of the deposit. Copper anodes are hung on each side of the rotating cylinder, and, where antimonial cradles are used, beneath as well.

Low-voltage high-amperage current is supplied to the bath by motor generators, preferably with separately excited field coils, or from metal rectifiers. Sufficient current should be available to deposit the required thickness of five to six one-thousandths of an inch in from one to two hours. This thin deposit, after the completion of the run, may be easily lifted at an edge with a knife and peeled from the base, when the base is re-treated and re-deposited ready for the next job.

Where great accuracy in cylinder size is not required, as for example in sheet-fed machines, the cylinders may with skill be deposited so smoothly that only a light polishing with a rotating mop and a tripoli composition is needed to produce a first-class finish. Modern high-speed rotaries, however, demand an accuracy of plus or minus one-quarter of one-thousandth of an inch, and it is usually necessary to lap the cylinders to the required size; preferably with stones of the Aldemite or Carborundum Intaglio type. The finest finish is got by the somewhat old-fashioned method of charcoaling, followed by polishing on a rotating mop, but this is an arduous job and requires great skill.

Thin copper plates are also used widely today. With some of the sheet-fed gravure presses the plate is a thin flat sheet of copper, ·03 in. in thickness, which can be fastened around the plate cylinder; the advantage of this to small printers is evident.

The deposited cylinder must now be

chemically cleaned by treating it with a 3 per cent solution of caustic soda and whiting, removing all grease. It is then washed with water and an acid solution, removing tarnish and neutralizing the remaining caustic soda applied, and after all this, once more washed to clear all traces of the chemicals.

To reduce the tanning effect of copper upon carbon tissue it is the practice of some firms to silver the chemically clean cylinder before laying the exposed carbon tissue, thus interposing a layer of silver between the copper and the gelatine surfaces.

The adhesion of the gelatine to the metal can be accomplished by two methods: wet, and dry mounting. In the case of the first method, the tissue is soaked in alcohol and water at a temperature of 60 deg.; this reduces the swelling and limits the stretch. When the tissue is limp it is placed in position around the cylinder, which has been previously wetted with the same solution, squeegeed and allowed to dry.

In dry mounting, the dry tissue is put in position on a dry mounting machine, secured by adhesive tape, the pressure roller is lowered on to the taped edge, the paper turned back and water is fed between the tissue and the cylinder which is slowly turned.

When exact register is essential, as it is in colour work, dry mounting is the rule, there being less stretch.

The backing paper is more easily removed, and the development time shortened, by swabbing the backing paper before development with methylated spirit or a wetting agent.

To develop the tissue, which has

CYLINDER WITH DEVELOPED RESIST

Fig. 4. *A photogravure cylinder with the carbon tissue laid and mounted upon it. The resist contains a photographic image of the original plus a superimposed print of the screen.*

now become the resist, the cylinder is rotated in a tank of hot water until the gelatine is softened sufficiently to permit the easy removal of the paper backing (Fig. 4).

The resist when quite dry has now to be protected with an acid resisting varnish in those portions which are not to be etched. This varnish is made from powdered bitumen diluted with turpentine and benzene to a liquid, workable quality (Fig. 5).

With a flexible celluloid ruler and a ruling pen, edges are outlined; and afterwards, with a brush, painted up to the margins around the pages. Spaces between the pictures and blanks where type is to be inserted later, are all painted out. The varnish should be applied thickly but nevertheless evenly, and any cracks or bubbles filled in. When this has been attended to, the cylinder is rotated in front of a fan and dried, and is then ready for etching.

Etching

Mordants available for gravure etching are few in number, and the only one in use today is a solution of ferric chloride. This is one of the few cheap chemicals possessing the high solubility necessary to produce the very dense solutions needed for the preferential penetration of the gelatine resist without attacking it.

The hardened gelatine resist upon the cylinder consists of an image of a gravure screen and a negative image of the subject positive transparency. The pigment incorporated in the gelatine makes it possible to inspect the image, and even to judge if the exposure has been correct. Since the action of light upon bichromated gelatine is to render it insoluble, then the solubility of an exposed carbon print will be an index of the light received. In the parts where the clear lines of the screen have exposed

the tissue to light there will be a network of insoluble gelatine, and the positive print will only modify the space between this network. Skies and other light tones will transmit most of the incident light, while darker tones will progressively restrict the passage of light, thus varying the solubility. When the resist has been developed upon the cylinder we shall have a continuous screen pattern of thick gelatine all over the cylinder, and, between the screen walls, the cells will contain a thick layer of gelatine in the sky tones, and a thinner layer in the darker tones, until the darkest tones are reached, when the copper will be almost bare.

Etching is started with a concentrated solution, and as the thicker layers of gelatine are reached it becomes necessary to weaken it by diluting with water to induce a more rapid penetration. The density of the mordant is determined by a number of factors, but the strongest bath does not, as a rule, exceed 44 or 45 deg. and the weakest 35 deg. on the Baumé scale.

It is advisable to use only the purest solution of ferric chloride containing no free acid. A measurement of the density of the solution can be taken with a Baumé hydrometer, and modification can be effected by the introduction of water until the desired strength is reached.

The etcher prepares a number of baths in advance, in strengths varying between 43 and 35 deg. Baumé, and puts them conveniently within arm's reach so that, starting with the most dense one, he can change down as rapidly as circumstances dictate.

The cylinder, mounted on a mandrel fitted with roller bearings for easy turning, is placed in a trough, the bottom of which slopes gently away to a hole through which the superfluous iron pours into a jug beneath.

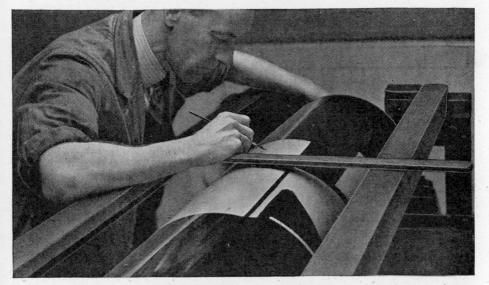

PAINTING OUT THE CYLINDER

Fig. 5. *Every part of the cylinder except that to be etched has been painted out with an acid-proof bitumen paint. The craftsman seen at work is filling in minute holes in the pictorial part of the resist which, unless treated, would etch in the form of black dots.*

With the jugs numbered according to their densities, the etcher, commencing with the 43 deg. solution, pours it over the cylinder in a steady lateral movement from one end to the other and back again, repeating this until his jug is empty. He then takes the jug from underneath the trough which has been draining off the residue of the perchloride of iron, puts in its place the one he has emptied, and continues pouring (Fig. 6).

These are the actual processes of etching. What, however, is happening and what is the action of the mordant?

Starting with a bath of 43 deg. it may be three or four minutes before any penetration is effected, but if any longer time elapses the etcher will change to the next weaker bath, and then, when etching commences, to lower ones in conformity with the prerequisite needs of the particular job.

Etching should be completed in anything from 15 to 30 minutes, but

this again is dependent upon a number of qualifications: the speed and quality of the carbon tissue, the temperature of the room, and the density of the positives and depth of etch required.

These factors are indeterminate, while the principles remain constant; varying conditions, shop customs and practices can affect the interpretation of them.

The first perceptible sign that etching has commenced will be the darkening of the heaviest tones; and then gradually the correct gradation of tones leading down from the middle and lighter tones to the lightest tone of all, will be manifest to the operator.

Etching Control

The very deepest and earliest etching should be rather slow in order to get the full amount of detail in the shadows, but it must be remembered that from start to finish the heavier tones are etching all the time. The man in control can

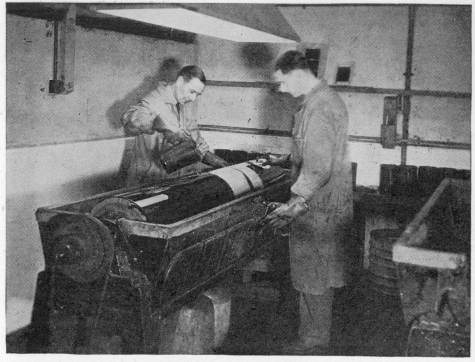

ETCHING THE CYLINDER

Fig. 6. *The etcher is shown pouring the iron perchloride in a lateral motion on to the exposed resist, while his assistant keeps the cylinder revolving continuously.*

examine at frequent intervals, with the aid of a magnifying glass, the depth of the cells; and by his judgment and experience he estimates when the iron has etched sufficiently short of breaking down the walls of the cells in the heavier blacks, and yet has provided sufficient covering over the lightest tones.

The mounting glass containing the positives should be placed in front of a diffused light, in a position where the latter can be examined during etching. The correct balancing of the positives should assure a regular and steady degree of penetration by the perchloride of iron, but if one subject or part of a subject is obstinate it can be encouraged by swabbing locally with a weaker solution.

A cylinder which is found lacking in essential tones after the conclusion of the etch may be "fine etched" later.

Type matter can be etched separately or with the pictures. When done separately it takes about one-third of the time of illustrated matter, and is usually accomplished in a bath of 37 or 38 deg. The reason for using a weaker bath for type is to ensure that the etching opens simultaneously, otherwise the type is apt to be patchy and uneven.

If, however, type and pictures are etched simultaneously the density of type should be slightly less than the pictures. Patented gravure processes in which type and illustrations are produced in one operation are described later in this chapter.

When etching is completed, the plate

A

(A) *Section of a nickel-plated gravure cylinder, showing the cell walls and cells (×120);* (B) *gravure cylinder, showing etched cells and screen walls (× about 100);* (C) *photomicrograph of an intaglio half-tone cylinder (× about 100);* (D) *portion of photogravure text matter (× about 8).*

(*Photos reproduced by courtesy of Mr. H. E. Boughay.*)

B

or cylinder is flooded with a stream of cold water, the remains of the gelatine washed away, and the bitumen cleaned off. Then it is swabbed with hot water and potash and dried. The plate or cylinder is thus finished and it is now ready for the machine.

Photogravure is notable for the long run with insignificant deterioration in quality of the reproduction printed from the metal; even longer runs with an indistinguishable measure of deterioration are obtained by chromium-facing the metal. Chromium, which is very hard and inert to most if not all of the inks and solvents used in gravure, may be easily removed without damage to the cylinder or the engraved surface. The cylinder to be chromium faced should be very well polished, since the facing exaggerates any surface defects. The deposit of chromium is usually about two ten-thousandths of an inch thick, and, if plated correctly from a warm bath, will be bright and shining, neither blue nor grey in colour. It should require little or no polishing, but when the plating is carried out from cold baths the grey matt deposits will certainly require more finishing.

Stringent regulations have been drawn up to cover the process of chromium plating. The regulations require special

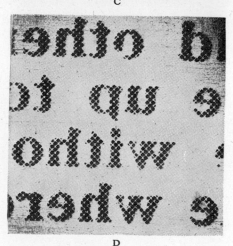

C

D

Fig. 7A *is the floor plan of a sixteen-unit Goss press, consisting of two eight-unit sections with two folders. Using one folder, it will print sixty-four pages of monochrome and colour. Each section of eight units will print eight pages of four colour, eight pages of two, and sixteen pages of monochrome at 30,000 per hour, stitched and counted.* Fig. 7B *shows one eight-unit section. Units 1 and 2 are two-colour; units 4, 5, 6 and 7 are four-colour; and units 3 and 8 are monochrome units. On unit 1,* A *is the impression cylinder,* B *the printing cylinder; between the two is the rubber-covered intermediate impression roller.*

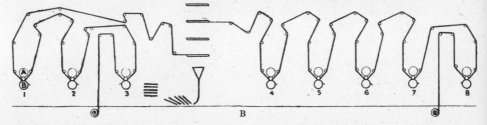

systems of ventilation; also medical inspections and protective clothing. The health hazards in this process are real and deserve every consideration.

Engraving and Re-etching

The amount of cylinder revision which may be successfully accomplished is of course limited, and in any case there is little point in spending excessive time upon a hopeless cylinder which may be easily duplicated. Nevertheless a great deal of revision can be carried out by re-etching; and, provided that the cylinder is not too deep already, individual tones or the whole subject may be successfully deepened in this way.

The cylinder to be re-etched is chemically cleaned; and, while rotating, is progressively inked until the maximum cover is obtained without filling in the tone to be etched. Obviously the sky tones can stand very little rolling up without filling in, but this is satisfactory for the slight etch required; while the heavier inking possible on the darker tones will withstand the heavier etching time necessary. Portions of the cylinder not to be fine-etched are stopped out with a bitumen solution, and an aerograph is very useful for applying this to vignetted edges of an illustration.

Re-etching is extensively employed for the correction of both colour and monochrome cylinders. Apart from tone correction, re-etching is employed for the balancing of type and making good worn cylinders.

Where the cylinder is too heavy, reduction by means of snakestone, charcoal and fine emery papers is carried out; and where high-lights require individual attention the burnisher is used. If the cylinder is very heavy in the darkest tones, there is not a great deal that can be done, as an amount of reduction that would affect the dark tones would remove the skies completely.

Missing type, white spots and similar defects are cut in with a graver, while additional tone may be added by means of a roulette—a tiny hardened steel wheel with sharp teeth arranged in a screen pattern. The roulette is applied to the cylinder with pressure, leaving a burred indented pattern upon the cylinder; the burr is removed with a scraper and the tone modified by burnishing.

The cylinder now put on the machine has an engraved surface etched with holes or cells, varying in depth according to the amount of colour required. In printing, these cells are filled with

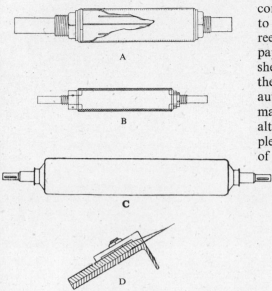

PHOTOGRAVURE CYLINDERS AND MANDRELS
Fig. 8. A *and* B *are sheet-fed type.* A *is an internally expanding mandrel; the cylinder is a copper-deposited steel sleeve.* B *is a taper mandrel, and the copper-deposited steel cylinder is machined with a taper bore to fit.* C *is a copper-deposited rotary cylinder, complete as illustrated; it has no removable mandrel.* D *is a diagram of a doctor, showing the protruding doctor and the backing strip.*

common use. Web is the term applied to a continuous band of paper on a reel, while sheet-fed implies that the paper is fed to the machine in single sheets from a stack. In the latter case the feeding may be done by hand or automatically. On both types of machine the makers frequently offer alternative printing surfaces. Complete cylinders, mandrels for the use of copper sleeves, or special mandrels to take thin copper sheets, may be used. In the latter case, means have to be provided to bridge the gap where the two ends of the copper sheet join; and the overcoming of this problem calls for great ingenuity.

The newspaper rotary intaglio press is composed of two or more pairs of cylinders coupled to a folding and collating mechanism; one of them in each pair is the etched cylinder; the other, the impression cylinder, has a steel base covered with vulcanized rubber.

The paper is fed from the web usually placed between the two press sections, and led through one pair of cylinders where it is printed on one side, and then over or through a drying process to be printed on the reverse side.

ink from the inking roller underneath the cylinder and the excess removed by a flexible steel blade, called the doctor blade. This doctor is in operation all the time the cylinder is revolving, keeping the cells full of ink and scraping the excess. The paper passes between the copper printing cylinder and intermediate rubber-covered roller to which pressure is applied by the larger main impression cylinder. It then passes over one or more heated cylinders or in front of air ducts, which dry the ink (Figs. 7, 8 and 9).

Flat-bed machines for printing from thick copper plates are now obsolete, although similar plates are still used for printing gravure on die presses. Sheet-fed and web machines are today in

Ink for Gravure

The speed of delivery of the printed copies from gravure machines nearly compares with that of the delivery from rotary letterpress machines, and in fact in the case of large-circulation periodicals is rapidly approaching newspaper speed. The rate of delivery in nearly all types of printing machines is determined by the time it takes the ink on each individual copy to dry. Intaglio printing necessitates the use of a fluid and highly volatile ink; firstly because thin ink readily fills the cells, and secondly

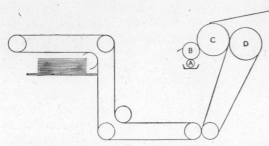

Fig. 9. *The diagram represents the Albert sheet-fed Palatia gravure machine illustrated at foot of page.* A *is the inking roller;* B *the copper printing cylinder;* C *the impression cylinder, and* D *the take-off cylinder. The paper passes from the take-off cylinder to the pile delivery by means of a system of chains and grippers.*

because the thin nature of such an ink is necessary to enable the doctor to function effectively.

In relief printing the inks, which are comparatively stiff, are compounded from pigments and drying oils and need the addition of metallic driers to accelerate the drying, which takes place by the oxidation of the oils. In photogravure the inks dry by the evaporation of the solvent, and compared to letterpress inks are of very thin consistency. They are usually solutions of bitumen or resins and pigment dissolved in zylol, toluol or other coal-tar distillates. Other inks have been used, including water inks, and these have not proved popular, but where adequate precautions against fire have been taken cellulose inks have been used with great success for rotary colour work.

The ink solvents are very expensive, and in this respect a highly desirable adjunct to the equipment of the large-

SHEET-FED GRAVURE PRINTING MACHINE
This type of press is used largely for high-class magazine and book work in which the runs are not long enough to justify the use of a rotary machine. Automatic feeding is used.

GOSS GRAVURE MACHINE DELIVERY

*The delivery end of a modern reel-fed gravure rotary press showing the continuous delivery
of a periodical, printed, folded and stitched at the rate of about 30,000 copies per hour.*

scale gravure printer is a solvent recovery system. Plants of this description have been applied with marked success to almost all industrial processes in which volatile solvents are used (Fig. 10).

Solvent recovery systems operate on the same principles as the familiar gas mask. Activated carbon is used to absorb gas or vapour contained in the air which passes through the absorbent material. In the commercial systems the absorbed vapours are recovered, and the carbons made available for constant re-use, by means of steam distillation. Large air ducts lead from the machines where air and the vapour from the printed surface are brought by an exhaust system to the absorbers. These

are large vessels containing activated carbon, and they are so arranged that, as soon as one has received its charge, the airborne vapour may be switched over to another absorber, thus keeping the plant in continuous operation. The absorbers which have received their charge are supplied with steam to vaporize the charge, and a mixture of steam and vapour finds its way to the condenser, where it is changed from vapour to liquid. The liquid is collected at a separator, where the lighter hydrocarbons, rising to the top of the water, permit easy separation.

It is not advisable to lay down any hard and fast rules concerning the suitability and practicability of particular papers for gravure printing.

SOLVENT RECOVERY INSTALLATION

Fig. 10. This plant is used for the recovery of the solvent in gravure inks. The latest presses include a recovery feature. Illustration shows the absorbers containing the activated carbon.

Excellent examples, printed in three and four colours on cheap paper and even on newsprint, are in daily and weekly circulation; and it has been clearly demonstrated that photogravure printing can more than hold its own with any other process on papers ranging from newsprint to the finest art.

Most of the cheap magazines, catalogues, leaflets, and in fact a good proportion of all commercial gravure printing is done on smooth, almost shiny paper, because it needs less ink and causes less wear to the copper surface than a rougher paper.

But to get the full richness, softness, and an exact photographic reproductive facsimile, a matt art, which is an unglazed coated paper with a soft, smooth, eggshell finish, is recommended.

To generalize, however, the paper should be absorbent enough to take the ink without the exertion of undue pressure. If the paper is not sufficiently absorbent the ink will mottle, because of the solvent evaporating before being absorbed by the paper. The moisture content plays an important part in rotary printing. A matt art, therefore, is the finest gravure printing surface. Any coated paper will give good results, but one of the chief attractions of the process is that it will equal the performance of any other process even on a non-coated paper.

It has been claimed that Karl Klic, the inventor of photogravure, created a complete process, and in its main and basic elements the invention of Klic has remained intact. The artistic reproductions which resulted from his collaboration with the Rembrandt Photogravure Company at Lancaster, founded in 1895, challenge comparison with the monochrome work of today.

But there have been modifications

and adaptations, mostly the result of a demand for the elimination of unnecessary manipulations in the separate workings of the process. Gravure can now challenge the older graphic processes both for speed and quality, and also commercially.

The patented Rinco process is extremely economical in the use of materials, easier to work and quicker, and with proper care and attention, can give results comparable with the older methods.

The type is set and printed on to a black glazed paper in white ink, on an ordinary proofing machine. The type is slightly dulled so that it approximates in tone to the lightest tone in the

COVER A SOOT STAIN WITH SALT AND BRUSH IT HARD WITH A STIFF BRUSH

SPOTS ON BROCADE AND VELVET

A coffee stain on a brocade upholstered chair can be treated with a liquid dry cleaning soap or, if you cannot get one, mix one yourself with ¼ oz. oleic acid (obtainable at the chemist), 1 dessertspoon methylated spirit, 1 dessertspoon ammonia and 1 teaspoon water.

Rub your dry cleaning soap over the stain and leave for several hours. Then rub with a cloth dipped in carbon tetrachloride and brush gently with a fairly stiff brush. Rub over again with a little of the solvent and dry with a clean cloth.

If your velvet or plush curtains have become spotted and stained through the rain blowing in through the open window, hold them in the steam from the spout of a boiling kettle, keeping them gently moving as you do it, until they are moist. Then remove them from the steam and shake till dry. You will find that all the marks will have

fullers earth mixed with carbon tetrachloride and leave on all night. Then wipe off carefully with a cloth dipped in the solvent.

If the stain is too obstinate to move at all, and you have a spare piece of the paper, the best remedy is to cover it with a patch. And when you do this, tear with your fingers a piece of paper the size you want instead of cutting it. The tearing leaves a very fine irregular edge which will be hardly noticeable when you have stuck the patch on the wall, whereas a cut edge would leave a hard line all round.

You may notice white stains on your polished linoleum, caused by spilling liquids on it. If these stains are obstinate to move, try rubbing them with vinegar and water—1 tablespoon vinegar to ¼ pint water—and then rinsing with clear water.

A rust-coloured stain, caused by a bottle of tonic or medicine containing iron left standing on a marble mantelpiece, can be removed with oxalic

REPRODUCTION OF A RINCO NEGATIVE

Fig. 11. A reproduction in half-tone of a continuous tone Rinco negative and type matter for gravure printing. There is, of course, no half-tone screen in the actual negative.

gradated scale of photographic tones on the negative that will later be mounted with it. The black paper must be perfectly opaque and free from wrinkles and blotches. The negatives are made on negative card, a special kind of bromide paper, retouched in the customary manner with dyes, and then either cut to size on a trimming machine or with scissors, or else it is painted round with a highly glazed and opaque varnish (Fig. 11).

With type, borders, folios and page limits clearly printed on the black paper, it is a comparatively simple matter for the planner to mount the negatives in position. The sheet is then sent to the studio, and the resultant positive made from it becomes a complete page, bearing all the type and pictorial matter together.

The positive will have the usual contrast. The type, while not quite so dense as ordinary line work, must yet be strong enough to give a bold and legible result. Here again the density of the type must be slightly less than the density of the strongest black of the picture.

The advantages of this process to the printer of catalogues, leaflets and folders are self-evident; but even in the production of really high-class magazines and periodicals, results leave nothing to be desired, providing that the initial photography and retouching are skilfully dealt with.

The Rinco process can be used for the production of magazines, periodicals, and all kinds of commercial work.

The process effects a considerable saving in labour and material costs, and although a little more care is required for the retouching, this is more than compensated for by the saving in the planning and etching time. It is a comparatively simple matter to place the negatives in position on the sheet of black paper upon which the type, folios and borders are already printed.

Invert Half-tone

A process which has attracted considerable attention by reason of its early employment for weekly colour-gravure newspaper supplements, is "invert half-tone." In this process a half-tone screen positive is made from a continuous tone negative and is sometimes printed directly on to a sensitized cylinder or plate, thus eliminating the use of carbon tissue. This method is specially suitable for colour work, though carbon tissue is often used.

The cylinder is sensitized with a cold enamel on a coating machine, and developed with denatured alcohol containing a purple dye. After this the sensitized cylinder is exposed on a direct transfer machine illuminated by a number of lamps and etched in a patented tank in which it is rotated for three to four minutes at a defined speed in a solution of 40 deg. Baumé.

Inverted half-tone is obviously an intaglio method, since the image lies below the surface; but, unlike gravure, the cell size varies with the tone instead of remaining constant.

Recent developments in gravure have tended towards discovering methods whereby the best of each system can be incorporated in a single entity.

One of the many new methods in inverted half-tone is governed mainly by variation in the areas of the etched cells, coupled with a variation in their depth.

The process is particularly suitable for colour work, as it does not depend upon the colour absorption or transparency of the ink. Separation negatives are made as in ordinary gravure, in continuous tone; but the negatives are illuminated by transmitted light in exposing the dot-formed positives, a cross-lined half-tone screen being used for the purpose. The positive exposure is made with a specially shaped aperture, the stop arranging the dots so that their sides are parallel to the screen lines: practically square but with slightly indented sides.

In the process the contrast is increased because the smaller dots do not etch as deeply as the larger ones. The positives are stripped on to a positive transfer glass, registration being effected on a precision table.

Another patented system embraces two different methods. The first utilizes half-tone positives exposed on cylinders sensitized with special solutions, and the second is based on the use of continuous tone positives employed in conjunction with a different sensitizer in the form of a bichromated proteid solution which is used as a resist.

Claims made for these adaptations are by no means extravagant. They embrace precision in register and greater fidelity in colour reproduction, since each image is an original; and thereby values are better controlled than in the case of separate positives which are printed down on carbon tissue.

Alco Gravure

The Alco process uses most highly volatile inks of the cellulose type, the solvent being extended ethyl acetate, and very rapid drying is assured without the use of steam drums. It would not be practicable to use such inks in an ordinary gravure press because the solvent by instantaneous evaporation would be constantly changing the ink consistency. Weiss, the inventor of the process, prevented this by revolving the cylinder in an enclosed metal box, at the top of which was a long slit through which a small section of the cylinder was exposed.

A blade of steel at each side of the slit nearly closes the gap between the revolving cylinder and the top of the box, restricting the entrance of air. This volatile ink is sprayed against the surface of the cylinder and the surplus scraped off by the doctor, the ink falling to the bottom of the box being filtered and pumped back for further use. The top blade is the doctor. The web, pressed by the impression cylinder against the engraved cylinder, takes up the coloured ink and passes immediately to the other cylinders, so that they are printed over each other in perfect register.

Gravure Tomorrow

It seems probable that the ultimate endeavours of photogravure research workers will reach towards the elimination of carbon tissue, and in the direction of photo-printing the positives directly on to specially sensitized cylinders. No process is static; the brains of men are for ever engaged upon the problem of making two blades of grass grow where there was only one.

SECURITY PRINTING

THE essential feature of security printing is, of course, the design, with its secret special markings, by which experts are able to detect at once any attempt at forgery. The original die of the design is first engraved on copper (Fig. 12), and it is then transferred to the copper cylinders and etched if the work is to be printed by photogravure.

Almost since the beginning of photogravure as a commercial process, it has been used extensively for the printing of bank notes, postage stamps, cheques and bonds. Postage stamps, which are printed as many as 500-up on a single

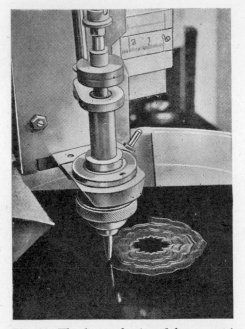

Fig. 12. *The diamond point of the geometric lathe which traces the black line effects which are a feature of the security of bank notes and similar printed matter.*

large quantities, because no other process can ensure such an exact duplication or maintain the highest printing quality during the long runs which such work entails. It can be said, however, that to the competent gravure worker, security printing offers no insoluble problems, as the principles are the same as in ordinary gravure work.

In the case of security printing direct from copper plates, the original die which has been prepared in steel, is hardened, and a soft steel cylinder is "taken up"—a process which produces a *relief* image of the original engraving. This soft steel cylinder is then hardened, and the design is duplicated on a steel or copper plate by means of rolling-in under great pressure. The image is repeated many times, in exact printing position, according to the size of the printing sheet (Fig. 13). After duplication the plate is dressed-off, i.e. the surface is cleaned and burnished free of all scratches and marks. The plate

cylinder, are perfected examples of the process.

The actual technical methods of printing are the same as in other forms of gravure production. From first to last the greatest care is taken to reproduce faithfully every line and tone of the original, and the cylinders are etched, and often re-etched, until an exact duplicate is achieved.

Gravure is the ideal medium for security printing in

PREPARING THE ORIGINAL DIE

Fig. 13. *Rolling-in the design on to the copper from the hardened cylinder in relief. The new image is shown half rolled-in.*

is next milled to a pre-determined gauge, and then chromium-faced, in order to resist wear during the course of printing.

The engraved printing plate is now firmly clamped to the cylinder, which is heated internally. Ink is then applied, after which the whole surface of the plate is polished clean of ink at every impression. The paper, which is damped for printing, then comes into contact with the plate under considerable pressure, the print being taken from the ink remaining in the recessed design on the printing plate.

The printed sheets are then dried, and the process repeated for every colour necessary to produce the design. After the final colour has been completed, the fully printed sheets are pressed so as to ensure that a perfectly smooth surface is obtained. Examination in sheet form then takes place, after which the sheets are numbered. Each sheet is then individually

sheared *by hand*. This is necessary owing to the fact that the sheets, being printed in a damp state, tend to stretch unevenly. The final cutting operation is performed by guillotine, and the notes receive the first "final" examination.

Rejected and imperfect notes are cancelled by means of large holes punched in them, being replaced by perfect notes bearing the same number. The waste notes and overs are shredded after the whole job has been finished.

The second "final" examination is now made; after which counting and sealing take place, followed by packing.

Throughout all the processes involved in security printing a receipt signature is secured every time a package or parcel changes hands; and the organization is such that, although millions of printed sheets are dealt with every year, the loss of a single sheet is almost unknown, and would be at once detected.

Security printing by the offset-litho process is described on page 190.

HAND PROOFING THE COPPER PLATE
There is no efficient substitute for the palm of the hand in cleaning the surface of the plate without removing ink from the more delicate parts of the engraving.

CHAPTER TWENTY-SIX

METHODS OF SCORE REPRODUCTION

EARLY METHODS. IMPORTANCE OF LEGIBILITY. MAKING ORIGINALS. HAND SETTING. ENGRAVING PROBLEMS. MODERN DEVELOPMENTS. PRINTING PROCESSES. SPECIAL IMPOSITION. TRADITION IN THE CRAFT. IMPORTANCE OF SPACING.

THE printing of music is so different in its very basic principles from the printing of letters in text or display, that it is necessary to understand the problem before considering the technical methods commonly employed. In music, everything relates to a stave, or grid, of five equally-spaced lines. It is thus obvious that all signs whatsoever—note-heads and tails and bar-lines—will cause the intersection of straight lines. It does not need much knowledge of practical type-setting to know the difficulties involved by this apparently simple demand.

Importance of Alignment

But there is yet one more complication, namely, that the whole sense of a passage of music depends upon exactness of up-and-down alignment. In letterpress, an A may be out of register, but it is still A; in music composition the note A out of register may sound as B or G. Special alignment is necessary also, with less absolute need for exactitude, because musical signs are read in clusters and not singly. For example, a word in brackets is read by convention as a separate word in separate brackets, but similar signs in music interlock much more closely in a musical sense. We determine pitch by vertical spacing, rhythm by horizontal spacing.

From the very early days of printing there has been a desire to print music, and the methods of overcoming the fundamental initial handicaps have occupied the attention of printers since before the sixteenth century.

Solving the Problem

At first, single separate notes with their staves attached were cut in wood by engravers, and fitted together piece by piece. The limitations of this system soon became obvious, and a development of the system, by means of which notes and staves and tails were made separately and joined together as an elaborately built-up type-page, dates from as early as 1500. The type-setting of music on this basis persists to our own times.

Hand-drawing for engraving by hand was another solution which was unsatisfactory; and also the obvious solution of double printing, by superimposing the signs on staves already printed. The question of exactitude of register created both difficulties and expense here.

It was later realized that the intersection of sunk channels is far more practical than the intersection of raised metal surfaces, and so the best solution of all, that of engraving, which provides a firm basis for flexible hand-work, was invented as early as 1525, when holograph or single punches are said to have been first used. This is the most general system in use in music printing today.

We must briefly discuss theory before describing practice. We must realize from the beginning that musical notation as printed on the page is not intended to be read in the same manner, or for the same reason, as letterpress type. The musical symbols convey not primarily a meaning of sense like a series of words, a noun and a verb, or a complete constructed sentence. They set out to convey to the reader his instructions to perform a series of actions, with his muscles or his breath and his always guiding ear, in order to enable him to make an audible sound.

Legibility of Printed Music

There are frequently two or more lines of symbols on one stave, and there are also often two or more staves set one above the other, to be simultaneously grasped by the eye and so transmitted to the body movements of the player. Moreover, there is not only the vertical aspect of the symbols; there is the horizontal as well. While each set of symbols must be vertically recognized instantaneously as an interval of a third, a fourth, or a fifth, there is also the fact that each chord or even single note must lead on, via the next, to the chords some way ahead.

Finally, it must be remembered that the receiver of the printed version, the player, or as we should call him in letterpress printing, the reader, is placed two and a half times as far from the page as the man holding a book or a newspaper; that is to say, two and a half feet is an average visual distance for music, one foot for ordinary reading.

The pictorial aspect of a page of music must never be forgotten. It is present in the musician's mind: the musician speaks in his ordinary talk of "high notes" and "low notes," and his

eye expects to see them relatively high or low in special relationship as he looks at his complex lines. Music printing deals with intersecting straight lines, but it also deals in curves, and its visual appeal is demanded by, and must be supplied to, the musical reader.

The sizes of founts of music are for these reasons comparatively restricted, but as in all other printing they need to be suitably chosen for the task in hand, whether it be the reproducing of short musical extracts in a letterpress book, a hymn-book for choir and congregation in a church, a song for home or concert-hall, an orchestral part for a symphony orchestra, or a mere sketch of a drum part for a jazz band.

The question of turning the pages is one of great importance. A good compositor, whether by hand or machine, avoids a hyphenated word at the end of a page, and a make-up compositor tries to avoid the commencement of a new paragraph on the last line of a page. These are niceties compared with the necessity of avoiding a turnover which no player can spare a hand to effect, without making wrong sounds on his instrument, or even no sound at all.

Production of Originals

It follows from all that has been said above that the production of an original from which to print off copies by some repeating method or another is in music printing a very much more precise and difficult matter than in letterpress printing. In music work the entire burden of good paging, and indeed of making proper sense at all, depends upon the compositor—or shall we call him for the moment the maker of the original?

Let us examine, then, how a good original can be made.

There is the method of hand-drawing. That does not affect the printer until it comes to its reproduction on a printing surface. Except as referred to below under new processes, paper is a difficult basis for music-work originals. We may dismiss it for the moment.

There is also the old method of type-setting by hand, which, however, is still very frequently used today.

Setting Music by Hand

The music compositor faces a complicated task. In his book, *Music Printing and Engraving*, Mr. W. Gamble says that "a bar of eight consecutive notes in 3/4 time, and with a tenor clef, contains at least seventy-eight characters, and there will be more if the measure contains accidentals or complicated harmony." The first difficulty is the extreme flexibility of musical notation, and the large number of sorts thus required.

Each sign which appears on or near a stave has to have attached to it the lines proper to its position on the stave for joining to the next piece of type. There are also tails, binds, bar-lines, note-heads of various durations, slurs, clefs, and a number of special sorts, apart from spaces. It is not surprising, therefore, that a case of music type contains about 350 sorts. It is unusual to find more than four sizes of music type in a printing office—semi-non-pareil, gem, diamond, and ruby.

Music type is costly and extremely fragile, and therefore printing is seldom carried out from the type itself. Stereos or electros are always taken and the type is "dissed"; apart from saving breakages, this practice has the advantage of closing up, to a certain extent, the innumerable join-spaces, and also of saving the printer from the heavy capital expenditure of large stocks of type. Sixteen pages are usually set and read, submitted to the author or customer, and, when corrected and

passed, immediately cast, so that the type may be released.

The type is set in a composing stick, in the usual way, but before the actual setting is commenced much preparation in the copy stage is essential. It is necessary to count or gauge by experience the number of symbols that will go to each line, and then roughly to allot the correct number of symbols into each bar. In some offices, it is a precautionary practice actually to set a single guide-line (not on a stave but on one line) to aid in the spacing. Correcting music type is difficult and expensive, and therefore accurate setting is imperative.

The use of words with music, as in a song or hymn, adds to the need for calculating the spacing, and the tonic sol-fa notation is frequently included in addition to the staff notation.

Hand-set music, properly composed and firmly cast, is a good original for limited purposes, but it is of its very nature unsuitable for elaborate musical work. As it is printed by the letterpress process, hand-setting is still much used for the examples illustrating musical textbooks and studies, and for any job involving a greater proportion of verbal text than musical notation.

Engraving Music

The enormous advantage that the drawing and engraving of a music original has over type does not depend entirely upon the intersection of lines. It depends, in this free-spaced craft, upon the simple fact that type-set music consists of building up mechanically a spaced original, whereas the pen and the graver have an open sheet, of paper or metal, on which spaces can be planned before action.

Imagine an army commander, without maps, building the plans of his movements with separate bricks!

TWO IMPORTANT PROCESSES IN MUSIC PRINTING

(Above) The use of steel punches for music engraving on pewter plates. Punches are used for all the conventional signs, other marks being produced by hand-cutting. (Below) Litho artist preparing a zinc machine-plate. Offset litho is largely used for music printing.

The freedom of the draughtsman's hand is always to some extent present in the craft of the music engraver. But the draughtsman is working on the unstable medium of paper in preparing his original. Paper drags under the pen. It is not easily fixed on a drawing-board. Even fine card, like Bristol board, is not satisfactory for the accurate drawing of five equally-spaced lines—our unit, let us not forget. Above all, there is no school or tradition that can keep a calligrapher or even map-draughtsman within the bounds of music's imperative demands.

The tradition of music engraving, on the other hand, with its stolid basis of metal to be cut, dates back for more than 400 years, and has a close kinship with the more expressive arts of wood-engraving, etching, and dry-point work on copper.

What the music engraver has to cultivate in his apprenticeship (apart from an innate knowledge of musical notation and composers' habits, of which more later) is the freedom of the draughtsman within the limits of a mechanically precise accuracy. He must make a music original that looks to the musician's eye a mechanical product, so clear and accurate is it. He can only attain that perfection of mechanical appearance by an innate understanding of the intelligible arrangement upon his plate of the composer's signs.

Pewter Plates

Music is engraved upon pewter plates by means of punches cut into the required shapes. The conventional signs—clefs, note-heads, quaver tails, pedal marks, accidentals, and so on—alone are provided in the fount. Any note-head will serve for any position on (or above and below) the stave. The stems of the notes, the binds, bar-lines, slurs, and crescendo marks are mostly produced by hand-cutting. This is not exhaustively true: where time and labour can be saved by the provision of holograph punches, proper provision is made.

Given his pewter plate, cut to the right size, and his skill, the music engraver needs only a small outfit of tools—a set of punches (some 150 against the 400 or so sorts of the hand-setter); a hammer or two; some callipers; some varied gravers (including a scorer or five-point cutter), and a metal rule. He must, too, have access to various cases of letter-punches and to cases of tonic sol-fa. It may be interesting to know that the punches have for many years been made mostly in Germany for use everywhere in the world, while the hard-metal cutters have (even in Germany) always been bought from Sheffield.

Engraver's Fount Sizes

The music engraver will find that he must have recourse to a larger number of fount-sizes than the hand-setter—at least eight. But the apparatus of storing is far simpler than with a fount of music type (*see* illustration on page 319). In the matter of style or choice of design in founts, there is little opening.

The style was set by J. G. Breitkopf and G. C. Härtel in the early part of the nineteenth century, and that the style was efficient is proved by a hundred years of practice.

There is no question of a central distributing agency for designs, and more's the pity. Such variations as have been made remain the property of individual firms, even down to the letter-punches (which are on the whole pretty poor, both in cut and in quality of design); but the design of lettering is influenced by the requirements of the printing process employed.

The question of spacing is as lively

DESIGNING A MUSIC COVER TITLE
*The attractive layout of a music title has an important effect on sales. A left-handed
artist is shown drawing the lettering for a song title by a well-known composer.*

a problem to the music engraver as it is
to the designer of a repeating pattern,
to a typographer, or to a poster artist.
He has a space to fill—in the engraver's
case, an oblong of metal. How does he
start? He (or his foreman) starts by
counting the symbols (or as the compositor would say, the ens) which go to
a line, including words, if any; he
watches his turnovers, makes easy
reading of each line, according to the
number of staves on each page (there
may be fifty or there may be five),
counts his stave spaces, above and
below, for vertical legibility; and then
he measures out his plate with his
callipers. Intelligent spacing is essential
to legibility, whether it be vertical or
horizontal.

Then, the music engraver marks out
his plate in rough, with a pin-point
scratching as a guide. Two things should
be realized here: first, the plate is soft
for working on; second, the engraver
has, of course, to prepare his original

backwards. Vertical spacing must come
first, as marking out can only be done
on an already engraved stave.

Once accepted, his marked-out plate
becomes his guide. He finally cuts his
five-pointed lines, punches in his note-
heads, and finishes with his gravers and
metal rule.

The fact that correcting is not a
difficult job does not remove one jot of
the responsibility from the engraver
in the first task of laying out his plate
right. Correcting on this soft plate is
done by marking with the callipers the
back of the plate at the spot to be
altered, and by hammering to flatness
the plate at that point. That is simply
described; but the process of flattening
and re-engraving demands skill not to
be defined in words. Finally the engraver
cleans up his plate for proofing.

Proofing is done, as in all intaglio
processes, by filling in the incisions
with ink, wiping the plate so that the
surface is clean and the incisions filled,

and printing under pressure. That is the ideal method; the usual way is to use green or even blue ink in the reverse way, so that the proofs appear with the engraved incisions showing white. This system is accepted but not generally liked by proof readers.

Alternative Methods

Partly owing to the shortage of engravers, partly because of the eternal search for more mechanical devices to reduce the cost of printing music, and partly because of the extensions in the use of the camera in printing, several new systems have been devised in recent years. The engravers themselves have assisted in this stifling of their own craft, for in Britain they have not admitted any new apprentices for a long period of years. It is to be hoped that the present increased interest in music in this country will enable this ban to be lifted.

Mostly, these systems are privately, some even secretly, owned by certain firms. The general principle of the Halstan process is to build up an original in a size much larger by many times than it is intended to print. The symbols are cut out like templates and are applied by hand, or stuck, on to an upright surface (like a wall). Little skill is required of the "setter" under this system, but the enormous photographic reduction does not make for legibility.

Technograph uses a machine for determining both vertical and horizontal positions with considerable exactness, and so eliminates the responsibility of the engraver; in place of muscular control of eye and hand it substitutes a precision-instrument. The notation is lightly stamped on to paper by holograph punch-like note-heads and other symbols. Apart from the instability of paper as an original, and the inevitable loss of the fluidity of freehand drawing, Technograph has made considerable progress.

Luxotype, a French system used in New York, differs from Technograph in the use of a tiny spotlight to assist positioning.

Musigraph is a process which has proved very successful in the production of full scores both in miniature and full size, surely the most exacting of all music. It is equally adaptable for producing all other kinds of printed music.

Many years of experiment and of building up a tradition are necessary before any of these attempts at simplification can produce anything which even approaches the perfection and stability of music engraving.

Printing Methods

As already pointed out, hand-set music is printed on letterpress machines, from stereotypes or electrotypes. Engraved music is printed by lithography. It is not necessary to dilate upon lithographic processes in this chapter, but certain points should be made clear.

First of all, lithography (usually offset) is invariably used in music printing today. Secondly, the original is laid down on to the stone or prepared zinc plate by photographic printing and not, as a rule, by direct transfer of inked proof to plate; though transfers from pewter plates are still used in some cases.

The traditions of imposition are different in music from those of book printing. The root reason for this is the fact that legibility in music is aided very considerably when the eye can take in a long phrase without turning to the next line. Margins in music are therefore usually much smaller than in books, even head margins. Nevertheless, bad practices have, through the years, crept in, and until a completely new set of traditions for margins was introduced, an unthinking acceptance of the bad

MUSIC PRINTING BY OFFSET ROTARY

A music cover title being printed in colour on a Mann two-colour rotary offset machine.
The actual printing of music does not differ from that of ordinary lithographic work.

old ways was universal in music printing, and still very widely remains.

Yet within the demands of music printing, it is possible to design a page with margins properly proportioned as to gutter and fore-edge which are both suitable to the function of the music and pleasing to the eye.

Music is issued mostly in quarto format, in oblong large octavo, or in upright large octavo. It is chiefly printed on paper of special sizes, or on royal sheets cut to special sizes. There is very considerable variation in customers' demands and practice, and a music printer has to be prepared to carry a large number of sizes of stock of both printers' and customers' paper. Imposition therefore is less a rule of thumb in music than in letterpress or even than in other kinds of litho work.

Any reader of the foregoing description of the processes of music printing may well be excused if he were to infer that the music engraver's job is easy compared with that of the ordinary compositor. He would be wrong. In addition to the clean and precise manual work demanded of him, involving a number of varied actions and processes, the engraver of music has a far greater editorial responsibility than the letterpress compositor, even if the latter be of the highest class, composing scholarly or specialist scientific books The traditions of the craft demand accuracy and pride in accuracy.

But it must be remembered that while the deciphering of author's copy in letterpress is difficult enough, the same task in music is very much more difficult, for common sense and everyday meaning are not there to assist, nor is there yet a musical typewriter; also there are very few composers of music or even copyists who have any knowledge of, or instinct for, the appearance of music upon the page, except in a very general way. Let us take one point only—the position of the tails of a crotchet or quaver sign.

The manual writer of music places his tail according to his whim, calligraphic or convenient as it happens. The music engraver, on the other hand, has to know that, though he must follow copy like any other printer, a tailed note must have its tail upward for notes that lie below the A of the treble clef, and down for notes that lie higher.

The rule is not rigid or invariable; it is at the mercy of demands of phrasing and other considerations. It does not hold necessarily with chords or with music written in "real parts," and so on, and it is conditioned by other needs of graphic appeal and common musical legibility. Accurate spacing is vital, whether horizontal or vertical, and can be obtained only by the most careful foresight and planning, to be followed by precision of manual skill.

It may truthfully be said of a printed page of music that any distinction or visual merit it possesses as a finished object is far more dependent on the engraver's skill than any page, even a display page, in letterpress work. The typographer, the layout man, can in music printing give only general instructions compared with their finished drawings for type-set pages; and in every piece of printed music, composer, editor, publisher, and machine-minder all throw far more responsibility on the engraver for accuracy and fineness of detail than is ever thrown upon the judgment of a compositor.

For all practical purposes, it may be assumed that there is only one style of fount available in musical notation, the alternatives being so restricted in use that only the employees of a single house can use this one, or of another that one—rather as if Caslon Old Face were confined to one printing office and Gill Sans exclusively to another.

This in its turn emphasizes the point once again. The writer has often heard from people, who judged only superficially, in praise of the "beautiful music type" used in certain productions. Actually, the "type" used was the same, and had perforce to be the same, as the type used for all other jobs.

What was mistaken for beauty of type-design was the arrangement of the spacing, which, by being intelligently planned, lent distinction and legibility to material of universal design.

Line reproduction of a music original of the Musigraph process for printing by photolitho.

CHAPTER TWENTY-SEVEN

STORAGE AND ISSUE OF STOCK

WHITE PAPER. STOCK ROOM CONDITIONS. SIMPLE PAPER TESTS. STOCK-KEEPING
SYSTEMS. ISSUE OF PAPER. CALCULATING OVERS. WAREHOUSE OPERATIONS. HAND
AND MACHINE FOLDING. GUILLOTINE WORK. WIRE STITCHERS.

WAREHOUSE work in the printing office falls into two main divisions, the handling and care of white paper being the first of these. The second is concerned with the paper after printing, in the process of transforming it into books, periodicals, catalogues and other sectional matter. There is a further subsection which includes the care of printed stock, which is quite properly related to the first division in warehouse work.

White Paper

The term "white paper" covers all paper of whatever colour in an unprinted condition, and the task of the warehouseman is the receipt, storage, checking, and issuing of such paper. As paper is the foundation on which the whole structure of printing rests, the importance of its care, handling and recording will be realized.

The paper store (Figs. 1 and 2) should be chosen for reasons of suitability, and not, as too frequently happens, for reasons of expediency. It should be light and airy, not the dark and dismal dungeon it too often is. The temperature should be constant, corresponding to 65 per cent moisture saturation of air, which approximates to 6 per cent moisture in the paper; this is about the normal amount. The racks should be solid, with flat shelves running parallel to the direction in which the paper will be inserted, and in no case less than 6 in. from the floor.

A free current of air should pass below all shelved stock. All papers coming into store will be checked as to quantity and quality: checking for quantity is routine; quality is too often taken for granted.

Whatever defects manifest themselves in the printing operation it is reasonable to suppose that the warehouseman will be called upon to deal with the trouble. Every department of the printing office is affected to a greater or lesser degree by quality and condition of paper, and the warehouseman's job is to keep his stock in prime condition.

Defects which occur in paper vary greatly according to class and quality. Often it is the reverse of economy to purchase the cheapest paper, yet cheap paper carefully chosen in relation to the job may frequently serve as well as a more expensive one.

Paper Testing

The experienced executive can effect tests of a rough and ready nature without accessories of any kind. He can recognize faults, often by observation alone; estimate thickness and weight by feel; and tell the composition of a sheet by look-through and handling. He can assess the quality of the

THE PAPER STORE

Fig. 1. *Ample handling space is essential in a well-arranged paper store, and the temperature should be controlled. Modern method of conveying stock is by platform trucks, as shown.*

sizing, or the amount of loading in a paper by virtue of his experience and a few simple experiments.

It is a good thing, however, to have available certain definite testing appliances for particular cases, such as a reliable micrometer for proving thickness and an apparatus for testing breaking strength. A few chemicals kept in carefully-stoppered bottles will serve to answer many questions. A few drops of ether for testing rosin sizing on a sheet of paper sized with rosin will produce a darkish earth-coloured ring. White iodine solution proves the presence of starch by producing a dark blue spot. Hydrochloric acid used in conjunction with ammonia will reveal the presence of casein. Phloroglucine acts as a detector of mechanical wood, a

spot on this kind of wood paper becoming brownish-red, the depth of the red being a dependable criterion of the proportion of mechanical wood.

Matching Sheets

There are other tests to which paper may be subjected, but the most useful testing method is experience; feel, appearance, rattle, look-through, are all reliable if the characteristics of these qualities are understood. Even the expert may have difficulty in judging an isolated sample; therefore doubtful parcels should be compared where possible with proved matching sheets, and any departure from standard of quality should be noted.

Management of the paper store should be vested in a single individual whose job will be the efficient running of the department: all movements of stock, receipts and issues will be his responsibility and he should have complete authority which should be rigidly enforced in the care of his stock. Without strict supervision much damage can be done. No unauthorized persons should be at liberty to help themselves to odd sheets, or to tear off corners at will, often leaving reams uncovered after doing so. Untidiness and exposure should be avoided; waste cannot be prevented if such practices are permitted.

All purchases will be faithfully recorded. Invoices must be copied into the purchase book as they come to hand, and the buying total summary extended monthly and annually.

Goods Received Book

A goods received book should also be kept. Into this will be noted details of all items received, together with particulars relating to quantity, contents, supplier, method of transport, and carriage paid or forward.

In this way an exact record of purchase and receipt is at all times on record. There may be some difference of opinion as to whether this recording should be done within the store or in the office. The point is, however, that it should be done and the man in charge should have such details under his control.

The consumption of stock must be recorded in detail and an accurate check be applied to the destination of each sheet; spoilage replacements should be issued only against spoilage tickets. There is a number of systems in use by which such records are kept, and it matters little which of these is used provided it is simple, accurate, and easily understood. The Master Printers' Federation official costing system has

much to recommend it on grounds of simple common sense and ease of working. It involves the use of a paper stock ledger. This is a loose-leaf book with a separate leaf for each item of stock carried. Full details of manufacturer, quality, specification, price and position in the warehouse are entered at the top of each page.

The remainder of the page is specially ruled to show amounts received and quantities issued; the balance in hand and its value can be seen at once if the book is kept up to date. Index leaves divide the different classes of paper, while an index at the front gives the page number of any paper to which it is desired to refer.

It will be seen from this that the complete transactions of the paper warehouse are on record and any query which may arise can be answered. Questions as to transport and deliveries which may have suffered damage *en route* are the immediate concern of the warehouseman, and should be taken up at once with the parties concerned.

The advantages of some such system as has been outlined need not be stressed. The work entailed will be reduced to a minimum; the value of the stock can be ascertained at any time; receipts can be balanced against consumption. Most important of all, odd lots of paper will be kept in full view to be used as opportunity offers.

Suitable Conditions

Provided that the temperature of the store is maintained constant and that slow-moving stocks are kept carefully wrapped, the condition should be uniformly satisfactory. Special papers will need to have more than ordinary care. Dampness is fatal where coated papers are housed, whilst manifolds, greaseproofs, carbons, vegetable parchments, must be kept in tight and ample wrappers. The careless habit of permitting deliveries of paper to lie exposed in the yard for quite long periods before transferring to the proper place should be regarded as a major offence against all the canons of good stock keeping.

Issue of Paper

The task of issuing the necessary paper for a particular job will be easy or difficult according to the system adopted in keeping the stock. In the majority of instances the work-ticket will show quite clearly the total amount of paper required to complete the job, such figures including overs. There are, however, many occasions when these figures will not be shown on the work-ticket, and the question of computing the quantity essential for the order with the necessary overs will be worked out in the paper warehouse. In addition, it is quite a usual procedure to ask the warehouse to work out the amount of paper for a job when the estimate is being prepared.

It follows, therefore, that the responsible head of the paper store should be able to arrive at the necessary paper allotment quickly and accurately. He should have knowledge of the processes which paper is called upon to undergo, for paper will be issued for ordinary printing, using black ink only, for two- or three-colour work, for lithographic printing, machine-ruling and account-book work, and die-stamping.

Calculating Quantities

Other processes call for the use of paper of different class and quality, such as art, imitation art, supercalendered, chromo, banks and handmade. In every case the nature of the operation or the class of paper, or both, will influence the number of overs needed in order to carry the printed job to a successful conclusion.

Finding the net amount of paper entailed in the production of a job (exclusive of overs) should present few difficulties to the man familiar with ordinary paper usage. To calculate this will be his first task. On the result and according to the operations involved in the particular job, the number of overs will be arrived at.

One example of this simple calculation may be given: 1,000 catalogues, crown 8vo, 112 pages. This is set out as follows:—

$$\frac{1,000 \text{ copies} \times 112 \text{ pages}}{16 \text{ page section} \times 500 \text{ (1 ream)}} = 14 \text{ reams}$$

Thus it is found that 14 reams is the absolute minimum needed for this job. To this quantity will be added the overs. In connection with this simple method of calculation there are one or two points to be kept well in mind. Remember that the denominator of the fraction is the key to the number of pages or leaves of such size which can be produced, either by folding or cutting, from the standard sized sheet.

Where *leaves* are required the figure in the denominator gives the number correctly; in the case of *pages* the denominator will be multiplied by 2. Errors arise very frequently by reason of confusion between pages and leaves: it is essential to *double the figure* in the subdivisional sign when pages are wanted as distinct from leaves. The following table is useful for reference:—

Standard sheet reduced to

8vo =	8 leaves	(16 pp.)
4to =	4 ,,	(8 pp.)
Folio =	2 ,,	(4 pp.)
12mo =	12 ,,	(24 pp.)
16mo =	16 ,,	(32 pp.)

This does not cover the whole range of sizes or subdivisions; it is intended only to illustrate difference in pages and leaves.

Overs depend on the number of times the sheet passes through the

PAPER REEL STOCK ROOM

Fig. 2. *The storage and handling of paper reels each weighing several hundredweights, requires special machinery. The illustration shows the reels being transferred to rotary machines on the floor above, the rewinding of the reel being carried through an opening in the floor.*

machine and on the number of formes used to print the job. It is neither possible nor advisable to lay down a scale for overs percentages, as these vary from one office to another. It can be said, however, that a certain definite number of sheets should be allowed for the first 500 run which will include make-ready, and for the balance of the run a percentage based on experience in relation to the process being worked, the quality of the job, and any other consideration which may be present.

On short runs the number of overs will naturally be higher in proportion than in the case of longer runs; on the other hand the overs percentage can be reduced within limits as the extent of the run increases. To sum up: the number of sheets to be issued as overs depends not on the net quantity which the job calls for, but on the number of times each sheet goes through the

machine. To this must be added the number of formes or plates which are used in the printing operation, because a certain amount of making-ready will nearly always be necessary each time that a new forme is put on the printing machine.

These are complex points which may be covered by a standard scale operating in particular printing offices. The warehouseman who is concerned with keeping *au fait* with his job, and the ever-changing conditions which are common to printing, will make it his business to keep careful records of requirements peculiar to the question of overs, always remembering that if the out-turn of a job exceeds the actual quantity ordered a custom of the trade permits a reasonable percentage to be charged for.

Few sections of the printing trade are so highly mechanized as the productive warehouse. The operations which the warehouse worker may be called upon to undertake differ considerably according to the house in which he is employed. In the larger jobbing offices where all classes of printed work may be turned out, folding, bundling, cutting and trimming, gathering, wiring, thread-stitching, thread-sewing, eyeletting, scoring, bending, wrappering, round-cornering, perforating, to mention a few of the more general processes, may easily form part of the daily routine.

Importance of Layout

The disposition of the plant and equipment is of first importance, for here, as in the bindery, bulky work is handled and completed. Thus, faulty alignment of mechanical units and work-benches will result in waste movement with consequent loss of output. Where detailed planning can be carried out a definite scheme of work travel should be aimed at the movement being continually forward from the point where sheets enter the department to that where the completed job passes to the packing room.

The printed sheet forms the basis of the warehouse job; it may come in the first instance from the machine department to "pass" for folding imposition; later for actual folding by hand or machine. Let us therefore consider the simple business of passing a sheet for imposition.

This must always be done in the case of a new job. Routine jobs which are repeated from time to time may not require the sheet to be O.K'd, but it is very dangerous to run-on a job which presents new features without having a sheet passed for position.

Many operators fight shy of accepting responsibility for this task. It is quite simple, however. The machine department sends two pulls to the ware-house. One of these will be folded carefully to print, trimmed to size and a stitch put in the fold to hold the sections securely in position. The second sheet remains in its unfolded condition and is laid out on the table.

The folded section is now considered page by page and checked with the dummy or layout, and any alteration of page position clearly marked on the flat sheet, and also on the folded section. When all the pages have been dealt with and the marking completed, the unfolded sheet, marked "press" if there should be no alterations, or "note alterations or corrections," is returned to machine. The folded and marked section is retained by the warehouse as a guide in marking the sections which are to follow.

A good method of paging up a blank folded section when trying out folding schemes is shown in Fig. 3. Fold the sheet to the desired scheme and lay it flat on a board, and cut a V right through as shown. The points of the V are now numbered 1, 3, 5, etc., on the front, the section turned over and the numbering 2, 4, 6, etc., repeated from the back. On opening out the sheet the pagination is correct and right way up; the sheet is practically intact and easily handled. This procedure takes but a few seconds.

Hand and Machine Folding

Although there is still a considerable proportion of folded work done by hand the operation does not require description, and machine folding is therefore dealt with. It is well to remember the advisability of using, wherever possible, an imposition common to hand and machine, for while the hand-folder can make any fold which is possible on the machine, time and expense are increased where unusual impositions have to be handled.

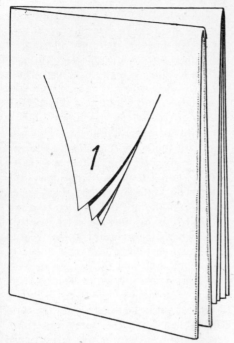

Fig. 3. *Any section, no matter how involved, can be paged correctly and the right way up by cutting a* V *through the paper and numbering throughout from both sides.*

There are two main features incorporated in modern folders: the knife, which dips between a couple of reciprocating rollers, and the plate which forms an envelope into which the sheet is propelled, bending or buckling along a desired line as it makes its exit (Figs. 4 and 5).

Most machines in common use employ one or other of these methods of producing the folds and certain machines include both principles in a single unit. Where faulty folding is delivered from the machine, it can be said that it is rarely the machine which is at fault, or if so, not directly. The cause can usually be traced to faulty operation or careless treatment of the machine, or faults in the register of the printed sheet.

In printing works where more than one type of machine is available it is a good plan to keep particular machines for certain classes of work as far as conditions will permit. The plate folder is ideal for parallel sections, and the knife folder is best for right-angle schemes. While right-angle sections can be folded on plate machines and done perfectly, experience shows that the degree of trouble is greater, more particularly as the stock becomes thinner, than where the knife-folder is used.

It should be the first duty of the operator to keep his machine clean and rollers, tapes, plates, should have regular attention. Chalk should not be strewn over folding rollers; tapes should be cleaned at least once a week. A pad of cotton wool soaked in benzoline pressed against the running tape in a safe spot is an effective method. Plates should not be left lying about on the floor when out of use but should be placed in racks under dust-proof covers. The amount of work spoiled through dents in plate lips by careless handling is simply astonishing.

A few maxims worthy of attention are offered to machine operators:—

In passing sheets from the printing department, be sure to check the lay edges.

If half-sheet work, slit on the printing machine, is being folded, make sure that the printer is using keen slitters; blunt ones will not cut straight.

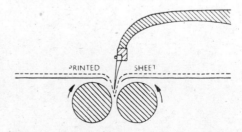

PRINTED SHEET

Fig. 4. *Knife folding is the most common folding method. The rollers are usually fluted steel. They can be rubber covered.*

Keep perforators in good condition; blunt perforators cause creases in the centre of the sections.

When using perforators, make sure that a suitable counterpart is fitted; a too-narrow groove cuts the section instead of perforating.

Look to the dip of the knife; see that it is not too low, otherwise the centre of the section may be rubbed.

On plate-folding machines the feed-roller must be adjusted to the folding length of the sheet by the plugging-in of a pin in a marked position on a cam-roller controlling the feed roller. This must not be overlooked.

Keep the front edge of sheets perfectly flat on plate machines. Any disposition to turn upwards becomes accentuated at the next fold, the sheet forming a V and catching, or failing to enter the following plate.

Where parallel work is being slit at delivery, keep the support rollers close up to the slitters, otherwise the cutting may be off the straight.

A good cutter must know his guillotine and be capable of making adjustments as they are required. The ideal machine is one having an easily-adjusted clamp, a knife with quick return which cannot over-run, a quickly-moving back gauge, and a safe and dependable safety guard. Most machines bearing well-known names fulfil these conditions. If, therefore, the cutter keeps his machine in good tune, dealing with the average job should present little difficulty. The knife should be so adjusted that it cuts the bottom sheet of the pile without dipping into the stick. With a knife which is beginning to grow dull it is much better to cut on a piece of card than to lower the knife.

When very thin wired sections are being cut, sometimes the backs will bulk to almost twice the thickness of the fore-edge; even when the wires are "staggered" the top sections will sag forward when front edges are being trimmed.

If the booklets have been wired before this trouble has been noticed the only thing to do is to press them up firmly against the back gauge, and to put a weight on top of the piles behind the clamp. Another plan is to trim front edges before wiring, thus

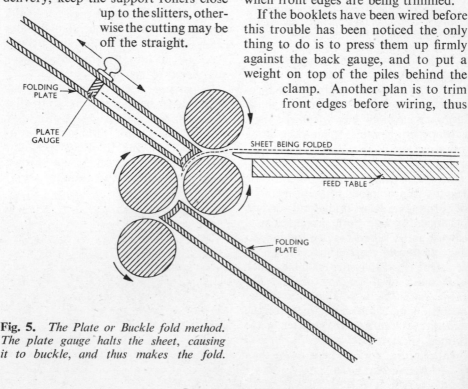

FOLDING PLATE

PLATE GAUGE

SHEET BEING FOLDED

FEED TABLE

FOLDING PLATE

Fig. 5. *The Plate or Buckle fold method. The plate gauge halts the sheet, causing it to buckle, and thus makes the fold.*

saving trouble and with more satisfactory results. The booklets are wired after the front edges are trimmed and returned to the machine to have heads and tails finished off.

Every cutter should keep at hand a few varying lengths of lead-cutting stick covered in clean paper for dealing with unusual difficulties. For instance, if warped cards come to the machine to be squared for the printer, the pile should be halved and each half faced, so that the convexes of the cards are made to face each other. A few weights placed on top behind the clamp will ensure their being cut square.

Pointers for Cutters

Keep a length of compositors' reglet (half-width) glued to the edge of a corresponding length of strawboard 4 in. wide to use under the clamp to take clamp pressure where set-off is likely to take place.

Every cutter should have a graduated cutting pad made of strawboard bevelled to a fine edge for use in trimming heads and tails of work which has undue swell in the back.

A mixture of graphite and soft soap rubbed on the "dolly" for wiping over the knife where hard stock is being cut will make the work of the knife easier.

Where forms of the repetition variety have to be cut dead to size to fit office machines or loose-leaf books, templets should be made of stout board or metal. These are placed against the back gauge and the knife lowered. The templet is turned forward until contact is established, the knife is run up, and if the gauge is locked the measure will be found to be correct.

To avoid tearing, always cut thick sections against the travel of the knife. In the case of square backs with wrappers drawn on it is best to do the trimming before the glue sets hard.

Bundling machines are very useful where much folded work has to be kept for any length of time; indeed, portable models which can be moved from one machine to another as the need arises should form part of modern warehouse equipment. In large departments handling periodicals and similar printed matter, fully-automatic wrappering machines are used, and they are a profitable investment. As such machines are very expensive to run, a much cheaper and simpler alternative for the small department is the glue-wrappering tank which supersedes the primitive glue-brush method of covering books.

Wire stitchers are so good in these days that they need but little attention. Where they turn out faulty stitching it is usually the wire or the setting of the machine which is to blame. There is, of course, more to learn about a wiring unit than how to depress a treadle.

To get an idea of how a wire-stitcher works the machine should be opened out to its widest stitching capacity and turned by hand while stitching a single sheet of paper. All the movements of forming the stitch can thus be seen in slow motion; and as the principle of wire-stitching is uniform in most machines the intelligent observer will learn much from this simple idea.

Value of Co-operation

Friendly relationship between departments should be fostered and encouraged under all circumstances. This is a necessary condition in all departments of a printing office, but it is of outstanding importance where the productive warehouse is concerned. The warehouse cannot afford to be difficult, for this department is so largely dependent on the good offices of the other sections that, in its own interest, where assistance or advice is sought its response should be instant.

CHAPTER TWENTY-EIGHT

PRINTING PAPERS AND THEIR MANUFACTURE

QUALITIES OF PAPER. RAG AND WOOD-PULP FIBRES. ADDITION OF LOADINGS. SIZING. ATMOSPHERIC CONDITIONS. HAND-MADE PAPERS. STATIC ELECTRICITY. EXPERIMENTAL RESEARCH. METHODS OF MANUFACTURE. PAPER-MAKING MACHINES. CONDITIONING.

BY far the greatest proportion of paper which is made throughout the world is used for printing. Enormous quantities of paper are used every day for producing books, newspapers, and periodicals of all kinds. There is a considerable variety in printing papers as regards the fibre used, the sizing or resistance to ink penetration, and the surface or finish; and papers vary greatly in price in consequence of these various characteristics.

Qualities of Paper

The chief qualities required for printing papers are good colour, not too hard sized, smooth surface, evenness of texture, fairly opaque, so that the sheets may be printed on both sides without the ink showing through; paper should have a clear look through, and be free from specks and spots on the surface. The price depends almost entirely upon the nature of the fibre which is used.

Printing papers may be made from pure rag, and will then be a beautiful white colour, soft to print upon, pleasant to handle, and very durable. A type face of moderate size, printed with a good black ink, gives a very rich appearance on such paper. These rag papers may be either hand-made, in which case they usually retain their deckle edges; cylinder-mould made, which means that they also have an imitation deckle edge; or they may be made on a paper-making machine, in much the same way as the cheaper wood-pulp papers. These classes of paper are used only for very special and expensive editions, and they are often watermarked.

Other high-grade printing papers are made from a mixture of rag and chemical wood-pulp fibres, and these together produce a soft paper which will take a good finish and have good opacity. Another very common blend of fibre, which is used for enormous quantities of book papers, is that of chemical wood-pulp and esparto grass (Figs. 1 and 2). This type of paper is largely made in Scotland, where it is produced with the greatest skill. The result is a paper which is good for printing half-tone blocks, and also for producing a rich appearance. Papers made from this mixture are often coated and used for high-class illustrated magazines.

Cheaper Grades

Going down the scale in quality, there are papers made from sulphite and soda wood-pulps, both from coniferous and deciduous trees, which, while excellent for many purposes, do not give the bulk and softness of those mentioned above.

Lastly we come to those printing papers commonly called newsprint, which are used for newspapers and other cheap productions; and these are made from a very high proportion (often 80 per cent) of mechanical wood, and sulphite or chemical wood-pulp.

This mechanical wood is simply ordinary soft wood from spruce trees, ground to sawdust by stone grinding wheels. In order to run this over a paper machine it is necessary to add a stiffening of from 15 to 25 per cent of long-fibred strong sulphite pulp, and the finished product is good for its purpose, but has no durability. Such paper easily discolours and disintegrates, and for this reason it is usual to print a few copies of newspapers on higher-class papers, such as that made from rags, so that they may be kept for record purposes. Papers made from ground wood and sulphite pulp are generally known as common printings.

In the manufacture of printing papers it is the invariable custom to add loadings. These may take the form of china clay—which is used in large quantities in common printings. Precipitated chalk, titanium oxide, barium sulphate, or other loadings are also used.

While some printers seem to be of the opinion that the adding of the loadings is an adulteration of the

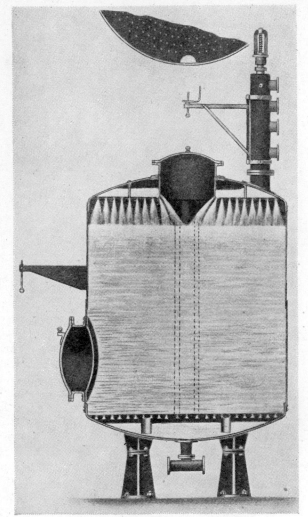

SINCLAIR ESPARTO PULP BOILER

Fig. 1. *The esparto grass is boiled in this stationary boiler with boiling liquor which is circulated by means of a pump which draws the liquor from the bottom, pumps it back and sprays it on to the grass. A small section of the perforated bottom is shown inset.*

papers, this is definitely not the case. For really successful printing on paper, and especially for fine printing results on high quality papers, it is necessary to add a filler of some kind, in order to fill up thoroughly the interstices between fibres, and also to produce a smooth

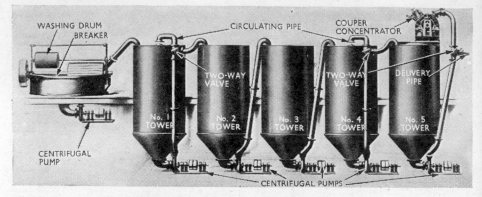

MASSON-SCOTT BLEACHING TOWERS

Fig. 2. The pulp is broken up and washed in the breaker and then pumped through the range of towers. By the time it reaches the last tower it is bleached white and ready for use. If necessary, however, the pulp may be circulated again in the bleaching towers.

surface which will take the print evenly.

Some high-class esparto printings, such as the well-known imitation arts made in Scotland, contain as much as 30 per cent of loading, and very fine printing results can thus be obtained upon them. For the many illustrations used in the production of a newspaper, the newsprint must be highly loaded with clay in order to give the solid printing results desired.

Sized Papers

In addition to the loadings, all printing papers are sized, which simply means that they contain a proportion of rosin and sulphate of alumina which makes them resistant to ink, and prevents the ink spreading on the surface and running through to the centre and to the other side of the paper. Most printing papers are not hard-sized in the same way that writing papers are hard-sized, but are only given sufficient size to economize in the consumption of ink and to provide a firmer-handling paper. If the paper is sized so that the surface is too hard the ink will not penetrate. Besides this sizing it is generally necessary to tint

with dyes all papers whether they be white or toned, as well as the deeply coloured papers. All white papers are coloured with blue and pink in varying proportions, in the same way that the laundryman uses blue in the water in which white things are to be washed. This neutralizes the natural greyness of most pulps, and gives the fine white or slightly toned shades which are generally desired by printers.

Paper is the only practical vehicle for printing, because it is adaptable to every requirement of the graphic arts; and H. G. Wells has declared that it is scarcely too much to say that paper made the Renaissance possible.

Paper-making Inventions

It is also true that printing created the potentialities of paper. The allied industries of paper-making and printing, however, depended upon mechanical and chemical inventions for their full development. The machine age has brought this about; and the many kinds of printing, each with its own peculiar technical requirements, have stimulated the introduction of a vast and growing variety of papers. The selection of the most suitable paper, to say nothing of the technical requirements of modern high-speed printing, necessitates a thorough understanding of certain fundamental facts about paper and its properties.

Quality in paper can no longer be determined by the materials from which it is made, or by its outward appearance. One has to know especially how it will function, and whether it is suitable in general for a given job. Moreover, it is necessary to understand certain conditions which sometimes interfere with the proper performance of papers which, for the most part, have seemed suitable for the work.

Atmospheric Conditions

Chief among these is the variability of atmospheric conditions, which is one of the prime causes of loss in the printing industry, and for difficulties between paper-makers and printers. It must be remembered that paper is not inert; it will take up water from the atmosphere and change its shape according to the amount of humidity it absorbs.

When the atmosphere becomes dry, paper loses some of this water, and again its shape alters. This causes endless trouble with the registering of printed matter. Under normal conditions of temperature and atmospheric pressure, most papers contain about 6 per cent of moisture; but they will take up and hold, under damp conditions, much more than this. In dry weather they will contain much less. The fibres of which paper is formed contract and expand under these variable conditions of humidity, and twist the paper or pull it out of shape.

It is only in comparatively recent times that paper-mills have introduced humidifying plants, which have enabled them to manufacture paper, in rolls and sheets, containing the amount of moisture which is most suitable for the normal conditions prevailing in various parts of the country. Previously it was a common thing for paper, especially that sold in rolls, to go out hot from the paper-mills, and perhaps be still warm and very dry when put into the presses. During the course of the printing, if atmospheric conditions were humid, the paper, on being unrolled and exposed to the atmosphere, rapidly took up moisture and so gave the printer endless trouble.

When paper was hand-made and hand-sized it was also air-dried, each sheet being left for days, and sometimes for weeks, lying flat or hung over a cow-hair rope in order to mature. Not very long ago some paper-makers would not send out paper for an order, no matter how urgent, until it had lain in the mill for a sufficient length of time to mature and reach a normal state of humidity and inertness. Nowadays the paper may be brought to this state, or at least to a state approximating to that achieved by maturing, by passing it over a conditioning machine in a constant humidity room during the ordinary course of manufacture (Fig. 3).

Static Electricity

Another common trouble in paper is caused by static electricity. This electricity is formed in the paper by friction and heat during the course of manufacture, and unless some means are employed to remove this electricity from the paper, sheets of paper will stick together and to anything metallic with which they come in contact, causing endless trouble on the presses. The conditioning of paper by the method mentioned above goes a long way in removing this static electricity.

Paper-makers in the past have often been blamed for faults which are not

HALL-KAY PAPER-CONDITIONING MACHINE

Fig. 3. *The paper is passed in a continuous web through a number of boxes containing treated air which brings the paper "into balance" with normal atmospheric temperature and humidity.*

inherent in their product; but most of the trouble has been due to lack of knowledge on these matters, on the part of both the printer and the paper-maker. Both have paid dearly in cash and peace of mind for their ignorance.

Printer and Paper-maker

Dr. G. L. Riddell blamed this condition on a serious lack of co-operation between the printing and paper-making industries in technical matters. "The result," he says, "is that the printer regards the paper-maker as being unable to produce two makings of paper alike, and the paper-maker gains the impression that the printer does not

know what he wants. However, the root of the trouble does not lie here. A situation akin to that of the Tower of Babel arises, for the two technicians do not speak the same language! The paper-maker, naturally, regards paper as a finished product, and all his attention has been directed towards the way in which variations in composition, beating, sizing and calendering can affect such properties as weight, strength, colour, gloss, handle and look-through. Now these properties are not among the most important which control the printing quality of paper; and since the printer evaluates paper by its behaviour under printing conditions, and by the printed result, little progress can be made. What is most urgently needed is that some common language between the paper-maker and printer be found."

The formation of the Printing and Allied Trades Research Association (PATRA) has gone a long way to smooth out the difficulties between paper-makers and printers, and now the Paper-Makers' Association of Great Britain and Ireland has formed its own Research Association which should still further help to eliminate the misunderstandings which have so often arisen between paper-makers and paper users, most of them caused by lack of knowledge of each other's problems.

Manufacturing Process

Paper has been described as an aqueous deposit of any vegetable fibre in the form of a sheet or web. This simply means that paper is made by floating vegetable fibres in water, and when the fibres are more or less evenly spread throughout the water, the water is drained away through a wire mesh cloth, leaving the fibres deposited and intertwined together on the top of the cloth, in the form of a fairly even mass.

Water plays an extremely important part in the manufacture of paper, and many thousands of gallons have to be used to make one ton of paper; thus the first requirement of a paper-mill is an abundant supply of the purest possible water.

In the case of high-grade printing papers made from esparto grass, the paper-mill first of all makes its own pulp from the raw grass just as it is received from North Africa or Spain. The grass arrives at the mill in large bales, and contains grit, sand, weeds, roots, and other foreign matter, which have to be removed. Esparto grass is pulled by hand, and not cut, in order

that the plant may survive, and therefore it is inevitable that roots are often included.

The grass is first of all put through a duster which removes a lot of the grit and sand, and is then either chopped or put straight into a large kier or digester, in which it is boiled with caustic soda. This process softens the grass and turns it into a brown pulpy mass, which is subsequently washed out of the digester and placed in washing-and-breaking engines, where it is broken up and washed free from the lignin and other substances which are present in the plant, and which must be disposed of before the pure cellulose which the paper-maker requires can be isolated.

If the boiling and washing have been thoroughly carried out, the addition of a bleaching solution made from chlorine causes the pulp to assume a pure white colour and to consist of practically pure cellulose (Fig. 2).

Chemical Wood-pulp

This pulp is now ready for making into paper, but it is usual to add varying proportions of chemical wood-pulp to the esparto-pulp in order to give the desired characteristics to the paper. The most bulky papers of all have the highest proportion of esparto; those which require to be stronger, and do not need to be so bulky, have less esparto and more wood-pulp.

The wood-pulp is produced from chips of wood of various trees, and the pulp is treated in almost the same way as esparto-pulp; that is, it is boiled, washed and bleached. The trees from which these pulps are made are usually spruce, poplar or aspen, the former giving the strongest pulp, and the two latter the softer and more bulky pulps.

The first process in the actual manufacture of the paper itself consists in blending various proportions of esparto-

MILNE'S PATENT BEATING MACHINE

Fig. 4. The blending of the correct portions of esparto and wood-pulp in paper manufacture is carried out by means of a beating engine. In this engine, which has a heavy roll containing steel knives, the fibres are cut to the correct length for making the sheet of paper in the substance required. The loading materials are added to the pulp while it is in the engine.

pulp and wood-pulp in a beating engine (Fig. 4), and there subjecting the mixture to the beating action of the steel or bronze knives in the roll and plate of the engine. The beating engine is a circular trough divided in the middle by a mid-feather, and having on one side a heavy iron roll fitted with bronze or steel knives. This roll revolves at a very high speed, immediately above a fixed iron plate containing a small number of sharp steel bars.

The action of the roll is to circulate the pulp and water round and round the trough, and to brush and cut the fibres between the edges of the knives on the roll and the edges of the fixed knives on the plate. This shortens, splits and frays the ends of the fibres, and reduces them to a condition suitable for being felted together on the wire of the paper-making machine.

When the pulp in the beater is almost ready, it is usual to add china clay and occasionally other materials, as loadings, in order to fill up the interstices

between the fibres, and render the finished sheet opaque and smooth to print upon. These loadings vary from as low as 5 per cent to as much as 30 per cent of the weight of the finished paper. Such papers as imitation art contain the very highest possible amount of loading in order to give the smooth printing surface required for half-tone blocks.

At this stage, also, alum and rosin size are added, so as to make the paper resistant to ink. If no alum and size were added, the paper would behave exactly like blotting paper, and thus soak up large quantities of ink, some of which would pass through to the other side of the sheet.

The china clay or other loading imparts opacity to the paper, which prevents the print on one side of the sheet showing through to the other side.

The pulp is now ready to be made into paper, and is emptied from the beating engine into storage chests, from which the paper machine is supplied.

The majority of printing papers are

made on a Fourdrinier paper machine (Fig. 5). This consists first of centrifugal cleaning machines such as erkensators (strainers which keep back knots and lumps), a wire part or wet end on which the sheet is formed, couch roll (Fig. 6) which removes some of the water and consolidates and smooths the sheet, drying cylinders which remove the final traces of water, and stacks of calenders which impart "machine finish" to the sheet (Fig. 7).

The centrifugal cleaning machines remove from the paper stock those impurities which are heavier or lighter than cellulose or china clay, and operate on much the same principle as milk-separating machines. Thus, if they are designed to pass through materials which have the specific gravity of cellulose, they will hold back lighter materials such as shives (light vegetable fibres), and throw out heavier materials such as grit, coal, dust, and small pieces of metal which may have been knocked off the bars of the beater roll.

The mixture of cellulose, water and clay passes on until it reaches the strainer, which consists of a vat in which is revolving a large phosphor-bronze drum. This drum is made up from plates with narrow slots cut in them, through which the fibres, water and clay may pass, but which will reject knots and lumps in the fibre. Everything which passes through the strainer gets on to the paper machine wire and will be found in the finished sheet.

The pulp, after passing through the strainer, has a consistency of about half to one per cent. This means that one part of cellulose fibre and clay is floating in about ninety-nine parts of water when it reaches the paper machine wire.

The wire, which consists of cloth woven from phosphor-bronze wires, usually has a mesh of about seventy-two to the inch. It is endless, and revolves continuously over a set of tube rolls which keeps it level and supports it

WIRE PART AND FORMATION TABLE OF PAPER-MAKING MACHINE

Fig. 5. This illustration shows that part of the paper machine on which the fibres are felted together in water on an endless wire cloth before they are pressed and dried. The water runs through the wire meshes and the remaining fibres form the sheet of paper.

SUCTION COUCH ROLL

Fig. 6. A close-up view of the suction couch showing wet-formed sheet of paper leaving the wire and passing on to the felt. The illustration shows a thin tissue paper passing over the couch roll at high speed. The vacuum in this roll may equal 20 in. of mercury.

during the time it is carrying the weight of water and fibre.

As soon as the pulp and water mixture flows on to the wire, the water begins to run through the meshes, and the fibres are gradually deposited, twisted and tangled together, on the wire cloth. In order that the fibres may not be inclined to face all in one direction, the wire is shaken laterally, and this helps to intertwine the fibres and give more or less even strength to the paper in both directions of the sheet.

Just before the wet web of fibres

leaves the wire, it comes under suction from vacuum boxes which draw out some of the water which has not drained through the wire mesh by gravity; and while it is passing over these vacuum boxes it also passes under the dandy roll.

The dandy roll consists of a brass framework to which is attached a laid or wove cover, with or without name or design as a watermark. A plain wove roll merely smooths and consolidates the surface of the paper, and improves its printing qualities; in the case of a watermarking roll, it transfers an impression of the bronze design on to the moist web of paper, and this mark remains in the paper and cannot be removed.

The web of wet paper is now sufficiently consolidated and strong to hold together without support, and it passes from the machine wire on to the wet felt.

The wet felt carries it through heavy press rolls which squeeze out more water and consolidate the sheet still further. There may be one, two or three separate sets of press rolls, but they all have the same effect, namely, water removal, consolidation of the fibres and smoothing of the surface of the sheet.

There now remains in the web of paper about 70 per cent of water, and this has to be reduced to about 5 per cent by drying the paper over steam-heated cylinders (Fig. 8). The moist web travels through the drying part of the machine, and during its passage through it is pressed by felts against the smooth hot surface of the drying cylinders which drive off the moisture in the form of steam. When the paper reaches the last drying cylinder it is quite dry and hot, and it is then passed through stacks of calenders which smooth and polish the surface and

BERTRAM 10-ROLL SUPER-CALENDERING MACHINE

Fig. 7. *Before paper is super-calendered it has to be damped, and then it is passed through the super-calender which has alternate steel and compressed paper rolls. Only one of these is driven; the paper driving the rest of the stack, thus imparting a very high finish to the paper.*

DRYING CYLINDERS OF PAPER-MAKING MACHINE

Fig. 8. *The paper leaving the presses of the machine contains nearly 70 per cent of moisture, and this is dried off by passing the paper between hot cylinders and woollen felts. When the reel of paper finally reaches the end of the drying cylinders it is almost bone dry.*

reduce the bulk to the required extent.

If the paper is to be a featherweight and as bulky as possible, it does not receive so much pressure in the wet presses already referred to, and it is not subjected to calendering; but if it is an imitation art, or a super-calendered printing, it receives the maximum finish which can be imparted to it on the machine calenders before it is reeled up at the end of the paper machine, to be re-damped and super-calendered.

A water finish is sometimes imparted to the paper on the paper machine, and this process is carried out on the machine calenders. It consists of running a film of water on to the machine calender rolls so that the surface of the paper is made slightly damp before it passes through the nips of the calenders.

When the paper is reeled up at the end of the machine, it is ready for the various finishing processes such as super-calendering, slitting, or cutting into sheets.

If paper is to be super-calendered it is first of all put through a damper which moistens the surface with a very fine film of water. The paper is then taken to the super-calender which consists of steel and compressed paper rolls, and the paper passes between the polished rollers of the calender, which are also heated, at high speed.

Conditioning the Paper

It is then usual for printing papers to be passed over the conditioning machine (Fig. 3) referred to at the beginning of this chapter, in order that any static electricity may be removed, and the paper brought to a proper state of humidity. The paper must be as inert as possible when it reaches the printer, and have the characteristics of a fully matured sheet.

After being conditioned the paper is ready to be slit into webs, or cut into sheets on the cutting machine. If it is being sold in webs no further examination by the paper-maker is possible, but if the paper is being sold in sheets it goes to the "salle" or finishing department, where each sheet is examined top and bottom by women examiners, and sorted into good, retree and broken. It is then made up into reams of so many sheets or so many quires; and the retree, which is sold at a cheaper price, may be put at the top and bottom of the perfect reams, or may be sold separately.

The good or perfect sheets should be free from all blemishes, specks and faults of every kind, while the retree may have very small blemishes not likely to cause much trouble to the printer, or it may be used for a cheaper job not requiring such perfect paper. Some printing papers are tub-sized, by which is meant that, if hand-made, the dried sheets of water-leaf are dipped into a vat containing a size made from animal glue, which is obtained from the skins and hooves of animals. These tub-sized sheets are then laid over cow-hair ropes, or on clean hessian, and allowed to dry naturally by air. After that they are usually plate glazed by being passed through rollers with pressure.

In the case of machine-made papers which are to be tub-sized, the roll of paper, when it comes from the paper machine, is unwound and passed through a vat containing animal size kept at a constant temperature. The surplus size is squeezed off by passing the paper through rollers, and then dried by leading it over an air drier, which consists of sparred drums with fans inside. This machine is installed in a room where a controlled system of hot air dries the paper. By this method of sizing, a thin skin of animal tub size, or gelatine, is left on the surface of the paper, and when this paper is written or printed upon, the print is actually carried on the thin film of gelatine. These papers have to be calendered before use, to give them an even surface.

Featherweight and India Papers

So-called "featherweight" printings are the exact opposite to these, as they are made to be bulky, and as light as possible. They are usually made from a very high percentage of esparto, which is beaten off very quickly in order that the pulp retains as much of its natural form as possible. These papers are made on a Fourdrinier machine with very light pressure when water is being removed, and little or no calendering; and they are in consequence very bulky.

Bible and Prayer Book papers are the other extreme. They are often made from hemp, and can be made very thin and yet extremely opaque, the thinnest of all being the so-called "India Bible Paper." While the best of these are made from rag or hemp, many beautiful thin opaque Bible papers are made from wood pulp. They are usually much more expensive than ordinary printing papers.

CHAPTER TWENTY-NINE

INKS FOR ALL PROCESSES

PIGMENTS AND MEDIA OF BLACK AND COLOURED INKS. LETTERPRESS INKS: NEWS, BOOK WORK AND JOBBING. INKS FOR LITHO, OFFSET AND COLLOTYPE. INTAGLIO INKS: COPPERPLATE, DIE STAMPING AND PHOTOGRAVURE. EASERS, REDUCERS AND DRIERS.

THE end of the eighteenth century marked a turning point in the history of printing ink manufacture. Before this time, ink-making was a normal part of the printer's job, each printer making his own ink from the materials then available, and adding the colour, consistency, and other desiderata which experience had taught to be requisite for each individual type of printing job.

About the turn of the century, the manufacture of ink began to develop into a separate industry; and although it remained for some time as a craft in the hands of printers, it inevitably produced its own specialists who had but a second-hand acquaintance with the craft of printing. The result of this development was the manufacture and distribution by so-called inkmakers of what amounted to little more than pigments ground into varnish, the printer being expected to turn these pastes into workable printing inks by the addition of driers, reducers and easers.

Scientific Study

Later, printing began to lose some of its craft character; inks were in the hands of machine minders, of necessity not skilled in the whole of the printing craft, but performing miracles of output on new high-speed machines about which the older craftsmen could teach them little. The advent of new processes and much faster machinery impelled a *scientific* study of inks and the printing processes, as a result of which the inkmakers' chemists could supply for most ordinary jobs trouble-free inks requiring little or no modification by the printer.

Small modifications of inks to compensate for varying conditions of paper and temperature, and also to cope with altogether exceptional jobs, are still necessary; and it is in this relation that some knowledge of the scientific principles underlying the formulation and production of inks is of considerable interest to the printer. The illustrative formulae given in most textbooks on printing inks are apt to be misleading: in the first place, because different materials sold under the same name vary so widely in their physical properties as to be comparable in no respect other than in chemical analysis; and secondly because raw materials, qualitatively and quantitatively identical, can, by different manufacturing procedures, be made to yield inks so unlike as to be unrecognizable as having identical composition.

Pigments and the Printing Processes

All printing processes are designed to produce a large number of objects whose essential characteristics are that they shall have a geometrically regular surface, some areas of which shall be contrasted in colour with the others. The ink is transferred to the material being printed by pressure, and the following are the properties demanded of the ink:—

(1) That it shall be capable of being deposited in a thin layer on the printing surface; (2) that it shall not be unduly deformed in shape during the transfer to its final position; (3) that deposited in its final position, it shall have the correct colour value; and (4) shall adhere permanently to the surface on which it is placed. (3) and (4) concern the finished article, irrespective of the specific printing process, and indicate that the *colours* used for all processes may be the same. In practice, this is usually found to be so. (1) and (2) are concerned with the printing process, (1) necessitating the ink being liquid.

How the colour shall be made liquid is determined by the physics and chemistry of the specific printing process being considered and hence, in all cases, the liquid part of the ink (the varnish, vehicle or medium) is peculiar to the printing process. It follows from the above statement that the varnish, being concerned only to a minor degree with the finished print, is reduced to a minimum in the ink formulation.

It is usually found most satisfactory to obtain colour by the use of finely divided particles of solid pigments, which are ground into the varnish.

Classification of Pigments

From the chemical point of view, it is most convenient to classify pigments according to their constitution, it being found that this classification also roughly indicates their stability. Inorganic pigments, for instance, are usually more stable (fast) than dyes.

To facilitate the subsequent description of individual pigments, the following table gives an outline of the classification of pigments by chemical constitution:—

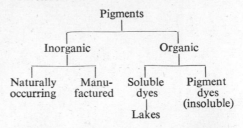

The printer, however, logically from his point of view, classifies inks mainly according to colour, and this system will be followed here, mention being made of the stability (fastness) or instability (fugitiveness) of the most important individual pigments. Where these terms are used without qualification, they are to be regarded as referring to stability towards light. Most pigments are sold under a variety of meaningless trade names, but, as far as possible, only the most informative or most commonly used name for each pigment will be used.

Blacks. Carbon in one of its forms is the pigment used in nearly all black inks. The very fine, high strength, gas black (made from American natural gas) is the pigment normally used, but for intaglio processes, where a coarser black is necessary, lamp blacks derived from the incomplete combustion of mineral oils or vegetable materials are used. Lamp blacks are essentially carbon, but have a colour strength less than half that of gas blacks.

For matt effects, a very dark iron oxide black is available, and aniline black (an organic colour) is also used. Blacks are occasionally prepared by mixing various organic colours. Carbon is stable to light and to nearly all destructive agents, but has an undesirable brown undertone, to compensate for which nearly all black inks are toned with other colours. The pigments used

General view showing the layout of the ink grinding plant in a large modern factory.

as toners are Prussian blue, basic dyes for news inks, and occasionally lake colours for special effects.

Transparent Whites. These are used for making transparent inks such as transparent tints and trichromatics for all processes, and in addition are used to give body to inks, without increasing the tack of the varnish. Alumina (aluminium hydroxide) gives inks of the greatest transparency and bulk, suitable for all processes. Colloidal china clay, magnesia, blanc fixe (barium sulphate), and precipitated mixtures of this last with alumina are used for certain grades of ink (e.g. poster inks), where absolute transparency is less important than cheapness. The cheap fillers are not suitable for use in offset or litho inks.

Opaque Whites. Opaque white pigments are necessary for cover inks, tin-printing whites, opaque tints, and in fact anywhere where obliteration of a background colour is necessary. Titanium dioxide is by far the most opaque pigment known, followed in this order by antimony oxide, lithopone, zinc oxide and flake white (basic lead carbonate). Flake white, once the commonest opaque white, has little opacity compared with the others, but is a good drier, and has good weathering properties. Zinc oxide (Chinese white) is a poor drier, but gives clean tints with good working properties. Chinese white inks do not keep well after mixing with driers.

The general stability of all these whites, as such, is good, but they reduce the fastness of colour pigments with which they are mixed. The fastness to light of tints varies according to laws not yet understood, and consequently fastness tests must be made on all tints.

Reds. For opaque full-strength reds, one has to rely on the inorganic colours which are fast to light, but heavy. Vermilion (red mercury sulphide) is the oldest and is very permanent, although it cannot be mixed with lead pigments or used in conjunction with copper blocks. It has largely been displaced by the lead molybdate chrome, whose only defect is lack of fastness to alkalis.

Special grades of red lead are also

used in inks to a small extent. Browner shades of red are obtainable by the use of hydrated iron oxides, which are also used together with cadmium selenide for lightfast flesh tints. These pigments are suitable for all processes, provided only the softest textured grades are used to avoid wear.

The basic dyes magenta and rhodamine are used in inks as such, and also precipitated with phospho-molybdic or phospho-tungsto-molybdic acids giving very strong fast pigments suitable for all processes. This method of preparing lakes is used for most of the basic dyes and has rendered obsolete the poisonous arsenical lakes which were formerly used.

Lakes from the acid dyes eosine, phloxine, rose bengal and erythrosine, are fugitive to light and bleed with alcohol, but are still valued for certain trichromatic reds and also for their heavy bronze. Madder lakes are largely used for inks which must be fast to light, oils and fats. For brightness and also strength, madder has been replaced by other organic colours. Barium or calcium lakes of the following colours provide the bulk of the red inks of medium fastness: lithol (strong but fugitive); pigment scarlet 3B (fast to light, heat and oils, useful for trichromatics); permanent reds 2B and 4B (dark bluish undertone, very strong); lake red C (heavy yellowish bronze); lake red P; lake red D.

Very strong colours, fast to light, acids and alkalis, are obtained by the use of one or more of the following pigment dyes: helio fast red R, permanent red R (scarlet); permanent red 2 G (orange scarlet); lithol rubine; para red (not fast to oils); and various permanent red dyestuffs designated by an initial letter F, e.g. permanent red FRL. Most of these pigment dyes are more fast to light than madder.

Orange and Yellows. All the shades of yellow from primrose to orange can be obtained by using various grades of lead chromate. This pigment, precipitated

Ink-blending equipment. Small-scale mills and mixers for blending finished inks to obtain special colours and other properties.

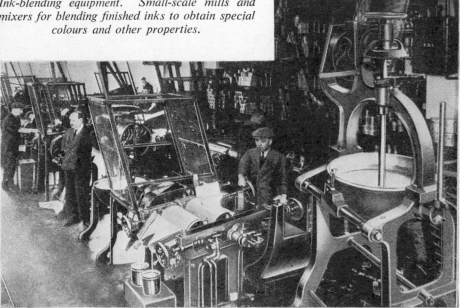

together with suitable substrata, gives opaque inks suitable for all processes, fast to light, but fugitive to alkalis.

The basic dye auramine O is used as such, and fugitive transparent lakes from the acid dyes tartrazine and quinoline, also find some use for the preparation of printing lacquers.

The shades of all the chrome yellows can be matched in transparent colours, very strong, fast to light and alkalis, by the use of the pigment dyestuffs known as hansa yellows (aceto-acetanilide dyes).

Browns. Half-tone browns are usually made by mixing organic colours. Precipitated iron oxide browns are also available for cheap, fast to light inks. Siennas, ochres and umbers (natural earths) have fallen into disuse owing to their coarseness and variability in colour and drying properties.

Blues. The iron blues (bronze blue, Prussian blue, etc.) are universally useful in all sorts of inks except where resistance to soaps or alkalis is required. This group of pigments has good colour strength, fastness to light, and excellent drying and general pigment properties.

The other representative of the inorganic colours among the blues is ultramarine. Owing to its hardness, coarseness, and water attractive nature, it can only be used in special media. It is very fast to light, but fugitive even to traces of mineral acids. Its use for posters is limited by its liability to bleach in atmospheres polluted with sulphur compounds.

The fugitive basic dyes, victoria blue, methylene blue and induline, are used alone in inks, and the fast to light lakes from victoria blue and greener basic dyes are useful for half-tone and offset inks. Reflex blue, used mainly as a toner for blacks on account of its lustre, is the only noteworthy representative of the acid blues, and pigment dye-stuffs are represented by indanthrene and monastral blue, of exceptional fastness to light and destructive agents.

Greens. The very poisonous Schweinfurth (emerald) green (copper arsenite) having been eliminated from modern inks, most inorganic greens are made by mixing lead chromes and iron blues, giving the chrome or Brunswick greens. Guignet's green (hydrated chromium oxide) is also occasionally used for pale tints very fast to light. The basic dyes brilliant green and malachite green are used as such and also precipitated in the form of lakes of high-colour strength, fastness to light, and a range of shades from grass green to deep blue-green. Acid and pigment greens are available, but are not important.

Violets. Various grades of methyl violet are in common use as basic dyes and derived fast lakes, which are largely used as toners for black inks.

There are available to the inkmaker several hundred pigments suitable for inks, each one of which has recommendations for some special purpose.

INKS FOR LETTERPRESS

A FURTHER analysis of the ink desiderata formulated on page 347, as applied particularly to letterpress or relief processes and machines, reveals that there are four phases in the normal life of an ink which must be provided for. These stages are (1) storage; (2) distribution; (3) impression; (4) drying: and the scientific approach to ink formulation involves making allowance for each one of these stages and embodying the result in one formula.

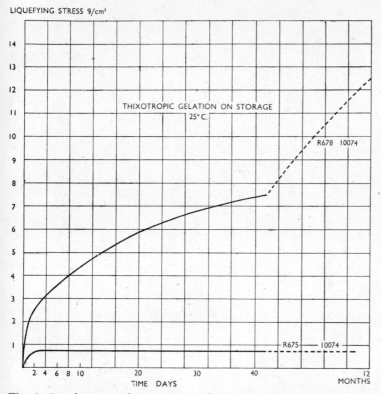

LIQUEFYING STRESS 9/cm²

THIXOTROPIC GELATION ON STORAGE
25°C.

R678 10074

R675 10074

TIME DAYS

MONTHS

Fig. 1. *Development of structure in ink storage. Ink must be kept to a consistency which can be easily liquefied by agitation.*

very gentle mechanical action of the duct, except in those rare cases where a duct agitator is used.

The action of the distributing rollers effects the complete breakdown of the ink structure, and the extent to which this occurs is illustrated in Fig. 2.

The distribution mechanism of the machine involves splitting the ink into finer and finer films which must still remain homogeneous and transferable from their penultimate position on the type face to the paper. Further, the ink must not thicken unduly or dry up during the time, which may be several hours, that it is on the machine. The ink must have sufficient tack to allow itself to be split in this way, and also to withstand the impression without being subject to undue lateral displacement as a result of the applied pressure.

In the production of ink for printing half-tone blocks, a certain amount of squash is allowed for, and in fact utilized in producing the desired result, but this must not be exceeded. The consistency of the ink has to be adjusted for the working speed of the machine and to avoid plucking the paper. Higher running speeds need thinner inks.

Nearly all inks set to a solid condition on storage, and it is important that this thickening should not go so far before the ink is used that it cannot be liquefied easily by mechanical agitation. The " Liquefying stress " axis in Fig. 1 can be regarded as representing the gel strength, and it is obvious that ink R678 would have livered or perished after a long period of storage, whereas R675 would be easily liquefiable at any time. New inks would need to conform to the R675 diagram owing to the fact that they are stored in tanks and pumped therefrom straight to the printing machine with a minimum of mechanical agitation.

The gel structure of the ink must be broken down in the first place by the

TORSIONAL COUPLE SCALE READINGS 25°C.

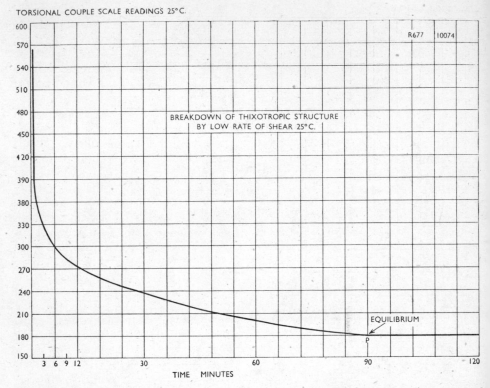

TIME   MINUTES

Fig. 2. *Diagram showing the reduction in consistency of an ink by means of stirring and rolling. The action of the rollers effects the complete breakdown of the ink structure.*

After being placed in the correct position on the paper and having the required colour contrast value, the ink film then has to become dry in as short a time as possible. Drying is accomplished by utilizing one or more of the phenomena of filtration, evaporation, and gelation.

Drying takes place on absorbent papers such as newsprint by partial filtration of the ink medium into the paper, leaving a highly pigmented film on the surface. This filtration must be very carefully controlled, otherwise too much medium is removed and powdering and bad drying result. The use of excess reducer, by lowering the viscosity of the ink medium, may result in excessive filtration and bad drying.

Evaporation drying is used only to a minor extent with normal letterpress inks, as the time which any given unit of ink is on the machine and the area over which it is spread are so large that only solvents of the slowest evaporation rates can be used—even paraffin in quantity evaporates too quickly.

With rotary letterpress rubber stereo printing, using methylated spirit inks, the drying is entirely by evaporation, and the ink distribution in consequence has to be reduced to a very elementary form.

Gelation enters into the drying of nearly all inks, but is sometimes hastened by the filtration of part of the ink into the paper, and sometimes by the oxidation of the ink by atmospheric oxygen aided by certain metallic compounds called driers. Drying by oxidation is a slow process and if accelerated too much by the addition of driers, may cause the inks to thicken up and finally dry on the machine during printing. Chemical processes such as this are also apt to be greatly accelerated by increases in temperature and irradiation by sunlight. Fig. 3 indicates the temperature effect on the drying time of a lithographic varnish containing cobalt driers. Inks behave very similarly, an increase in temperature of 10 deg. C. (18 deg. F.) roughly halving the drying time.

Finally in this analysis, the ink must not wear or chemically react with any of the surfaces with which it makes contact, e.g. machine, rollers and printing surfaces.

News Inks must be thin, non-drying on the machine to avoid the necessity of washing up, and need only be of low colour value. As mentioned above, they must not gel on storage. Drying is entirely by the process of filtration. About 10 per cent carbon is used as pigment, toned with basic dyes, the

medium nowadays being a heavy mineral oil. Some makers favour the admixture of some resin oil, but whether the value of this is purely traditional or not has never been proved.

Magazine Inks are used on rotary presses running more slowly than news presses. The consistency is

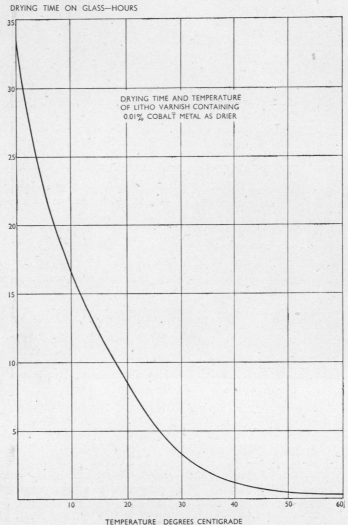

DRYING TIME ON GLASS—HOURS

DRYING TIME AND TEMPERATURE OF LITHO VARNISH CONTAINING 0.01% COBALT METAL AS DRIER

TEMPERATURE DEGREES CENTIGRADE

Fig. 3. *Graph showing the temperature effect on the drying time of a lithographic varnish containing cobalt metal as a drier. This curve illustrates the relationship which exists between the temperature and drying time, as applied to non-absorbent surfaces.*

P.T.G.—M

HEAVY DUTY INK MILL

A close-up view of an offset ink being ground on a triple-roll mill: depending upon the hardness of the pigment passing through the mill, three or more grindings may be necessary.

formulation gives a print which dries hard after a few days, and has a finish which a news ink never attains.

Book Inks vary according to the type of paper being used. For absorbent papers, inks rather stouter in body than magazine inks, and having more litho varnish than mineral oil, are used. Resin may also enter largely into the formulation of the medium. For harder papers, soft inks similar in composition to half-tone inks (see below) and drying largely by gelation may be necessary.

Jobbing Inks are intended for platen machines, and are short and stiff in body. They are normally slow drying, using filtration and oxidation processes balanced according to the absorbency of the paper. The medium which is heavy bodied will normally consist of mineral oil, resin and litho varnish, and the colour strength will be weaker than that of inks for flat-bed machines.

Half-tone Inks are generally used on flat-bed machines which require soft inks because of the high peripheral speeds of the cylinders, particularly of the two-revolution presses. In order to

somewhat above that of news inks, as are also the carbon content and the amount and quality of toners. The medium for the ink is usually a mixture of mineral oil and litho varnish (heat bodied linseed oil). Some driers are used, but insufficient to cause the ink to dry on the machine overnight, or to oxidize the rubber rollers. This type of maintain accurate reproduction on a long run, the film thickness must be reduced to a minimum, and this entails high colour strength and special grinding of the strongest and finest pigments available. Litho varnishes or synthetic resins constitute the usual media, drying being by gelation, and filtration according to the paper being used. The filtration drying mechanism is used in inks for the first printing on a perfecting press, to allow the ink to set rapidly before the sheet is backed up.

Quick Setting Inks, which are particularly useful for avoiding interleaving on art papers, are generally made by the use of a synthetic medium, part of which filters into the paper very rapidly, leaving a hard resinous film to bind the pigments, and subsequently hardening off to give a rub-proof film.

The principles outlined above apply equally to trichromatic and other coloured inks, the softest pigments only being chosen, particularly if printing from rubber half-tone blocks. Where more than one colour is to be printed, particular care has to be taken to adjust the drying of the first colour or colours, so that it has not dried too hard before the other colours are superimposed. Once a colour has crystallized, there is no satisfactory method of obtaining adhesion of an ink superimposed on it.

Bond, Cover and Hard-paper Inks. The drying of such inks has to be entirely by gelation, and the medium used is usually a quick drying resin-oil combination. A little paraffin or other solvent may be added to improve adhesion to difficult surfaces such as cellulose film, and as gloss is usually required, the inks must have full flow and a comparatively low pigment content. Opacity with inks other than blacks is obtained by the use of titanium oxide and lead chromes.

Spirit Inks for Rotary Rubber Stereo Printing. These inks are low viscosity fluids of two types: (1) fugitive aniline inks, consisting of basic dyes, dissolved in methylated spirit, sometimes admixed with glycerine; and (2) pigmented spirit inks using normal ink pigments ground into a medium consisting of shellac or synthetic resins dissolved in methylated spirit. The pigmented spirit inks can be made fast to light, but are much more difficult to handle on the press, owing to the fact that the dried film tends to build up on the forme.

Spirit inks dry mainly by evaporation of the spirit, and hence can be used successfully for printing on completely non-absorbent materials, such as cellulose and synthetic resin films. The older type of spirit inks containing a large quantity of glycerine or other non-volatile liquid, are much easier to handle, but their use is restricted to absorbent materials such as sulphite papers for bags and boards for cartons.

INKS FOR PLANOGRAPHIC PROCESSES

THE fact that a greasy image on an otherwise non-greasy surface can be selectively wetted by a greasy ink is the basis of all lithographic printing processes. The production of inks for the various planographic processes (those in which the image is in the same plane as the non-printing areas) depends on the control of a number of new properties, *in addition to* those already discussed for letterpress inks.

Planographic inks must not dissolve or disperse in water. This applies both to varnish and pigment. If the pigment dissolves even slightly in water, a tinted bleed appears over the whole of the non-printed area. There is no remedy for this condition except the use of pigments absolutely insoluble in water.

If the ink medium tends to disperse in the water, it will carry some of the pigment with it and give rise to a gradual enlargement of the image, and in bad cases, the appearance of spots of ink in the non-printing areas. This condition is known as scumming, or greasing, and in most cases can be overcome by the addition of a small amount of strong varnish to the ink.

Water Absorption

Planographic inks must not absorb water. This statement is only partially true, as the best planographic inks absorb water to a definite small limit. Inks which continue to absorb water, gradually become more buttery or plastic on the machine, and eventually become waterlogged. A waterlogged ink will not distribute satisfactorily, causing spare printing and bad drying. The absorption of water may not occur over the whole of the plate, but only along the edges or in certain other parts depending on the type of work being printed; this accounts for a great deal of the variation experienced during a run. The water absorption may be reduced by the incorporation of certain wax compounds usually containing tallow as the active ingredient.

Planographic inks must not wear or otherwise remove the image from the plate. Inks containing hard or imperfectly ground pigments often cause wear to the soft image, particularly if this is not rendered resistant with a fairly heavy coating of asphaltum. There is also a certain amount of evidence that some inks tend to dissolve the image from the plate. In both cases, the image becomes reduced in size, appears to be wearing thin, and the job is stated to be "working sharp." This condition, which is quite rare, is remedied by adjusting the acidity of the ink medium.

Planographic inks must be unaffected by solutions of chromic and phosphoric acids, various ammonium salts, gum arabic, and other materials used as etches, both on the plate and in the damping water. It is a common, but quite unnecessary, practice to keep damping water slightly acid to maintain clean working. The action of these acids on the ink is to increase the tendency of certain pigments to bleed. This point must not be overlooked in selecting pigments. If a bleed is caused by the use of etches in damping water, it can be eliminated by running the ink a bit stiffer, and using pure water for damping.

The drying of planographic inks must not be impaired by the action of water. The emulsification of water, particularly if containing salt etches, often causes retardation of drying. Poor drying may in turn give rise to powdering. To attempt to overcome bad drying caused in this way by the addition of further driers is apt to give rise to greasing. The correct procedure is to run the ink with as little reducer as possible, and to make a small addition of a wax compound to keep water out.

Offset Inks

The introduction of the offset process, involving the further step of first offsetting from the litho plate on to rubber and thence on to the paper, introduced yet further difficulties in producing satisfactory inks. The very thin ink film which finally reaches the paper by this method, necessitates the ink having extremely high colour value, and the avoidance of solvents, oils and driers which will attack and soften the rubber.

Litho Inks. By direct litho printing,

COLOUR MATCHING OF INKS
Large stocks of standard inks are maintained by the manufacturer from which the required colours are selected. Special shades are obtained by mixing the standard inks.

it is possible to transfer more ink to the paper than with printing offset, and hence litho inks need not be so strong tinctorially as offset inks. Pigments are carefully selected to conform to the criteria listed above, and litho varnish is almost universally used as a medium, a small amount of wax compound and strong varnish usually being added.

For some reason not yet explained, it is possible to print litho inks considerably more tacky than can be used at the same speed letterpress. The extra body of the inks helps to suppress scumming.

Offset Inks. The highest possible colour strength is needed for offset inks which must also have somewhat less tack than direct litho inks. Tint litho

varnish or burnt oil is the usual medium, a minimum of driers being added together with wax compound and strong varnish. In printing offset, the ink must not be allowed to penetrate and oxidize the rubber blanket. Use of solvents, particularly turpentine, is thus forbidden, and driers must be cut down to the minimum.

Offset inks should be short in body, and brighter and cleaner printing is obtained if very stiff inks are made workable by a duct agitator or other device. Heating does not have the effect of thinning an offset ink. Cheaper offset inks are made for special poster work in which high quality printing and durability are not required. Such inks, the working properties of which are not good, are prepared by using second quality pigments and a proportion of mineral oil in the medium.

Tin-printing Inks. Tinplate is printed by the offset process, and the sheets are subsequently baked dry at temperatures averaging 220 deg. F. The lithographic properties of the inks must be of a high standard, and in addition, no colour change must take place on stoving. The first colour printed may have to withstand stoving four or five times before the whole job is finished.

Good adhesion and elasticity of the dried ink film are necessary to ensure good performance in making up the tin box or other article. The stoving of the ink gives a film which is better in adhesion than an air-dried film, and attempts to improve this property still further have been made by substituting various synthetic resins for the litho varnishes in the ink media. Opacity is generally required of tin-printing inks, and as most work is subsequently varnished, oil-soluble pigments should not be used, as these often bleed during the stoving of the varnish.

Collotype. An increasing amount of fine work is printed by the collotype process, which is a planographic process, printing from hardened gelatine. Collotype inks are formulated on the general lines of offset inks, but are pigmented to the extreme limit with the softest pigments available. Extra resistance to the water and glycerine used on the plates is conferred by the addition of wax to the lithographic varnish used as the ink medium.

INKS FOR INTAGLIO PROCESSES

THE various intaglio processes call for inks with yet another set of specialized properties. They must all be of such a nature that, under the specific conditions obtained, the inks completely fill the engraving. The great variety of tones which is the beauty of intaglio printing is produced by wide variations in the amount of ink transferred to the paper.

The maximum amount of ink possible is many times that used even in heavy letterpress printing, and consequently intaglio inks need to be only moderately strong tinctorially. They must not be too stiff, otherwise it will be difficult to fill the engraving completely; they must not be very tacky, otherwise there will be a tendency to drag the ink from the engraving when wiping the plate.

In order to obtain a perfectly clean wipe, the effective pigment particles in the ink must be larger than the grain size or other unevennesses on the non-printing areas of the plate or cylinder. Very fine dispersion of finely divided pigments is undesirable, and a high degree of pigmentation helps to flocculate (join together the fine particles) the pigment and reduce the tack of the ink.

Inks for all intaglio processes should be readily absorbed by the paper or other material being printed. The ink has to be withdrawn from the etching or engraving by the paper. The absorption of the ink medium into the paper creates a paper/ink adhesion greater than the ink/metal adhesion, and thus allows the ink to be removed from the engraving. This absorption is facilitated by the use of a thin, non-tacky medium and a high degree of pigmentation.

Copper Plate and Steel Plate Engravings. These inks are made from a very lightly bodied burnt linseed oil, having little tack and little tendency to adhere to the plate. The tinctorial value of the inks need only be low, and the high degree of pigmentation necessary is obtained by the incorporation of a large amount of inert pigment of negligible colour strength. The coarser grades of black such as vegetable blacks are exclusively used. Such inks dry by the gelation process, and a small amount of driers needs to be added.

Die-stamping and Embossing. Inks for these processes are midway in general properties between copper plate and photogravure inks. The types in general use are (1) that in which the medium consists of a resin dissolved in a slow drying solvent; and (2) the medium of which consists of an aqueous solution of gum arabic possibly admixed with other water-soluble materials. Both types are pigmented, the former giving a high gloss result, the latter a matt finish. Drying in both cases is by filtration into the paper, and evaporation of solvent, and is slow compared with photogravure inks.

The production of gloss results is attended by incomplete withdrawal of ink from the die, which consequently needs to be cleaned out occasionally with a powerful solvent such as xylol. Imitation die-stamping is done by printing letterpress, dusting the still wet print with a powder wax-resin composition, and then passing the print underneath a heating element, which fuses the powder. This type of work can easily be distinguished from genuine die-stamping by observation of the paper with a low-powered lens.

Photogravure Inks

Photogravure Inks conform to type in being highly pigmented, although this is not apparent because of the presence of a large quantity of inert solvent, reducing the ink to a liquid consistency. This latter property enables the etch to be filled completely with ink at the very high speeds common to photogravure printing. For fine colour work, the medium will consist of a pale natural resin such as dammar, or synthetic resin dissolved in a suitable solvent.

Solvents

The choice of solvent will depend on the type of work, particularly the speed of drying necessary. Xylol is the solvent in most general use, but toluole is sometimes used for quicker drying, and petroleum fractions for slower drying inks. It is essential that the resin chosen should be such that it will allow the solvent to evaporate completely without going through a sticky phase. Solvent and resin must be carefully tested to ensure that neither contains any impurity which will attack the copper plate or cylinder.

Although the most finely dispersed pigments are too fine to give a clean wipe in photogravure, one must carefully distinguish between fineness and hardness in photogravure pigments. Only the very softest pigments are permissible owing to the danger of scratching the soft copper.

Precautions in Drying

Drying is ultimately by evaporation of the solvent, aided by application of heat and air blasts. The presence of the solvent vapours in the air gives rise to health and fire hazards. It is an unfortunate fact that all the useful solvents are either inflammable, or, if not inflammable, are dangerous to health after long periods of exposure. In large plants, the air containing solvent vapour is withdrawn from the machine room and purified, the solvent being recovered (see page 310).

Photogravure inks for high-speed magazine printing are formulated according to the general principles just given, using darker grades of resin up to and including hard asphalts instead of the more expensive pale resins. Practically all the cheaper solvents having the requisite evaporation rates have been used in photogravure inks. Satisfactory inks can be made using water as the solvent, the drying being mainly by penetration into the paper in the first place.

Inks based on cellulose derivatives, and using mixed solvents including alcohol, give excellent printing quality. There is a much greater variety of media in use for photogravure inks than for other processes. Each type of ink must be reduced with the appropriate solvent mixture, and the composition of the furnishing roller must be such that it is not attacked by the solvents being used.

Owing to large variations occurring in the depth of etching of photogravure plates and cylinders, and the fact that the photogravure printer has no control over the film thickness of ink transferred to the paper, it is necessary for him to be able to vary the colour value of his ink over a fairly wide range, in order to produce consistent results from different depths of etchings. The colour strength of photogravure inks is varied by the addition of a colourless medium, which is in all respects a complete ink except that it has no colour. As many types of photogravure inks are not miscible with each other, each type must be mixed with a medium of its own class.

INK MANIPULATION, EASERS AND REDUCERS

AS already stated, the up-to-date inkmaker can formulate for any specific conditions, trouble-free inks requiring little or no modification by the printer. On the other hand, owing to the diversity of jobs and conditions of printing, and the urgent necessity of keeping the number of standard inks down to a minimum, the printer is frequently constrained to modify his inks in the machine room. The best printing results in all processes are obtained by using inks as stout as will distribute with ease.

All inks thicken to a greater or lesser degree on storage, particularly at a low temperature, and it is essential to make sure that any such mechanically or thermally reversible body is broken down by appropriate means before having recourse to modifying the ink by other means.

The purpose for which such modifications may be justified can be roughly classified as : (1) easing of distribution; (2) improvement of filtration into the paper; (3) elimination of plucking; (4) reduction of set-off; (5) improvement of speed of drying; (6) alteration of shade or reduction of colour strength; (7) improvement of ink properties peculiar to the printing process, especially lithographic and photogravure; (8) production of special effects such as gloss.

All inks consist of two phases: the continuous phase (varnish or medium), and the disperse phase (usually pigment). The continuous phase which looks after the printing of the ink is that to which additions can be made most easily, but it must be remembered that inks are not true fluids, and additions must be incorporated with great care in order to ensure the ink remaining homogeneous.

The necessity for easing usually implies that the ink contains too much pigment for certain conditions, and this is remedied by the addition of varnish similar to that on which the ink is based. For letterpress and litho inks, litho varnishes or boiled oils can be used. Highly pigmented inks require less easer to effect an ink reduction in viscosity than do inks having less pigment. In Fig. 4, point Y represents a copperplate ink, and point X a litho ink. From the curves it can be seen that the addition of 5 lb. of varnish to 100 lb. of ink X will reduce its pigment content to 33·3 per cent and hence its viscosity from 140 to 137 poises, i.e. 2·1 per cent; a similar addition to ink Y will reduce its viscosity from 100 to 82 poises, i.e. 18 per cent.

The rate of filtration into the paper (often referred to as penetration) is increased by reducing the viscosity of the ink medium. This also tends to reduce plucking and minimizes set-off. When two liquids are mixed, the viscosity of the mixture is generally lower than the arithmetical mean of the viscosities of the two components. This is illustrated by Fig. 5 in which the heavy lines represent the viscosities of mixtures experimentally determined.

It will be seen that the deviation from the arithmetical mean (i.e. the dotted line) increases as the viscosity difference between the two components becomes greater. Liquids of very low viscosity, provided they are miscible with the varnish and do not evaporate too rapidly, will thus be most effective as reducers. This effect from a practical point of view is best instanced for the case of paraffin. A 5 per cent addition of paraffin *to the varnish* reduces the viscosity by roughly 50 per cent. Such very thin oils must be used with extreme caution to avoid the removal of too much varnish from the pigment, and yet to give reduction without loss of colour.

P.T.G.—M*

It is difficult to reduce a stiff ink with a thin oil, and hence the popularity of petroleum jelly in ink easers. This material, although solid and easy to handle, has a high reducing value. If used in large quantities, however, petroleum jelly will retard the drying and result in a greasy film.

Driers contain metal compounds which assist the gelation process of drying. Paste driers are manufactured to have the consistency of an ink, whereas liquid driers also act as reducers. Terebene, which is a drier dissolved in turpentine, is the most powerful available drier combined with reducer. Driers obviously cannot be effective in

VISCOSITY-POISES AT 25º C. AT CONSTANT RATE OF SHEAR

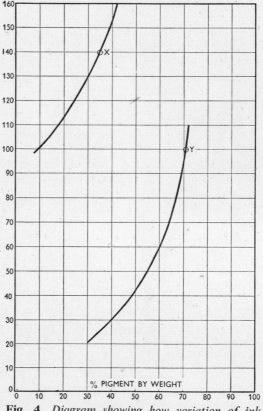

% PIGMENT BY WEIGHT

Fig. 4. *Diagram showing how variation of ink consistency is obtained by increase or decrease of the amount of pigment.*

news inks, photogravure and other inks made with non-oxidizing materials.

Letterpress Reducers. Litho varnish, boiled oils and linseed oil are the most satisfactory reducers, as they do not interfere with the drying. Paraffin and mineral oils may be used with care on absorbent papers.

Lithographic Reducers. The lithographic process is so finely balanced that extreme caution has to be used in manipulating offset and litho inks. Prudence suggests that reduction should be confined to high-grade litho varnishes, as solvents and driers may cause trouble. Linseed oil may give rise to greasing, and turpentine must be barred completely in order to preserve the rubber blanket. Increased water resistance can be imparted to litho and offset inks by the addition of small amounts of tallow, and scumming stopped by the addition of strong varnish.

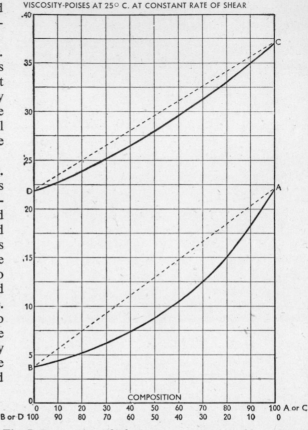

VISCOSITY-POISES AT 25° C. AT CONSTANT RATE OF SHEAR

Fig. 5. *Penetration of ink into paper is increased by reducing the viscosity of the ink medium. The curves above represent the viscosities which are obtainable with all the possible blends of two pairs of ink media.*

Photogravure Reducers. In order to compensate for depth of etch, it may be necessary to add medium to photogravure inks. Broken cell reproduction usually indicates that the ink has too high a viscosity, and should be reduced with the appropriate solvent. This must be done with caution, as too thin an ink leads to the ink flowing out and printing the screen lines instead of the cells.

Of all the materials that the printer is called upon to handle, ink is the only one that he can modify considerably. Such modification can only take the form of making additions to ink, and an ink badly at fault may indicate that it is necessary to remove something from it, rather than add something to it. Such surgical operations no one can do, and such inks are better rejected and replaced entirely.

On the other hand, the printer may be tempted to try to remedy defects of all sorts in his printing materials by means of ink manipulation. Sometimes this method succeeds; but where it does not, it does not follow that it is the ink which should take the blame. There are many other possible sources of trouble which are unconnected with the ink.

CHAPTER THIRTY

COUNTING THE COST

IMPORTANCE OF COSTING. PRINCIPLES OF FEDERATION SYSTEM. EXPENSES OF A BUSINESS. DISTRIBUTION OF DEPARTMENTAL COSTS. FORMS AND DOCKETS. PROBLEMS OF ESTIMATING. REASONS FOR VARIATIONS. ANALYSING THE JOB. SELECTION OF PAPER. LABOUR AND MATERIAL. STANDARD CONDITIONS.

SO far this book has dealt with details and methods of production, but the financial side of the printing trade must not be overlooked. A prosperous industry is good both for employers and employees. If profits are made, improved machinery and plant can be purchased, better and cleaner works maintained and higher wages paid. An unsuccessful industry cannot develop nor afford good wages. Printers must charge customers the *whole cost* of producing work, and a reasonable profit besides.

All business firms keep books to record the facts of income and expenditure as they occur, and a balance sheet is prepared periodically to ascertain the financial position of the concern. General information such as the value of sales, the total wages paid, the cost of materials purchased, the amounts of the different expense items, and the ultimate profit or loss for the period can be derived from the ordinary accounts, but these relate to external transactions only.

The financial books do not show the cost of individual orders; the details of stages of jobs; nor where profits or losses occur; and as printing involves both manufacturing and merchanting processes, it is necessary to introduce a method of analysing the expenditure of time and money to obtain further information to assist the management.

COSTING

COSTING is the means of finding out the actual cost of individual jobs in order to charge fair prices; to furnish data for accurate estimating; and to assist the management by revealing such items as excessive cost, waste and inadequate output. The system devised by the Federation of Master Printers is now recognized as the most accurate method of achieving these objects, and a study of Fig. 1 in conjunction with the following notes

will show the lines on which the system operates. The panels in Fig. 1 are numbered for reference.

There are eight main principles of the system laid down in the Federation Costing Text Book (Tenth Edition). These are reprinted below, and will be referred to as they occur.

1. Management is an item of expense to the business. If not shown as such in the audited accounts an amount must be included in the cost of the

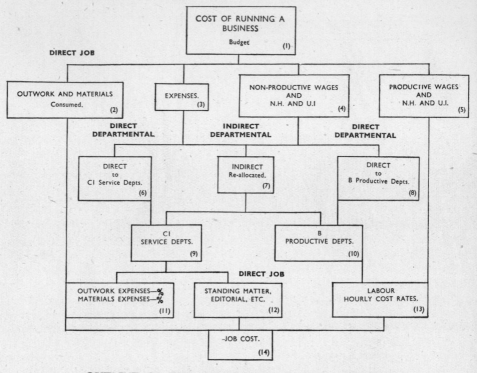

OUTLINE OF THE FEDERATION COSTING SYSTEM

Fig. 1. *Showing how the elements of cost—wages, outwork and materials and expenses, which make up the cost of a business—are transformed into labour hourly cost rates and outwork and materials departments' costs, and distributed equitably to every job produced.*

business equal to that which would have to be paid to employees for giving similar service.

2. An amount must be included in cost for interest on the capital of the business made use of during the year.

3. The cost of buying, storing, handling and selling outwork and materials must be ascertained.

4. Before attempting to distribute elements comprising the cost of a business to jobs they must first be equitably allocated to each of its departments.

5. Departmental management of all kinds must be allocated to each productive department in proportion to the sum of its productive wages, plus direct departmental expenses.

6. Indirect departmental expenses must be allocated to each productive department in proportion to the sum of its productive wages, plus direct departmental expenses.

7. The unit of labour cost is a rate for the directly chargeable hour. This rate is inclusive of productive wages, non-productive wages, all materials and expenses both directly and indirectly chargeable to the department, and the wages paid for all indirectly chargeable operations.

8. The cost of buying, storing, handling and selling outwork and materials, ascertained in accordance with the third principle, must be distributed to each job by the addition of a percentage to the cost of quantity used.

The main purpose of a costing system, simply expressed, is to distribute the cost of the business over every job produced. It follows, therefore, that the first step must be to ascertain the actual cost of running the business for the ensuing year. An estimate or budget of the anticipated annual expenditure is prepared (Fig. 1, panel 1), based on figures extracted from the trading accounts and the profit and loss accounts of previous years. When these expenses have been ascertained they are grouped under the following headings:—

Outwork and materials consumed (panel 2); expenses—direct and indirect (panel 3); non-productive wages (panel 4); productive wages (panel 5).

General management expenses (e.g. all managerial salaries) and interest on capital, if not shown in the financial accounts, are added to the expenses (first and second principles) for costing purposes.

In order to compile the first form of the system, Form 1a, summary of expenses, adjustments are made to the above four groups. Outwork is separated from materials, and the latter are analysed as follows: retail, direct job (paper, ink, binding); and direct departmental sundries. The figures for the last item, together with non-productive wages and holiday payments, are transferred to expenses. An example of Form 1a is shown in Fig. 2.

Departmental Costs

The departments of a printing business are classified into three groups: (A) retail; (B) productive; (C) service.

(C) departments are of two kinds: (1) departments whose cost must be distributed direct to jobs; (2) departments whose cost must be re-allocated as circumstances demand.

A small letterpress firm would prob-ably include: (A) shop; (B) hand composing; lino or intertype; monotype keyboard and caster; machine; binding. (C1) Outwork expenses; materials expenses. (C2) Indirect departmental expenses.

There are various other examples of (A), (B), (C1) and (C2) departments, but in practice it is found that a small number of departments can be drawn up to suit the costing requirements.

The next step is to distribute accurately the budgeted expenses from Form 1a (Fig. 2). For this purpose a Statement of Expenses, Form 1, is drawn up, with a total column and columns for all departments required. To assist in the departmentalization of the expenses (third and fourth principles) which is the real function of the form, the following particulars are obtained and entered in the headings of the departmental columns:

Value of assets, such as plant, fixtures and fittings; values of metals and materials stocks, work in progress, and amount of working capital; superficial area; aggregate h.p. of the motors used; number of employees; budgeted amount of productive wages to be paid weekly in each department.

The skeleton statement of expenses is now ready for the distribution of expenses, and for many of the items the basis of allocation is perfectly straightforward.

Area Expenses. Rent, rates, lighting and heating, according to the superficial area of each department.

Value Expenses. Interest on capital, on the amount of capital invested in the department; depreciation of plant, on the diminishing working value of the plant and fixtures; fire insurance, on the value of the plant, fixtures, fittings and stock; depreciation of metal, which is an amount sufficient to cover the loss due to frequent remelting.

FORM 1a
Summary of Expenses

	% of *	£	£
SHOP PURCHASES	6·30		1470·00
WAGES (productive)	21·95		5100·00
EXPENSES (direct and indirect)	42·75		9940·00
OUTWORK	8·90		2070·00
MATERIALS (direct)—			
PAPER		4070·00	
INK	20·10	280·00	
BINDING		330·00	
			4680·00
TURNOVER AT COST	100·00		*£23260·00

Fig. 2. *Compiled from the last year's Trading and Profit and Loss Accounts and Balance Sheet. If some expenses will change, owing for example to the purchase of additional plant, increase of staff, abnormal overtime or loss of business, adjustments must be made.*

Expenses such as water, gas or electricity for process heating and power are allocated according to actual departmental requirements. The last expense, however, may be distributed in proportion to total h.p. of motors used in each department, if details of actual consumption are not available.

Repairs, renewals and direct departmental sundries, are costed by analysis of invoices and petty cash payments.

Employers' liability insurance and holiday payments are in proportion to aggregate wages paid to employees in productive departments.

Certain expenses related to the amount of D.J. (direct job) materials, such as carriage, storekeeper's wages, packer's wages and packing material, are allocated to materials expenses department.

Other items of expense: travellers' salaries, commissions and expenses, office expenses such as advertising, postages, telephone, discounts, bank charges, audit and legal fees, bad debts and house printing spoilage, are allocated at this stage to the I.D. (indirect departmental) expenses depart-

ment. General management and office salaries require individual consideration, and are distributed between C1 and C2 departments according to circumstances.

When all the expense items (Fig. 1, panels 6, 7 and 8) have been distributed the statement of expenses should be cast. The sum of the departmental totals must agree with the budget figure in the first column, in order to prove that all expenses, both direct and indirect, and the non-productive wages have been accounted for. Finally, with the re-allocation of a portion of the indirect (I.D.) expenses to C1 departments (Fig. 1, panel 9) and the apportionment of departmental management costs (fifth principle), the statement of expenses is completed and an annual total of budgeted direct departmental (D.D.) expenses is obtained by this method for each of the A, B and C1 departments.

In order to adjust the burden of I.D. expenses *pro rata* to the fluctuation of output in the individual B departments, it is next necessary to establish a reliable basis for their distribution. The Federation Costing System lays down that these expenses must be allocated to each productive department in the proportion which they bear to the sum of its productive wages plus direct departmental expenses (sixth principle). To do this Form 1b (Fig. 3) is prepared. A glance at this form will show the I.D. expenses total expressed as a percentage, and this percentage is applied week by week throughout the year to the direct departmental cost of the B departments in order to arrive at their total weekly budgeted cost of production.

The method of recovering the costs of the A and C1 departments is also set out in Form 1b, viz: to the budgeted totals of shop purchases and consumption of outwork and materials (from Form 1a) are added their respective D.D. costs (from the statement of expenses). These costs are also expressed as percentages which are used later for shop costing purposes and on job cost sheets for recovery of outwork and materials expenses. A study of the figures in Form 1b will show that all the budgeted costs in the original summary of expenses (Fig. 2) have been distributed to each of the departments, thereby ensuring the recovery of the budgeted costs.

Distribution of Costs

The B departmental annual costs are at this stage simply expressed by amounts of money. These costs have now to be equitably distributed to every job to be produced in the ensuing year, and the basis for this distribution is a unit—one hour—except in cases where piece scales are in operation.

The units of time worked on operations in B departments are identical in every job, and are related to the time on which wages are usually reckoned.

It is not possible, however, to say that every hour worked is directly chargeable to a job number, so a distinction is made between direct job (D.J.) and indirect job (I.J.) hours. A list of operations under these two headings is given on page 368. It will be noted that the D.J. operations are each given a designation number, and the I.J. operations a designation letter.

Hourly rates for all D.J. operations

FORM 1b
Method of Recovering Expenses

A DEPTS.

			£	£
SHOP	....		1470·00	
EXPENSES	....	36%	530·90	2000·90

B DEPTS.

WAGES (productive)		5100·00	
DIRECT DEPTL. EXPENSES		3228·90	
		8328·90	
INDIRECT DEPTL. EXPENSES (SAY) †40%		3365·30	11694·20

C1 DEPTS.

DIRECT JOB OUTWORK		2070·00	
EXPENSES .... ‡14·1%		292·40	2362·40
DIRECT JOB MATERIALS		4680·00	
EXPENSES .... ‡25%		1174·05	5854·05
DIRECT JOB EDITORIAL EXPENSES§			1348·45
			£23260·00

† For use on Statement of Budgeted and Recorded Cost.

‡ Note how these expenses will *not be distributed* unless the requisite percentage is added to outwork and materials *on every job.*

§ Carried Direct to Weekly News Cost Sheet in appropriate portions.

Fig. 3. *By the allocation of expenses in the Statement of Expenses (Form 1) the estimated annual expenditure has been equitably distributed to the retail, productive and servicing departments. The total agrees with the budgeted expenses in Form 1a.*

TABLE OF DIRECT JOB AND INDIRECT JOB OPERATIONS

Composing Department
1. Composing
2. Imposing
3. Author's Corrections, Hand
4. Machine Revises

5. Pulling Proofs
6. Handling Mech. Comp.
7. Layouts

A. Distribution
B. Picking for Sorts
C. Waiting (state reason)
J. Reading
M. Miscellaneous

Linotype
3. Author's Corrections
9. Keyboard

C. Waiting (state reason)
D. Changing (state reason)
E. Melting Metal
F. Oiling and Cleaning
G. Repairs
M. Miscellaneous

Monotype
3. Author's Corrections
9. Keyboard
10. Casting
11. New Founts
12. Renewals

C. Waiting (state reason)
D. Changing (state reason)
E. Melting Metal
F. Oiling and Cleaning
G. Repairs
M. Miscellaneous

Foundry
11. Casting
14. Moulding
15. Depositing
16. Routing and Finishing

17. Mounting
18. Alterations

C. Waiting (state reason)
E. Melting Metal
F. Oiling and Cleaning
G. Repairs
M. Miscellaneous

Letterpress Machines
3. Author's Corrections
4. Machine Revises
5. Pulling Proofs
20. Make Ready, Registering, Adjusting Feeder, etc.
21. Assisting Make Ready
22. Preparing Overlays
23. Wash Up for Colour

24. Running On
25. Interleaving and Taking Out
26. Bronzing, Hand
27. „ M/c

C. Waiting (state reason)
F. Oiling and Cleaning
G. Repairs
H. General Wash Up
K. Materials
L. Packing
M. Miscellaneous
N. Feeding

Binding and Ruling
30. Cutting
35. Knocking Up
37. Binding
38. Marbling
39. Indexing

40. Finishing
41. Blocking
43. Casemaking, M/c
44. Casing in M/c
45. Setting Pens and Ruling

C. Waiting (state reason)
D. Changing or Rubbing-up Knife
F. Oiling and Cleaning
G. Repairs
H. General Wash Up
K. Materials
L. Packing
M. Miscellaneous
N. Feeding

Women's Department
5. Proofs
30. Cutting
31. Folding, Hand
32. „ M/c
33. Punching
34. Eyeletting
35. Knocking Up
36. Tying or Stringing
37. Binding
42. Laying Gold and Taking Off
46. Inserting and Gathering
47. Sewing, Hand
48. „ M/c

49. Perforating, M/c
50. Wire Stitch, M/c
51. Numbering, M/c
52. Punching, Bending, Tabbing, M/c
53. Gluing, Pasting, Gumming
54. Covering
55. Banding, etc.
56. Varnishing, M/c
57. Die-stamping
58. Rotary Cutting, Creasing, Perforating, etc.
59. Mounting, M/c

C. Waiting (state reason)
D. Changing (state reason)
F. Oiling and Cleaning
G. Repairs
K. Materials
L. Packing
M. Miscellaneous
N. Feeding

FORM 2

DAILY DOCKET (UNIVERSAL)

Name.. *Date*..................................*194*........

Job. No.	Customer's Name (*abbreviated*)	Description of Job (*abbreviated*)	Opera-tion No.	Machine	Ordinary Hrs. Min.	Overtime Hrs. Min.

If Forme Standing write "Standing" opposite Job No.

Total Hours

Examined by................................... FOR OFFICE USE ONLY { Directly Chargeable / Indirectly Chargeable

OPERATIONS

1. Comp., Hand
2. Imposing
3. Author's Corrs., Hand
5. Pulling Proofs
6. Handling Mech. Comp.
9. Keyboard (Lino or Mono)
10. Casting (Mono)
11. New Founts
12. Renewals
20. Make Ready, etc.
23. Wash Up for Colour
24. Running on
30. Cutting

31. Folding, Hand
32. ,, M/c
33. Punching
34. Eyeletting
37. Binding
46. Inserting, Gathering
47. Sewing, Hand
48. ,, M/c
49. Perforating, M/c
50. Wire Stitch, M/c
51. Numbering, M/c
53. Gluing, Pasting, Gumming
55. Banding, etc.

A. Distribution
B. Picking for Sorts
C. Waiting (state reason)
D. Changing (state reason)
E. Melting Metal
F. Oiling and Cleaning
G. Repairs
H. General Wash Up
J. Reading
K. "Handling" Materials
L. Packing
M. Miscellaneous
N. Feeding

COST SHEET (For Small Business)   D.B. (or Led.) Fol................   JOB No.

COMPOSING

Date	Hours	Date Br. For.	Hours	Date Br. For.	Hours
3/5/	4				
,,	3				
,,	1				
5/5/	8				
,,	8				
6/5/	2			Author's	Corrs.
	26			7/5/	2
Car. For.		Car. For.			

Total Hours 28 @ 6/9 per Hour.   £9 : 9 : 0

MECHANICAL COMPOSITION

Date	Hours	Date	Hours	Date	Hours
				Author's	Corrs.
Car. For.		Car. For.			

Total Hours   @   per Hour. £ : :

MACHINE ROOM

Date	Mach.	Hours	At	£	s.	d.
8/5/	3	5	5/6	1	7	6

OUTWORK

Date	Firm and Description	£	s.	d.
	Outwork Expenses.... %			

BINDING OR WAREHOUSE

Date	Op. No.	Hours	At	£	s.	d.
9/5/	31	2½	2/-		5	0
,,	50	2	2/9		5	6
	30	½	5/6		2	9
					13	3

MATERIALS

		£	s.	d.
56/1,000 *Demy Ptg.* 520 @ 35/-			18	2
Wire, 2,000 @ 4*d.*				8
Inks, ½ *lb.* @ 4/-			2	0
		1	0	10
Materials Expenses 20%			4	2
		1	5	0

SUMMARY

	£	s.	d.
Composing (Hand).........................	8	15	6
,, (Machine)			
Author's Corrections		13	6
Machine	1	7	6
Binding, Cutting, etc.		13	3
Materials	1	5	0
Outwork			
Standing Matter			
....			
Cost....	12	14	9

Add for Net Profit........%.............

Previous Price £........................

       CHARGE....

Quoted Price £........................

JOB. No.

This sheet must accompany the Job through each process (copy and proofs to be attached) and returned to Office immediately the order has been delivered.

Date Order Received.......3........day...........*May*...........194.....................

Customer...................*Stone & Co.,* ....

.... *19 Joyce Park, N.E.*...

Quantity............*1,000*...........Size............*Demy 8vo*................................

Description...............*Price List, 8 pp. Printed Blue Ink*...........................

....*Stitched two wires*..

Remarks ....

Proof Wanted.....................*May 6*...

Proof Out...........*May 6*...........Returned...............*May 7*........................

Order Wanted........*May 11*...........Delivered...........*May 11*.....................

Deliver to...

MATERIALS

Price per M 35/-

	Sheets	£	s.	d.
Paper....56/1000 *Demy Ptg.*	500		..17	6
.......................*Overs* 4%	20			8
	520			
Cards				

Value of Standing Forme £   :   :

Inks...lb.   @..

Extras ....

....

OUTWORK.—Ruling ....

Binding...

Litho.   ....

are based on the following principle: the total D.J. hours in a department are recorded for a year (or estimated, if figures are not available) and divided into the department's annual cost. The result will be a cost rate per D.J. unit (Fig. 1, panel 13), which is inclusive of those hours which are indirectly chargeable (seventh principle). The actual procedure for determining hourly rates for operations varies in the different departments according to the nature of the work, but it should be clearly understood that for hand operations the various rates are for D.J. time spent by individual workers, and for machine operations the various rates are for the D.J. time the machines are in use, which includes the wages of all the workers on the machines.

Daily Dockets

Daily dockets are used for recording the hours worked by productive workers and machines, and it must be realized that the accuracy of all cost records depends entirely on accurate daily dockets. The example given (Form 2, page 369) embraces all operations and is suitable for small businesses. Medium or large-sized businesses will have dockets printed for use in the different departments in accordance with their own particular operations. It will be noted that the designation numbers and letters of operation are printed at the foot of the docket for reference, and are recorded in column 4 by the worker when filling in details of the day's work. This distinction has its value for the costing clerk when clearing the docket. For the purpose of cost recording the clerk posts D.J. hours only to the individual job cost sheets. An example of a typical cost sheet is shown on page 370.

Records of total D.J. and I.J. hours are also kept by the costing clerk on weekly recorded cost of production sheets in order that progressive statements of budgeted and recorded cost of production may be compiled for the business as a whole, and for each of the departments. The latter form indicates to the management whether or not the budgeted cost is being recovered by the hourly rates in use and enables an investigation to be made if the comparative figures show any great variation.

Outwork and Materials Expenses

The directly chargeable (D.J.) materials in a printing business are: paper (a comprehensive term which includes all the materials bought, stored and issued by the "white paper" warehouse for printing and binding orders); ink; and binding materials (such as wire, thread, glue, cloth, and strawboards).

Reference was made earlier to the addition of a percentage to record the expenses allocated to the materials department. This percentage is added to the purchase price of all D.J.

materials recorded on the job cost sheet. In this way a share of the department's expenses is recorded against every job. Outwork is treated in the same manner, but the percentage to be added to the amounts paid to other firms will be found lower than that for materials, as certain items of materials expenses do not occur in the case of outwork (eighth principle).

Job Costs

When a job is completely delivered and all the daily dockets have been cleared, the job cost sheet (page 370) is completed in the following manner: details of all operations are checked and the hours recorded are extended at the appropriate hourly rates; quantities of materials consumed and outwork costs are checked and priced out, and their respective expenses added. After totalling, the job cost sheet, with the works instruction sheet (page 371) and file copy, is passed forward to the appropriate authority for pricing out before being invoiced by the accounts department.

The foregoing pages have endeavoured to show that the Federation Costing System, commencing with the various elements making up the cost of the business, distributes them equitably between the productive and servicing departments (fourth principle). The system thus transforms the productive departments' expenses into hourly cost rates for labour, and the outwork and materials departments' costs into expense percentages, so that every job, whether an ordinary letter heading or an illustrated catalogue, involving blocks, intricate setting, printing in several colours, various papers or boards, and many operations in the binding department, shall bear its proportionate share of all the elements of costs associated with its production.

The information supplied by the daily dockets and the job cost sheets also provides production records, which give valuable data for estimating purposes. The statistical information furnished by the various forms used in connection with the system, if rightly interpreted, also enables the business to be managed on the basis of fact, and the efficiency of one department examined and compared with another. This gives effective control, as excessive and unremunerative expenses are thus quickly detected and eliminated.

ESTIMATING

A STUDY of estimating methods should form part of the technical training of every person engaged in the printing trade. All who aspire to executive positions will find it of great advantage to be able to determine the times required and calculate the comparative cost of different schemes of working, in order to decide on the most economical or expeditious means of production.

It has been shown that the costing system determines hourly rates for labour and machine operations and percentages for the materials and outwork expenses. These rates and percentages are made full use of in the preparation of estimates.

An estimate is, in fact, an advance calculation of the costs incidental to the production of a prospective order; in other words, an assessment or forecast of the operational times expected to be incurred in the different stages of the work calculated at the various hourly rates, plus the anticipated cost of materials and outwork and the expenses thereon.

Adding the Profit

To the total cost, a reasonable amount must, of course, be added for profit. No printer should seek to secure business by quoting figures lower than his estimated cost of production, if for no other reason than because one job taken at a loss requires two further jobs taken at a profit, each equal to the loss, before the business is in the same position as if the first job had been taken at a profit.

The importance of efficient estimating cannot be over-emphasized, because many quotations are in competition with those of other printers, and orders usually go to the printer whose price is most favourable. An extravagantly figured estimate will probably lose the job. A carefully thought out quotation is a proposition based on the firm's capabilities and costs. It must not be assumed, however, that an unsuccessful quotation means an unsound estimate.

Price Variations

There are many factors which account for the variation in printers' prices, and the more important ones should be noted as follows:—

Variation in the quality of printing and the specification quoted on; varying efficiency of the plant and organization; variation in the estimates of time on the various processes, and in the working scheme adopted; different hour rates for these times; difference in the purchase price of the materials and outwork used; variation in the handling charges on materials and outwork; different amounts which have been added as profit.

Generally, if the estimating is sound, it follows that a firm obtains the class of work for which its plant is most

DETAILS REQUIRED FOR THE PREPARATION OF AN ESTIMATE

Customer's name..   Date ....
Address ....   Traveller..

Nature of Customer's business.........................   Estimate wanted by.............................
Purpose for which printing required.................   Job completed by.................................
....   Dummy to be sent.................................
References or other status information.............
....

GENERAL DETAILS
 Quantity................................ Process.......................................   Size (depth* first)......................
 Title or description...........................
 Envelopes or other extras wanted..
 No. pages or folds..................................   Cover...

COMPOSITION (insert any composing machines in use)
 Type ....   Style ....   Impose ....

ILLUSTRATIONS ....   Kind ....   Who supplies.........................

PRINTING
 Quality..
 Number of colours or workings..
 Score...   Crease...
 Embossed ....   Dies..............................   Who supplies ....
 Inks..   Body ....   Cover ....

BINDING
 Folding..   Cutting...
 Inserted or gathered into sections..
 Stitched at fold, or stab...
 Wired ....   Thread sewn ....   Ribboned or corded...............
 Cover drawn on.............................   Pasted on ....   Overhanging ....
 Binding ....   Lettering..............................   Indexing ....
 Carbons...   Tinfoil..................................   Numbered ....
 Perforated ....   Padded ....   Round-cornered ....
 Loose leaf, punched......................   No. of slots.........................   Kind of slots............................
 Cut out (or punched).................   Eyeletted..............................   Strung......................................
 Varnished..   Strip gummed ....
 Ruling ....   Colours ....
 Die stamping..................................   Dies....................................   Who supplies.........................

SPECIAL DEPARTMENTS (for example)
 Artists' instructions...   Kind of sketch.................................
 Litho instructions : Direct...........................Offset.. No. of colours........
 Photogravure instructions and those for any other special process in use by firm.

MATERIAL
 Paper inside :   Kind........................ Colour...................   Size and weight per 1,000.....................
  ,, inserts :   Kind........................ Colour...................   Size and weight per 1,000.....................
 Cover :   Kind........................ Colour...................   Size and weight per 1,000.....................

GENERAL DETAILS
 Is matter to be kept standing?...
 How goods to be packed................................... How sent...............   Who pays carriage...................
 If posted : how..   No. of inserts.....................
 How flap dealt with, if wrapper folded or rolled ....

* Or "width first," whichever is the custom of the house, but one or other needs to be stated, as a standard house custom avoids errors.

suited, and of which its staff has most experience.

Estimating should be under the control of an experienced man, who has devoted a considerable time to the study of printing, knows the ramifications of the trade, and possesses the gift of foreseeing the difficulties which may arise in the production of work.

It is essential that he should know every detail about his firm and its methods, the personnel of the departments (classification of operatives, wages, overtime rates and conditions); details of its plant (types and machinery for mechanical setting, printing and binding)—their capabilities and shortcomings; and the average standards of output on different classes of work.

Qualifications for Estimating

The estimator should have a working knowledge of paper, so that he is able to approximate the weight in any stock size; determine the class and finish on examination; judge the price to within a $\frac{1}{4}$d. per lb.; and anticipate every difficulty or peculiar behaviour of paper during printing.

He should be acquainted with schedules of prices for all the allied processes, which are outside the scope of his firm's activities, e.g. ruling, blockmaking, die-stamping, gumming, varnishing and other methods of finishing, and similar processes.

The estimator should be temperamentally suited for his position, and tactful in dealing with departmental overseers, because he must consult and collaborate with them on all important and intricate jobs. On the other hand, he should not waste their time with estimates for standard types of inquiry. He should also be helpful when dealing with customers, and be able to interpret their ideas and make suggestions for putting them into practice.

When an inquiry is received, either by telephone, through the post, from a personal call, or brought in by a representative of the firm, the job should be visualized and all essential particulars settled. A form similar to that shown on page 374 is in use in many businesses to ensure that no technical detail is overlooked.

Estimate Forms

An estimate form (pages 376 and 377), drawn up according to the printing processes involved, is used for the purpose of bringing together the items of cost. The specification, which is filled in at the head of the form, should be a complete description of the job in not too technical language.

It is from the wording in this form that the actual quotation form is typed; and later, when the order is received, the order clerk is in possession of a description of the job in a concise form. It will be noticed that preparation (composition, make-ready, and preliminary outwork) is separated from working (running-on, binding, and final outwork) in order that the estimate may be made up for more than one printing number, if desired.

Casting Off MS.

At the outset it will be necessary to determine the size and number of pages of a job from the copy submitted. After casting off the manuscript to find the approximate number of words, consideration must be given to the size and face of the type to be used and the page requirements of the work, allowance being made for incidental pages, blocks, and white space.

When the number of pages and general format has been decided, the method of compiling the estimating costs and filling in the form usually proceeds on the following lines:—

ESTIMATE FORM

Est. No. *34*
Name—*Messrs. John Smith & Co.*,
Address—
Description—
   Catalogues "Greenhouses"
   printed 8 pages and cover flush, discount slip 8 × 5½ printed
   in red, tipped in, stitched two wires
Quantity—*2000*.

Size—*10″ × 7½″*

Date—*6th Oct., 194....*

Enquiry *per*
Traveller.............................
Letter ....
Verbal ....
'Phone.............................

PREPARATION

Operation	Hrs.	Rate	£	s.	d.
COMPOSITION					
Hand	10	6/9	3	7	6
Mono—Keyboard	6	7/-	2	2	–
Do. —Caster	5	8/-	2	–	–
Mono Corrections	2	6/9		13	6
Lino or Intertype					
Do. Corrections					
Making up	20½	6/9	6	18	5
Proof (galley)	1	6/9		6	9
Imposition	5½	6/9	1	17	2
Proof (mach.)					
Author's Corrections					
Standing Matter—					
Cost of Alterations					
,, Looking out					
FOUNDRY					
Stereos					
Electros					
Laying-down Plates					
ARTISTS					
Designers					
Reproducers					
PROCESS, ETC.					
Camera					
Retouching					
Planning					
Printing down					
Carbon					
Etching					
Stones, Plates					
or Cylinders					
Size Number @					
TRANSFERRING					
Press					
Machine					
PROVING					
Press					
Machine					
OUTWORK					
Outwork Expenses %					

MAKE-READY

Mc. No. or size	No. of Formes	Size of Formes	Hours: M.R.	W.U.	£	s.	d.
6	1	8pp	4½	4½ 6/4	1	8	6
6	1	Cover 4pp	2	2 5/6		11	-
2		Slip	½	½ 1 3/9		3	9
Preparing Overlays							

RULING
Setting Pens

TOTAL (*carried to Summary*).... **£** 19 | 8 | 7

WORKING

M/c No. or Size	No. of Cols.	No. of formes	Sizes of formes	Extra W.U's.	Hrs.	Rate	£	s.	d.	Hrs.	£	s.	d.
6	1	1	8 pp	—	2½	6/4	15	10					
6 (cover)	1	1	4 pp	—	2½	5/6	13	9					
2 (slip)	1	1	—	—	2½	3/9	9	5					

Bronzing, Hand
  Do.   Machine
Interleaving & Taking out

TOTAL (*carried to Summary*) .... **£** 1 | 19 | .

MATERIALS

2000

	£	s.	d.	£	s.	d.
PAPER, BOARDS, etc.—Weight Size x Out of Sheet						
Stock No. 32 White S/C Ptg. D/Crn. 60/1000 @ 7d. 35/-						
1000 sh.	1	17	1			
Overs 60						
Toned Ptg. D/Crn. 80/1000 @ 8½d. - 56/8 500 sh.	1	9	6			
Overs 20						
Slips White M.F. Demy 40/1000 @ 7d. - 23/4 250 sh.		6	7			
Overs 30						
INK, VARNISH, BRONZE, etc.		5	–			
BINDING MATERIALS						
Leather Cloth Linen Buckram Boards						
End Papers Thread Joint Gold Sundries		1	4			
Marbled Paper Wire* Eyelets Hangers						
Ribbons Cord String						
	3	19	6			
Materials Expenses 20%		15	11			
TOTAL (*trans. to other side*)	4	15	5			

OUTWORK (*if not preparation*)

Outwork Expenses............%

TOTAL (*trans. to other side*)

MACHINE BINDING

OPERATION	QUANTITIES 2000								OPERATION	QUANTITIES 2000							
	Hrs.	Rate	£	s.	d.	Hrs.	£	s.	d.		Hrs.	Rate	£	s.	d.	Hrs.	£	s.	d.
Guillotine (Splitting)	¾	5/6		15	2					*Brought forward*				15	2			
„ (Trimming)	2									Eyeletting								
„ (ditto)										Stitching—Wire	3½	2/9		7	7			
Rotary Cutting										Thread								
Gold Blocking										Round Cornering								
Casemaking										Scoring								
Folding—Book										Creasing								
										Indexing								
										Drilling								
Parallel										Punching								
										Mounting								
										Varnishing								
Sewing										Gumming								
Paging																		
Perforating—Rotary																		
Foot																		
Carried forward				15	2					TOTAL (*carried to Summary*)			1	2	9			

HAND BINDING

OPERATION	QUANTITIES 2000								OPERATION	QUANTITIES 2000							
	Hrs	Rate	£	s	d	Hrs	£	s	d		Hrs	Rate	£	s.	d.	Hrs	£	s.	d.
Folding	8									*Brought forward*			1	4	–			
Making-up										Gluing								
Inserting	3	2/-	1	4	–					Pasting								
Gathering										Tip in	6	2/-		12	–			
Collating	1									Mounting								
Sewing										Varnishing								
Stitching										Gumming								
Binding										Padding								
Nipping										Banding in .... s								
Finishing										Packing (special)								
Gold—laying on																		
Lettering																		
Casemaking																		
Numbering																		
Indexing																		
Carried forward			1	4	–					TOTAL (*carried to Summary*)			1	16	–			

SUMMARY

	QUANTITIES 2000												
	£	s.	d.	£	s.	d.	£	s.	d.	£	s.	d.
PREPARATION	19	8	7									
WORKING	1	19	–									
BINDING—Machine	1	2	9									
„ Hand	1	16	–									
MATERIALS	4	15	5									
OUTWORK	–	–	–									
Cost	29	1	9									
Profit 10%	2	18	3									
Spcl. Carriage or Commission	–	–	–									
„ Discounts	–	–	–									
TERMS *Net* QUOTED £32 : 0 : 0	32	–	–									

NOTES AND OTHER DETAILS

The first step for work other than book jobs is to decide the paper or papers to be used. These come within two categories, those available from stock and those to be specially purchased from a wholesale stationer or merchant, or to be bought from a mill through the mill agent. Until the size or sizes obtainable are known it is useless to consider the estimate scheme.

Selection of Paper

The size of paper has a bearing on the following points: the method of imposition, and number of formes to be printed; and whether in view of the machines at the disposal of the estimator, it is of advantage to print the job sheet-work, or half-sheet work, or from more than one set of type or plates.

The selection of paper suitable for the particular job is also an important matter. For half-tone work, the fineness or coarseness of the screen of the blocks must be taken into account in order to obtain satisfactory results.

In working out paper costs, the working size should include the allowance for trimming when necessary, and an extra allowance for grippers in full-out work and when blocks or rules bleed.

Methods of cutting out should be studied. For straight cutting, the Monotype chart of sub-divisions of paper is an excellent booklet. "Staggered" cutting will often enable paper to be used economically for odd sizes, and for jobs where the only available stock size appears at first to be wasteful.

Allowance for Overs

Working out quantities is a simple calculation when the fraction of the sheet or number of sheets required for each copy is known; but to the bare quantity needed must be added an adequate percentage for overs, according to the number of colours or workings, to allow for proofs, spoilage, and house files. When the total number of sheets is known, the full cost of paper at current value can be ascertained easily, and the appropriate handling expenses added thereto.

The paper and scheme of working having been decided upon, the estimator proceeds to assess the operational times needed by those departments through which the work will pass.

Composing and Machining Times

The amount of time estimated for composition will include all directly chargeable hours from commencement of setting until finally sending to machine, but excluding author's corrections. When mechanical composition is decided on the number of ens to be set must be calculated before an estimate can be made of the hours required: (a) on the Linotype or other slug-setting machine; or (b) on the Monotype keyboard and on the casting machine. The nature of the copy, measure and size of type all have a bearing on the times required for mechanical setting.

The allowance for hand work will take into account the hours required for first proof corrections to machine-set matter (i.e. placing corrected slugs in Linotype galleys or correcting Monotype galleys after casting); for straightforward composition from case; and for all the difficulties encountered in display work, such as letter-spacing, justifications, rules and borders, inserting and spacing blocks. House corrections before proofing must also be allowed for, as well as the operations of making-up into pages or formes, imposing in chases, and putting to press, or to foundry if the job is to be produced from plates.

When preparing an estimate for the

machine department costs, the size and number of formes, printing capacities and speeds of machines, and length of run must be borne in mind when selecting the machines for the work. The time required for making-ready will be affected by many factors, e.g. the nature of type forme, number of blocks, whether hand-cut or mechanical overlays, register of colours, and kind of paper used.

Running times will be determined by the expected output on the particular class of job, whether hand or automatic feed, and other factors such as the necessity for interleaving or spraying, or double rolling. Special jobs have their difficulties and these must be taken into account. Allowance must be made for extra washing-up for colour, at beginning, during and on conclusion of the run, and fluffy paper also may cause delays for additional wash-ups during the run.

The correct amount of ink required is frequently difficult to decide. Many tables have been published giving average ink consumption for formes of different sizes, classes of work, and grades of paper, but as jobs vary considerably only years of experience will enable the estimator to avoid the pitfalls in this connection.

Binding and Warehouse Operations

These cover a wide field. The estimator should be conversant with the sequence of the many different processes entailed, and be able to work out detailed costs in that order. Pamphlet and bookwork can be calculated on standard outputs or on the piece-work scales. The capabilities of the folding, wire- and thread-stitching and sewing machines, and the hourly outputs of women workers for everyday operations such as insetting, gathering, collating, and pasting should be noted for reference.

A wider experience is necessary for estimating miscellaneous vellum or account-book binding, where the work is handled in batches and the time spent each day is allocated to individual jobs. Cased work, too, is in a class of its own and if mainly mechanized, the capabilities of the machines employed for nipping, rounding and backing, triple lining, case-making, blocking, and casing-in, must be carefully studied. The work of the guillotine cutter in the various stages of binding must not be overlooked when making up estimates.

Binding Materials

Materials used in binding are varied, and are difficult to calculate. Scales should be compiled showing the values of: wire, per 1,000 staples in the various gauges and qualities; thread, per 1,000 stitches, according to the length required for each style of machine, and per 1,000 sections on the different book-sewers. Tables are available giving sizes and substances of strawboards and other boards for various classes of books. The cutting out of boards and cloth is a straightforward calculation, but working out the cost of leathers requires practical experience. Due allowance should be made in every case for normal wastage; and the cost of paste, glue and other sundries must always be included. The appropriate expense percentage must be added to the costs of these materials.

Outwork

A great many firms find it necessary to obtain the help of specialist houses for blocks, and for processes for which there is only an occasional demand. This is more economical than installing separate departments in their own businesses requiring special plant and operatives, when there is not sufficient work to keep them fully employed.

To all outwork costs must be added the percentage for expenses.

When all estimated costs are completed and the individual amounts checked, the form is totalled and passed to the management for fixing the price for the work. At this stage consideration is given to items which are not covered by the hourly rates or expense percentages, e.g. carriage charges, special discounts, long credit, split deliveries, and finally, the amount of profit.

A specially printed form is used for sending the quotation to the customer. The typed specification should be explicit and show what processes are included. Any variation from the details can then be charged as an extra. If the quotation is for a repetition job the full details are unnecessary: "as your pattern" covers most of the details. If a sample of paper is to accompany the quotation this should be stated.

Standard Conditions

The Standard Conditions of the printing industry should be printed in full on the back of the quotation form sent to the customer, and attention drawn to them on the front of the form. They are as follows:—

1. PRELIMINARY WORK — Work produced, whether experimentally or otherwise, at customer's request will be charged for.

2. PROOFS—Author's corrections on and after first proof, including alterations in style, will be charged extra. Proofs of all work may be submitted for customer's approval, and no responsibility will be accepted for any errors in proofs which may be passed by him.

3. DELIVERY AND PAYMENT—In the absence of any agreement to the contrary, goods will be delivered when completed and payment for the goods shall be made against delivery.

4. EXPEDITED DELIVERY—Should delivery of work be required sooner than the normal time requisite for its proper production, every effort will be made to secure freedom from defects, but reasonable allowance must be made by the customer in such cases. Should such delivery necessitate overtime being worked or other

additional cost being incurred, a charge will be made to cover the increased cost.

5. QUANTITY DELIVERED—Every endeavour will be made to deliver the correct quantity ordered, but, owing to the difficulty of producing exact quantities, quotations are conditional upon a margin of 5 per cent (in colour work 10 per cent) being allowed for overs or shortage, the same to be charged for or deducted.

6. CLAIMS—Any complaint must be made within ten days of receipt of goods.

7. STANDING MATTER AND PRINTERS' MATERIALS—Type may be distributed and/or lithographic, photogravure, or other work effaced immediately after the order is executed, unless written arrangements are made to the contrary. In the latter event, rent shall be paid unless any other specific arrangement has been made.

8. CUSTOMER'S PROPERTY—Customer's property when supplied will be held at customer's risk. Every care will be taken to secure the best results where materials are supplied by customers, but responsibility will not be accepted for imperfect work caused by defects in or unsuitability of materials so supplied.

9. ILLEGAL MATTER—The printer shall not be required to print any matter which in their opinion is of an illegal nature.

10. PERIODICAL PUBLICATIONS—In the absence of any agreement to the contrary, quotations are given upon the condition that not less than three months' notice is given to terminate the contract for the printing of monthly publications and not less than one month's notice in the case of weekly publications.

11. CONSEQUENTIAL LOSS—Responsibility will not be accepted for consequential loss or damage occasioned by errors, or by delay in delivery.

12. FORCE MAJEURE—Every effort will be made to carry out any contract based on a quotation, but the due performance of it is subject to variation or cancellation owing to an Act of God, War, Strikes, Lock-outs, Fire, Flood, Drought, or any other cause beyond control, or owing to inability to procure materials or articles except at increased prices due to any of the foregoing causes.

13. COST VARIATION—Quotations are based on the current cost of production (materials, working hours and wages), and are subject to amendment on or after acceptance to meet any recognized rise or fall in such cost.

The standard conditions for bookwork vary slightly from the above.

CHAPTER THIRTY-ONE

LETTERPRESS BINDING

DISSECTING A COVER. FOLDING SUBDIVISIONS. PASTING IN PLATES. GATHERING AND
COLLATING. SEWING. END-PAPERS. CUTTING. GLUING. ROUNDING AND BACKING.
TREATMENT OF EDGES. ATTACHING BOARDS. LINING AND COVERING. FORWARDING.
LEATHER BINDINGS. FINISHING. LETTERING. BLOCKING MACHINES.

THE work of the bookbinder consists in uniting printed matter or ruled leaves in such a manner that each page is readily available for reading or for writing as the case may be; also when not actually in use, the contents are to be protected from damage while ready for immediate reference when required. This may be obvious, but nevertheless, if constantly borne in mind, the purpose of the operations about to be described will be more readily understood.

Letterpress and Stationery Binding Compared. A book is something to be read, or something in which accounts are kept. This statement clearly divides the trade into two main branches and there is a clearly defined line between them. The purpose, construction and method of using the two classes of books are so different that their production is considered as quite different branches of the trade.

Hand and Machine Processes

In this chapter a description of the hand processes will be given, followed by an explanation of some of the machines that undertake the work. These machines, however, are many and varied and are ever undergoing changes; the hand processes must therefore form the basis for instruction.

Examination of a Dissected Leather Binding. Valuable knowledge will be gained if the instructions given below, showing the dissection of a book, are carried out.

The book may be full-bound, or what is known as half-bound; that is, the leather may fully cover the boards or it may cover the back portion and corner pieces only, the remainder of the boards being lined cloth or paper. For our purpose we will assume it is a half binding (Fig. 1).

Remove the cloth side by inserting a thin knife under the edge where it is turned in and notice how comparatively easy it is to peel the cloth away. If the sides consist of marbled or coloured paper it will not be possible to do this, the stronger cloth side proving to be less durable than the paper.

One of the leather corners may now be removed in a similar manner and without tearing, if possible. It will be found that the leather sticks to the board more firmly than the cloth; this is due to the fact that the cloth is of a similar fibrous nature to the board. Notice the way the extreme corner has been turned in and the manner in which the leather has been passed round the edges.

Next lift the leather from the board as far as the joint, cutting the material

381

Fig. 1. *Dissection of a half-bound letter-press book. The detached portion shows the leather corner after it has been removed.*

at the turn-in to enable this to be done. It will now be observed that the boards are held to the book by three or more cords. These are the cords upon which the sections have been sewn and the boards are said to be "laced on." Should these cords not have been laced through the boards the binding is what is known as a cased book, a cheaper style described under cloth work. Notice how the corners of the boards have been neatly cut out to enable the book to be tied up at the time of covering.

Now examine the spine of the volume. If it is possible to insert a thin bone folder between the leather and the sewing, the book is said to be bound "hollow" back, but if the leather is attached direct to the back sections, it is said to have a "tight" back.

The binding most probably has a hollow back, the said hollow being made up of a strong brown paper. With a sharp thin knife this paper may be slit along the joint, thus exposing the linings which, however, cover up the sewing. On a hollow-back book any raised bands will be found to be built up from pieces of leather and form no

contribution to the durability of the binding. Should, however, the specimen be found to have a tight back, considerable effort will be required to remove it and the leather probably destroyed in doing so, thus illustrating the effectiveness of leather as a binding material.

The setting of the leather at the head and tail should be noticed as well as the piece of worked silk known as the head band. Examine the leather and endeavour to identify it; it will probably be calf, morocco, or sheepskin. Test the rigidity of the boards; strawboards may be broken with ease but this is not the case with grey or rope millboard. Rope millboards will be dark in colour and will be found to be very heavy.

Inside the Book

We may now turn our attention to the inside of the book by opening the front cover. The front leaves will be a different quality paper to that used for the printed matter. These are the end-papers and are supplied by the binder. One leaf forms a lining for the board and is known as the board-paper while the other leaves are known as fly-leaves.

The remaining leaves are supplied by the printer and are known as the text body of the book. The operation of examining a book for missing leaves or other imperfections is known as *collating*, and is a very important one when handling rare and valuable items. A typical make-up of a printed volume is as follows: the half-title is the front leaf containing a brief title in the centre of the page; the illustration that faces the title-page is the frontispiece; then follow the title-page, copyright or printer's imprint, preface, contents and list of illustrations. These items are printed last, as the necessary details are not available until the rest of the book is printed, and for this reason are often numbered in roman figures. Page one of chapter one starts on the right-hand page and the numbers continue throughout the book. Although the index is compiled after the rest of the printed matter is completed, the pages can be numbered, as they follow, and not precede, the text. Illustrations printed with the text are numbered with it, but those printed on special paper are not, and their position is determined by the list of plates.

The leaves of the book are proportioned out into sections (usually eight, sixteen or thirty-two pages) which are identified by a letter or number printed at the foot. These letters are known as the *signature*, and are used to denote the order in which the book is made up. This term is also applied to the sections themselves.

There may also be printed at the foot of the signature, a series of letters corresponding to the title of the book. These are used in making up, to identify the particular title from another of a similar size which may be in process of binding at the same time. These marks are usually referred to as *designation marks*.

The book previously examined has been bound by hand, and it will have been noticed that the operations involved are too complicated to be undertaken by machines. The cased binding is, however, more suitable for machine, and as most books are bound by this method, the dissection of a specimen on similar lines will serve to illustrate the difference between the two methods.

Cased Bindings

For the purpose, an ordinary inexpensive cloth-bound book will be required. Upon opening the front board an examination will usually show three or four tapes and a piece of coarse muslin underneath the board paper; these hold the book in its case. If the two boards are opened right back and held firmly in the left hand and the leaves grasped in the right hand, a firm wrench will remove the book completely from its case.

These cases, consisting of two boards, a paper hollow and the cloth, are produced on the case-making machine (Fig. 18). An examination of the book will show the tapes attached by the sewing, the first lining of coarse muslin and the second lining of paper. The endpapers consist of two folded sheets edged with paste to the outside leaves. Notice that the spine has been hammered to a rounded shape which gives the familiar round hollow to the foreedge, also the shoulder which has been formed from the boards by an operation which is known as backing.

Examining the Sewing

If the book has been in use for some time it may be possible to remove the back linings and expose the sewing. A machine has been used for this purpose and our specimen will be useful when this operation is described. A few sections may be removed from the front of the book by cutting through the threads on the inside. Notice if each section consists of sixteen or thirty-two pages and confirm the make-up of signature A.

New books are supplied to the binder in flat sheets ready for folding. A completely folded copy should be available to indicate how the work is intended to be made up. These sheets will be one of the standard size printing papers or a multiple of one of these sizes (Fig. 2).

The name of the paper together with its subdivision indicates the book size, i.e. a foolscap folio book would be about $13\frac{1}{4} \times 8\frac{1}{4}$ in. when trimmed. Some of the more familiar book sizes are as follow:—

The Folios. Here the sheet is folded

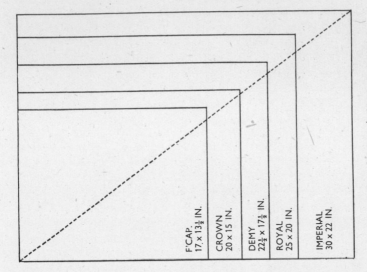

F'CAP.
17. x 13½ IN.

CROWN
20 x 15 IN.

DEMY
22½ x 17½ IN.

ROYAL
25 x 20 IN.

IMPERIAL
30 x 22 IN.

Fig. 2. *Printing paper sizes drawn to scale. The diagram shows clearly the lack of system in standard paper sizes. The broken diagonal line indicates that certain papers are more oblong than others, which naturally affects the relative shape of the finished book page.*

once, but as a single sheet would make an unsuitable section for sewing, the double or the quad size paper would be used and the sheets inserted one within the other, the formes being imposed accordingly. The folios form a series of very large books. They are not so popular as they were at one time but are still used for atlases, books on architecture and the like. Being outside the popular range, machines which require large quantities to be economical are not designed to handle them.

The Quarto. Here the sheet is folded twice, dividing it into four. The quartos form a series of rather large square-shaped books. They are very suitable for illustrated works of travel, for the reproduction of pictures and for children's books. Printed on double size paper or two sheets inserted, the more usual sixteen page section is produced.

The Octavos. The sheet for this size book is folded three times, forming sixteen pages direct. If printed two up the binder must cut in half before folding. The octavos form a series of books more commonly used than all the other sizes put together. The crown octavo has become a standard size for works of fiction, being suitable to handle, for the case and even for the pocket. Demy octavo is the next in popularity, being a good size for technical books with their illustrations and diagrams.

The Twelvemo. Here the sheet is folded twice one way, dividing the sheet into three, and then twice the other way, dividing it into four. The twelvemos form a series of small, attractive, square-shaped books useful for gifts. They are not very popular, perhaps because they tend to make the bookshelf untidy.

The Sixteenmo. A section of thirty-two pages is rather awkward to fold by hand and is more suited to machine folding. The sections will be found to be printed two on a sheet and folded as for octavo. The sixteenmos are used for Bibles and hymn-books, for small ready reckoners and handbooks.

Certain illustrations which are prepared by a process other than letterpress cannot be printed with the text, as a special paper is required. These are known as plates and are usually supplied to the binders as single leaves. Having no back folds they cannot be sewn and require special treatment by the binder.

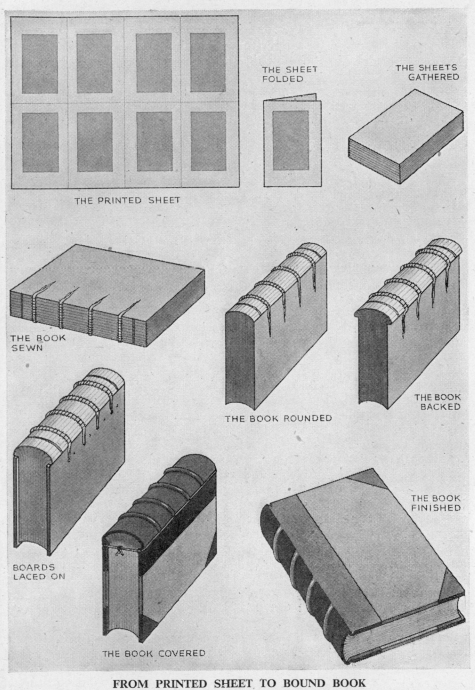

THE PRINTED SHEET

THE SHEET FOLDED

THE SHEETS GATHERED

THE BOOK SEWN

THE BOOK ROUNDED

THE BOOK BACKED

BOARDS LACED ON

THE BOOK COVERED

THE BOOK FINISHED

FROM PRINTED SHEET TO BOUND BOOK

Fig. 3. *Various stages from the printed sheet to the finished book bound in half leather. The sheet is usually folded to print and not to paper edge, as this ensures better register.*

The dummy copy will indicate to the binder how the sheets are intended to be folded, although the make-up of the book is determined by the way the sheets are imposed by the printer. As such factors as thickness of paper and size of book affect the thickness of the section, consultation should take place between the two departments.

Folding

The bone folding stick is the only tool required for hand work and the operation itself is simple, but the success of the binding depends upon several important details. A pile of sheets is taken and placed before the operator with the lowest page number on the underneath, bottom, left-hand corner. Registration is very important and concerns the accurate placing of the printed matter one above the other. Folding to the edge of the paper is no guaranteed assurance that the pages will register correctly unless special precautions have been taken to obtain this result; otherwise it is necessary to "fold to print" which entails the careful placing of type matter at each fold (Fig. 3).

Folding the sheets three times making eight leaves or sixteen pages is the commonest of all the folds as it gives the correct thickness of section for the average paper. Thinner sections increase the cost of sewing without adding to the strength of the binding, whereas thicker sections cause difficulties in folding by hand.

Experiments with folding sheets of paper should be tried out by the student at this stage. The difficulty referred to usually occurs at the fourth fold, and appears as an unsightly crease on the inside at the top of the section. The best remedy is to cut through the bolt—the term given to the folded edge—before the last fold is made. This can be done with the folding stick, which by releasing the paper, avoids the crease. Folding along the length of the paper first is another means of avoiding the trouble, but the printer must, of course, impose his pages accordingly.

Hand folding is slow and when quantities are large a machine is used. It is an operation that is particularly suited to mechanization and a wide variety of machines which are both accurate and fast is available. The demand for such work is very great and has created a supply of folding machines which handle very large sheets, and also cut and insert them.

Worked in collaboration with the printing machines, difficulties of register are completely overcome and being adjustable to numerous folds they are indispensable to the wholesale bookbinder. The choice of a machine requires careful consideration, for although their range is wide, some are specially designed to suit particular classes of work; therefore the output of the printing department must be taken into account, and once the folding machine is installed, the work can be planned accordingly (Fig. 4).

Preparation for Sewing

Pasting In. Any leaves of a book which have no folds in the back cannot be sewn in the usual way, and require special treatment from the binder. The usual method is to edge them in with paste. This is by far the easiest and most convenient way of overcoming the difficulty, but there are one or two serious objections, and in describing the operation an attempt will be made to reduce these objections as far as possible.

If a book with a pasted-in plate is examined it will be found that the leaf to which it is attached is dragged up

FOLDING MACHINE

Fig. 4. *An efficient machine producing perfect register. It receives a sheet of 64 pages and slits and delivers two sections of 32 pages (16 inserted into 16), or four 16-page sections.*

with it each time the book is opened. The leaf is weakened thereby and eventually both will be broken away. If, however, the pasted portion is kept very narrow, the attachment is kept well into the binding and the strain on the leaves is so reduced that very little harm is done. The other objection is caused by the cockling of the paper by the moisture in the paste. It occurs when the machine direction of the paper runs across the book, especially when the paper is heavily sized. This should be taken into consideration when the selection of the paper is made.

The position of the plates is determined by the list of illustrations or from the dummy copy. They may require to be trimmed to size with careful consideration given to the margins. About twenty plates are taken, fanned out to the required width and evenly pasted to the extent of $\frac{1}{8}$ in. The quality of the paste is important because if too thin it will penetrate between the leaves, and if too stiff, it will dry too quickly. Cleanliness is very important.

Guarding is an alternative method of attaching plates. Half-inch strips of paper are pasted out, attached to the plate and carried round the section. Under these conditions the attachment is independent of other leaves and the guard is sewn in. If numerous, however, these guards add to the thickness of the back and, apart from the increased cost, cause the book to take a bad shape.

Oversewing is another method to be used when plates and single leaves are very numerous, but this is not always satisfactory.

Gathering and Collating

Gathering. The signatures are now ready to be gathered together in their proper order to form the complete book. The operation is simple but precaution must be taken against misplacement of the sections. The folded sheets are placed on a table in such a way that the operator can take one from each until the book is completed. Place alternately back and fore-edge when stacking completed volumes in order to balance the pile. In large, modern binderies the gathering is usually done by a gathering machine (Figs. 5 and 6).

Collating is the term given to the operation of examining a book to ensure it is complete and in order. It is of great importance as an imperfect book is valueless; and for this reason examination is sometimes undertaken both before and after sewing. Sometimes marks, called collating marks, are printed at the fold of each signature, every successive mark occurring a fraction lower than its neighbour. The series of steps formed across the back readily indicates that the sections are in proper order, for any break in the sequence is easily seen and remedied accordingly (see page 56).

Pulling. The operations described up to the present apply to new books only. Re-binding, however, is an important branch of the trade, and the work involved, up to the stage of sewing, being quite different, may now receive attention. The old binding having been removed, the book must be pulled to pieces with as little damage as possible to the leaves. As much of the lining material as possible is removed from the back, and if the original backing is beaten out with a round-faced hammer, the glue will be broken up and the removal of the linings made easier. Soaking the back with water should be avoided for although the glue is softened the paper is also weakened, and tears in the paper are likely to occur.

If all the threads are cut on the inside of the section, it may be pulled away from the rest of the book with very little danger, and as the operation

proceeds any lining material that has remained may be removed with ease. A point to remember is that any threads left uncut will themselves cut the paper and trouble will occur when re-sewing. The creases formed by the original operation of backing should now be hammered out on some solid metal or smooth stone base, and any leaves that have become separated must be treated as described for plates.

Pressing precedes sewing in the case of hand-bound work but machine-sewn books are pressed after sewing. The thicker threads used by hand sewers cause a considerable increase in the thickness of the back and pressing would do harm under these circumstances. The press is associated with a number of operations during the course of binding and is the most important appliance in the workshop. Used at this stage, its purpose is to obtain that solidity always associated with good bindings. Its effect upon the paper is to bring the leaves in perfect contact, even to the extent of causing the grain of the paper to fit together, and its effect is retained throughout the life of the book.

This result is obtained only by a heavy pressure over a period of at least ten hours; shorter periods merely have the effect of driving the air out of the paper which returns to its original state when the leaves are opened. Books must be knocked up perfectly square during pressing, for should any sections become misplaced, they will become permanently set in that position, and subsequent operations will fail to replace them. The total weight that can be applied by means of the screw and lever is considerable, and certain precautions must be taken to avoid damage to the apparatus or the books. All work must be placed directly under the centre, otherwise

SECTIONS GATHERED AND WIRED

BOOKS WRAPPERED

COVERS PASSING TO BOOKS

COMPLETE MARTINI BINDER

Fig. 5. *This machine gathers the sections and inserts the wire stitches. It also glues and fixes the paper covers on magazines and similar paper-covered work at high speed. In the event of a section being missed during gathering the machine stops automatically.*

strains will be imposed which tend to bend the screw. Large and small books should not be pressed together and wherever there is a variation in size strong wooden boards must be placed between. Further use of the press will be described in this section, when dealing with the later stages of binding work.

Sewing

Three methods of sewing will be described: hand sewing on cords for leather binding with boards drawn on; hand sewing on tapes suitable for library bindings; and machine sewing for publishers' cloth-cased work.

In the case of the first and second styles the position of the cords or tapes is marked across the back by means of shallow saw cuts. These ensure the accurate placing of the cords or tapes and assist the sewer, especially if the paper is hard. They also make slots for the cords and the knots formed at each end of the signatures, which is called the kettle stitch, leaving the back sections quite smooth and level. The saw cuts must not be more than $\frac{1}{32}$ in. deep or the threads will not grip and the sewing will be weakened.

The book is placed between a pair of strawboards and firmly held in a laying press. For the marking a compass and set square are required, but sets of cards may be kept in hand for the various sizes of books and used as required; the saw may be an ordinary carpenter's tenon saw.

The thickness of the cord depends

upon the size of the book but should fit into the saw cut; it should consist of good quality hemp or flax which is capable of being unravelled without losing strength. The thread should be linen and the thickness to be used must receive careful consideration. Its presence in the back of the book causes what is known as the "swelling," which must not be allowed to become too great; therefore if the sections are thin the thickness of the sewing thread should be kept down.

The frame having been fitted up with the cords or tapes, whichever are chosen, the first section is placed in position with the left arm inside. The needle travels in and out the saw cuts along the length of the book securing the cords on its way. The next section is then placed into position and the operation repeated in the opposite direction, the threads being tied to the previous section at the top or bottom saw cut, called the kettle stitch. The knots formed when the needle lengths are joined together must be made close to the short end as they cannot be drawn through the paper. On the completion of a volume a second may be sewn on the same frame, provided it is the same size and that the cord or tape is sufficient to allow two inches each side of the book, as this amount must be left when cutting off on completion.

Machine Sewing. The skilled hand sewer can average only three books per hour, therefore machines are necessary where quantities are large. The principles involved are based upon hand work, with the exception that instead of a thread running along the length of the section, the sewing is made up of a series of separate components each with its tape and two kettle stitches.

GATHERING AND SEWING MACHINES

Fig. 6. *A battery of sewing machines showing the delivery of the folded and sewn sections. In the background is a gathering machine supplying the sewing machines with folded sheets.*

SMYTH No. 12 SEWING MACHINE

Fig. 7. *The gathered and folded sheets are fed, one section at a time, on to the arm of the machine. The finished books are removed periodically from the back of the machine by the operator.*

extra wear and tear to which the outside leaves are subjected and so protect the preliminary pages. The paper used should be selected to meet all the above requirements, i.e. it should be fairly strong in order to form a satisfactory joint, but not hard sized or it will be difficult to paste down without creases. It should be opaque as it must cover up the turn-in material. A coloured paper may be used as a help to the general appearance of the binding. The end-paper must also withstand the extra handling without becoming soiled. The thinner kinds of cartridge or quiet-tinted cover papers are usually quite suitable (Fig. 8).

The advantage of this, when necessary to change over from larger to smaller books, is clear when it is pointed out that one or more needle units can be put out of action as desired.

In action the operator places the sections upon the arm of the machine which sews them at the rate of 60 to 90 signatures a minute, depending on type of machine used and the class of work. The work is continuous and an additional operator is required to separate the individual books at the rear of the machine. A machine is shown in Fig. 7.

End-papers are used in bookbinding for the following reasons: to form the inside joint; to form the lining for the inside of the boards; to take the

For a leather-bound book one form of end-paper is here described. A folder of tinted paper and two folders of white paper are required for each end. The tinted folder is pasted on to the white and the pair edged with paste are inserted into the remaining folder of white. The end-paper may be sewn to the book as a section or it may be pasted in. If pasted, the end-paper must

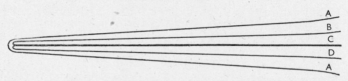

Fig. 8. *The letterpress " made " end-paper.* (A) *Waste ;* (B) *board paper ;* (C) *stiffened fly-leaf ;* (D) *extra fly-leaf.*

be in line with the back of the book, otherwise it will drag the first page and eventually loosen the binding. The outside leaves of these end-papers are waste and must be removed prior to pasting down the board paper later on in the process of binding.

Fixing the End-paper

A cloth joint end-paper is used for library bindings and gives the extra strength which these books require. They must, however, be sewn on through the cloth in order to be effective. Smooth bookbinder's cloth is a suitable material. A strip one inch wide, two folders of white paper and two single leaves of tinted, are required for each end. The strip of cloth is glued, the two folders of white are laid on each half-way over and with the folded edge touching. The tinted papers are pasted and placed on, each side just overlapping the edges of the cloth. When dry and folded down the centre the ends are ready to be sewn on. Here again it will be noticed that the outside leaf is waste and has to be removed prior to the final paste down of the end-paper on to the board.

The single folded sheet edged to the outside of the book is the usual end-paper for cloth bindings for both hand and machine work. To save handling the heavy books, they may be attached to the section before gathering, thereby forming a protection during that and the sewing operations.

Cutting the Edges

The Guillotine as used by printers for cutting paper is also suitable for trimming the edges of books. The important parts are the knife, the platen, the clamp and the gauges (Fig. 9).

The Knife. A 30-in. blade is sufficient for all bookbinding work. The edge must be kept in good condition as any notches will readily produce a very disfiguring mark on the trimmed edges of the books.

The Platen must be kept free of oil from the bearings, as the smallest quantity will penetrate through a large number of leaves of paper.

The Clamps. All work cut in a guillotine must be securely clamped. Difficulties are encountered because sewn books are not solid like flat paper.

The Gauges must be kept accurate as lack of squareness is very disfiguring in bookwork.

The fore-edges of books are the first to receive attention. The slips and cords must not be allowed to come between the gauges and the sections, or the cutting will be thrown out of true. Any swelling in the back sections due to sewing will cause the front end-paper to be wider than the back and should be hammered out before trimming. The trouble is unlikely to be met with in the case of machine-sewn books as the swelling is only slight.

Trimming Head and Tail

The tail is the next edge to be trimmed. The head is placed against the back gauge and any projecting end-papers will throw the cutting out and must be cut away. The engraved lines on the machine table will assist in obtaining an accurate trimming and these should be parallel with the length of the book. The swelling is likely to cause trouble again as it is not wise to allow the clamp to press it out. The remedy consists in packing up the forepart of the book with a block of paper until the whole is level.

The head is the last edge to be trimmed and the operation is similar to that described for the tail.

The extent to which the edges of books are cut varies considerably in practice. The bad appearance of reduced

THE GUILLOTINE

Fig. 9. *Massive construction is necessary for cutting heavy piles of paper, but the machine may also be used for trimming. The safety bar shown in foreground is automatically raised while the knife descends thus avoiding danger to operator's hands, and is lowered only after the completion of the cut in order to permit of the work being removed.*

margins has resulted in a fashion against trimming. The dust-collecting uncut edges with the leaves difficult to turn has become an accepted habit without inquiry into its origin. If the love of wide margins is the sole reason the printer is in a position to supply the answer. However, books are sometimes cut top edge only; others have the fore-edge and tail trimmed, but not to the extent as to make the edges solid; the uncut leaves give proof that the book has not been unduly cut down.

Gluing is a comparatively simple operation, but one or two important points require consideration. Thin glue

is worked into the back sections whereby the sewing is set firm. The glue that finds its way between the sections is effective and any deposited on the outside merely cracks and breaks when the book is opened. It is important also to prevent the glue getting on the end-paper, slips and edges. The book must be knocked up quite square, for when once glued it can never be altered. Several may be glued up at the same time, a partly worn brush being best for the purpose, as the shorter hairs force the glue between the sections.

In large binderies the backs are glued up automatically, the books, in piles of

GLUING MACHINE

Fig. 10. *The machine is shown gluing the backs of a pile of books. Cleanliness and complete control over the distribution of the glue are ensured by the use of this machine.*

five or six, are fed between caterpillar tracks and are carried over first a glue cylinder and then a very stiff brush which rises to meet the book and brushes off the glue between the sections (Fig. 10). The glue used for this operation should be flexible in nature and should not dry sufficiently hard to cause cracking.

Hand-bound books are glued up before cutting as the sections cannot become disturbed and spoil the smooth edges, but in machine work the stiffened backs cause clamping difficulties.

If the book is taken in the hands after the glue has set but before it has been allowed to dry hard, it will be found that it is possible to mould the back into its familiar rounded shape with ease. Under workshop conditions it is seldom

possible to get the glue in the right condition and so the hammer is used. Any swelling in the back disappears after *rounding*, which is the main purpose of the operation. Its effect upon the fore-edge is to produce a concave shape, and whenever attempts are made to keep the backs flat, attractive as they may appear when new, they sink inwards with use, causing the fore-edge to take a convex form (Fig. 11).

Backing is an operation exclusive to letterpress work and its importance is seldom realized even by some bookbinders. The learner is advised to make the following test: take from your shelf a book that has been backed and also one that has not, lay them open side by side and compare them. It will be noticed that the former does not open right into the back but uses the fold in the paper formed by the backing operations. On the other hand the unbacked book opens right into the sewing as though it had been broken over. It will be clear that the strain on the unbacked binding will be much greater than that on the backed one, and in consequence its life will be reduced.

Letterpress books are not required to open right into the back for reading

purposes and, provided the paper is not too stiff, its usefulness is unimpaired, and gives greater durability.

Backing serves yet another purpose, for its effect upon the sections is to bind them firmly together independently of the sewing and give them the necessary support when standing on the bookshelf.

Hand-backing requires the laying press, a pair of wooden backing boards and the round-faced bookbinder's hammer. The backing boards are placed

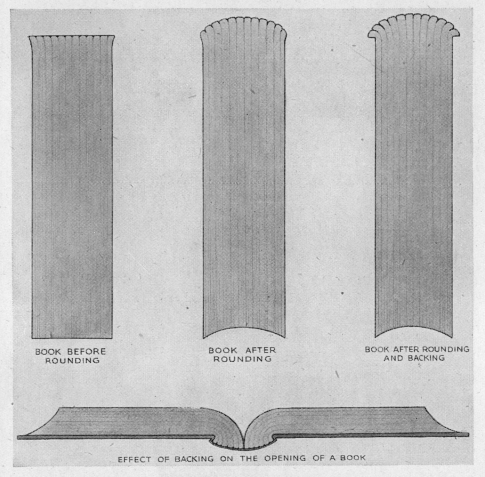

BOOK BEFORE ROUNDING

BOOK AFTER ROUNDING

BOOK AFTER ROUNDING AND BACKING

EFFECT OF BACKING ON THE OPENING OF A BOOK

ROUNDING AND BACKING
Fig. 11. *Showing the effect of the operation of backing and rounding on the opening of a book.*

TRIMMING THREE EDGES AT ONE OPERATION

Three edges (top, foot and fore-edge) are being trimmed continuously at this machine—the trimmed book being delivered to the moving platform shown in the foreground. The cuttings are automatically drawn away into sacks, forming valuable white-paper waste.

HAND-FED THREE EDGE TRIMMER

Although the above machine is hand-fed and has no automatic delivery, it trims three edges at one operation at a speed depending only on the skill of the operator.

$\frac{1}{8}$ in. from the joint on each side of the book which is then lowered into the press and screwed firmly. The sections are now hammered over on each side to form the familiar backed shape. It is not sufficient to batter the book into shape. The outside sections are beaten over first, to be followed by the more central ones, while the actual top of the round is not hammered, for if this happens the paper will be badly creased. When taken out of the press the groove so formed on each side must not be allowed to be pressed out of the book by its own weight, but the book must be placed with the back projecting.

A machine for backing books has been on the market for at least fifty years. The fact that it has remained unchanged over this period is a sure proof of the efficiency of its original design. It is hand worked and employs a heavy roller in place of the hammer and is certainly less noisy and less laborious than the hand method. Being quickly adjusted to a wide range of sizes it has become popular even in small workshops.

The more recent power machine combines the operation of rounding and backing using clamping irons or rollers to work the book into the rounded shape and the roller or wiper principle for backing. Being fast and positive in action, it is in general use in publishers' binding houses (Figs. 12 and 13).

Treatment of the Edges

White edges form a harsh contrast to the coloured cover and readily become soiled. Marbling, which at one time was very popular, is not used today. This is due principally to the use of uncut edges, to the elaborate apparatus and to the experience required which make it uneconomical for miscellaneous work.

Water-colours take very well to the

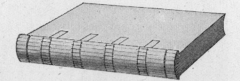

Book sewn on tapes.

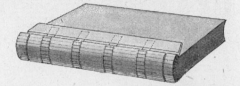

Book cut, rounded and backed.

The split board opened ready for insertion.

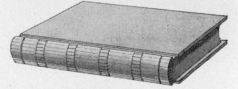

End-papers folded back and glued over the tapes before insertion in the split boards.

Split boards attached.

The book covered.

LETTERPRESS BINDING : LIBRARY STYLE WITH FRENCH GROOVE

ROUNDING AND BACKING MACHINE

Fig. 12. *The books are fed at the right where they are rounded and passed on to the centre of the machine for backing. Fig. 13 shows a close-up view of the machine.*

edges of books if they are cut solid, and form a ready and effective means of giving a finish to this part of the binding. The shades should be carefully selected and be quiet in tone to help the general appearance of the whole book. They are best applied by means of a small wad of cotton wool and when dry a semi-burnish may be given with a stiff brush.

Gilt edges are still the best form of book-edge decoration with the added value of exclusion of light and dust. They would be more popular but for the cost; the method used today, however, is just the same as it was a hundred years ago. The necessary firm base for gilding is obtained by placing a pair of wedge-shaped boards flush with the edge and clamping firmly in the laying press. A steel scraper and sandpaper are used to give the extra smoothness required. A mixture of gilder's red

chalk and blacklead with water to form a paste is then applied to fill the pores of the paper which, when dry, is burnished with a stiff brush.

The adhesive for the gold consists of the white of egg, or albumen, diluted with six parts of water, beaten up and strained. The gold leaf is cut ready and immediately after the edge has been painted over with the size, it is applied to the edge by means of the gold tip. With experience the last operation can be done quickly, leaving the gold flat upon the edge free from creases and breaks. When dry, the edge will have a matt appearance which is not unpleasant, although burnishing is usually preferred. This is done by means of a polished agate set in a handle which is worked backwards and forwards across the edge after a slight greasing with a bees-waxed rag.

Edge decoration is most conveniently

undertaken immediately after trimming; but better quality work results if left until after the rounding and backing operations, as the book is firmer and so disturbance of the sections cannot take place, causing "starts."

Binders' Boards

Boards are made from various fibres obtained from straw, wood, wastepaper, rope and string; also from by-products of other industries. They range in quality and price according to the raw materials used, and it is for the bookbinder to judge the particular quality suited to his requirements. The familiar yellow strawboard has now been replaced by a British product which is grey in colour. These boards are used for wholesale cloth binding in very large quantities. The price is low and, generally speaking, these boards are quite suited to this class of work. This grade of board is not strong enough for library binding and for hand work it is not in keeping with the cost of labour spent on the work.

At the other end of the range of boards is the black millboard made from rope. This is extremely tough and rather heavy, and should be used only when the quality of the other material is in keeping with it. A middle quality is most useful, and one known as grey machine millboard is suitable for general work.

The warping of boards is perhaps the bookbinder's greatest problem and, in attempting to find a solution, one must first know the cause. Boards swell or shrink according to the amount of

FEEDING THE ROUNDING AND BACKING MACHINE

Fig. 13. *A book is shown entering the rounding station. After the jaws have given the back its rounded shape the book passes on to another part of the machine which carries out the backing.*

moisture and, if the drying or wetting is uneven, warping results. The moisture is supplied by the glue and paste used during the process of binding. This is absorbed by the paper or cloth, and finds its way into the boards. The drying occurs on the outside of the binding which is exposed to the atmosphere, and warping results.

Publishers' binders are not troubled with warping to the same extent as miscellaneous binders, as the boards are not so hard and the weight of the books is sufficient to keep them fairly flat. Hard boards such as are used by leather binders are not easily straightened after warping. A sheet of thin paper pasted to one side of a millboard and exposed to the air will pull the board towards it, and if the lined side is placed inside, it will act as a counter warp against any undue tendency to pull outwards.

Board Cutting. Accurate board cutting is essential in all branches of bookbinding and while the guillotine cuts thin cards quite easily, there is always a slight difference between the sizes of the top and bottom of a pile. The rotary card cutter, which consists of pairs of rotating knives set on adjustable spindles is extremely accurate when once the gauges are set. The scissors-like action of the rotary machine enables thicker boards to be cut without undue strain. The board chopping machine is useful for miscellaneous cutting and will cut boards up to $\frac{1}{4}$ in. in thickness, but beyond this there is a risk of damage to any machine. When thicker boards are required, it is necessary to use two or more thin ones and glue them together after cutting to size.

The Squares. When the boards are made larger than the book the portions that overlap are termed the squares. Where there is no overlap and the boards are trimmed with the book, they are said to be cut flush. The squares account for the necessity for accurate cutting as the appearance of the book is marred should they be ill-proportioned or out of true. The student is again asked to study the books in his possession, taking notice of the proportions for several sizes, and noting that the fore-edge square is slightly larger than the other two. If you happen to have a library binding, notice that the boards are a short distance away from the joint, forming what is generally known as the French groove.

Attaching the Boards

Drawn-in Work. The cords upon which the sections were sewn are laced through the boards for this class of binding, and the first operation consists of fraying them out so that they become soft tufts of fibres. Mark the position of these cords upon the boards, and pierce holes—two for each cord—immediately opposite, about half an inch from the edge and from each other. The frayed slips are pasted and laced through the holes from the outside and returned from the inside when they may be cut off flush. By means of the round-faced hammer and a knocking-down iron the holes are closed, levelling the boards again and firmly holding the cords. A pressing between tin plates will further help to level the boards, and while in the press the backs of the books are sponged free of loose glue ready for the linings (Fig. 14).

Library Bindings. Split boards are used for this work. They are made by pasting a thick and a thin board together leaving a split about $1\frac{1}{2}$ in. wide. The waste sheets of the end-paper and the tapes are reduced to such a width that they may be inserted within these splits, glued and afterwards pressed. Allowance has to be made for the French groove by keeping the boards

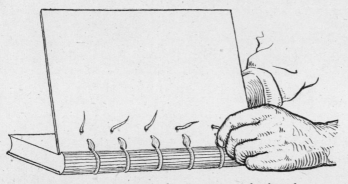

Fig. 14. *Drawn-in work. Lacing on the boards.*

away from the joint about $\frac{1}{8}$ in. The purpose of this groove is to allow thick leather to be used and yet to have a free opening board, giving that extra strength and durability required for this class of work.

Cloth Bindings. The boards are not attached at this stage, as cases are made for the book which are attached later.

Lining the Backs

There are four factors which determine whether a book will remain flat when placed upon the reading-desk, but only one of these is under the control of the binder. The factors are: the thickness of the paper; the direction of the paper grain; the size and weight of the book; and the back linings. Music as a class is required to open flat, but as thick paper is often used the amount of material used for lining should be kept down; on the other hand, an altar book is large and the paper thin, therefore the linings may be increased in order to afford greater strength and durability.

The Hollow Back. Drawn-in work is usually lined with a hollow. It is made of brown paper which should be strong but pliable; some of the better quality Kraft packing papers are particularly suitable. If the machine direction is arranged to run parallel with the back

sections the pliability will be increased and the work of forming the back will be easier.

Strips of worked silk to be seen at the head and tail of leather bindings are known as the headbands. For the best work they are sewn and worked direct on to the book but it is now more usual to purchase silk by the yard and glue it to the back; the worked headband gives strength which is lacking in the stuck-on form.

The operation of making and fixing the hollow is as follows: cut a strip of brown paper wide enough to cover the length of the back. Glue the back sections freely, lay the paper level with one joint, rub down and fold over at the other joint. Cut completely off the book, glue first lining on book and lay the paper $\frac{1}{8}$ in. from the joint, leaving a strip of glue showing, rub down and fold over at the other joint, rubbing down again. Now give this lining another coat of glue, fold the paper over and cut off at the opposite joint. This leaves two linings to the book and two outer linings forming our hollow. This of course can be varied to suit the book we are binding. Rub down well with the folding stick and level the ends with the shears to make them flush with the boards.

The Fixed Back. If the covering material is attached direct to the back it is naturally creased each time the book is opened. This may be a serious objection with certain classes of work, but in library binding, where strength and durability are of first importance, the fixed back may be used and the stronger and more pliable leather

GENERAL VIEW OF MODERN BINDERY

In the background are the folding machines, the bundled and folded sheets and the gathering machine. The sewing machines and gluers are shown in the foreground.

allowed to replace the brown paper. In these circumstances the books are not lined at this stage of the binding unless they are extra heavy, when the layer of leather or canvas may be a definite advantage.

Cased Bindings. These receive a lining of coarse muslin and one layer of paper. The muslin is allowed to extend $1\frac{1}{2}$ in. over the end-papers to assist the tapes in holding the book in its case. The glue used must be flexible and not too thick or cracks will occur as the book is opened, but the paper should be well rubbed down with the folder. The glue must be confined to the back sections.

In large binderies the lining is done by machines capable of applying linings to the book at the rate of 2,000 per hour. On one machine the book is fed into a trough, where it is gripped by overhead travelling clamps and carried to a station where it receives a coating of glue and then passes to the next station where a piece of muslin is automatically cut the required width and applied to the book. As it passes the next stations it receives more glue and a crêpe-paper

lining, finally being rubbed down with wet rubber rollers, the dampness allowing the crêpe-paper to shrink to the book. This machine can also apply head and tail bands at the same time (Fig. 15), if this should be necessary.

Book Covering Materials

The requirements of a covering material for books are as follows: it should be pleasant to handle, its colour and general appearance should be good, it should be fairly soft and pliable and it should not easily soil or be affected by slight moisture. Last but not least it should be strong and durable. The student is advised to study these requirements and see how far they have been met in his own books.

Leather. Morocco, which is the skin of the goat, is perhaps the only material that meets all the above requirements. Calf is even more popular but it is not so strong or so durable as morocco. Pigskin, on the other hand, being less pliable, is more suited to heavy work. Sheepskins form a very useful series of inexpensive leathers but the surface is easily bruised and certain tannages rapidly deteriorate. Split sheepskins under the name of skivers lose two-thirds of their strength in the process of splitting and are less durable than cloth. Attention is being given to the problem of the deterioration of modern leathers, and unless a solution is found their popularity will decline in spite of their attractive feel and appearance.

Cloth. The range of cloths suitable for bookbinding is very wide and the strength and wearing qualities vary greatly. Cloths do not deteriorate on exposure to air, therefore the simple test by tearing will indicate at once their wearing qualities. Cloths are not suitable for drawn-in work as they are not pliable enough and their general appearance and feel do not justify the labour required for this class of work; but the strongest, such as certain leather cloths and buckrams, may be used for library bindings while the cheaper varieties, including art linen, are popular for cloth cased work.

Papers. These are used for the sides of half bindings, but they should be free from excessive loading materials and artificial surfaces. Good quality papers have considerable durability.

A full binding is covered all over in one piece, but a half binding has a leather back and corner pieces and cloth or paper sides. A quarter binding has a leather back only. When cutting, allow at least $\frac{3}{4}$ in. for the turn-in for the average book with proportional increases for the larger sizes (Fig. 16).

Leather requires to be pared down before covering, but this paring need only be round the edges with particular attention to the corners and the turn-in at the head and tail. A disused lithographic stone is very useful for paring and for leather work in general as its smooth, hard surface forms an excellent covering table. The shoemaker's knife is used by many for paring leather, but

BACK LINING MACHINE

Fig. 15. *Applying the mull and brown paper linings to the backs of books has proved to be one of the most difficult operations to mechanize. But this machine is capable of applying linings to the backs at the rate of about 2,000 copies per hour.*

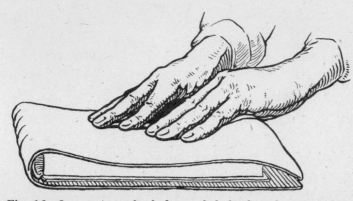

Fig. 16. *In covering a book for a whole binding the material is all in one piece. Note the allowance made for the turn-in.*

a strip of steel 1½ in. wide ground obliquely at one end has a wider range of uses. Naturally these knives have to be kept very sharp, and as leather removes the edge very quickly the oilstone and strop should be ready to hand.

Edge paring which consists of thinning the leather all round the edges is usually sufficient and is not difficult. It is best done on a lithographic stone. The turn-in requires care, and a number of trials should be made with the corners of half bindings before attempting full covers. The turn-in at the head and tail requires to be thinned down to reduce the distortion by the double thickness of leather.

Paste is used for leather as it is slow in drying thus allowing time for the covering operation. The cold water paste powders are very convenient and answer the purpose very well, but glue must not be used as it soaks through and hardens the leather. The extra moisture in paste helps to soften the leather while working it and allows it to be moulded into position. The folder and stone must be clean and dry as the damp leather is sensitive to stains.

After gaining experience with corners a back may be attempted. If you have

decided to have raised bands, narrow strips of leather may be glued across the back before covering. Notice how the back corners of the dissected books are cut and that the hollow is slit to enable the leather to be inserted.

After the leather has been pasted and allowed to soak a little it is drawn over the back and equally over the sides. The turn-in at the head and tail is undertaken either by opening the boards and standing the book on end, or by using an assistant to hold the book on the stone with the boards open, leaving both hands free to work the leather into position. To set the head, the book is tied up with twine which passes along the back edges of the board, across the book, and is tightly tied. The leather at the head and tail may now be moulded into shape, the raised bands set with the folder and flat stick or with special nippers, and the whole cover set and allowed to dry.

Styles of Binding

For *Library Bindings* the method is similar but has the following differences —the tight back requires both leather and back sections pasting to ensure sticking; there are no raised bands; the French groove must be set with the folder and thicker twine used for tying up to fit this groove; silk headbands are not used, but in their place a short length of string is inserted in the fold of the leather and neatly set.

The Cloth Case. The following is the method for making a cloth-case book. It is used wherever single volumes are

Fig. 17. *Casing in the cloth-cased book by hand after the end-papers have been pasted.*

being bound, or to obtain the original pattern case used for the case-making machine. The boards, the strip of brown paper for the hollow, and the cloth cover are cut to size. The boards are placed in their correct position on the book and thin glue applied to the cloth. The book is placed in the correct position on the cloth which is then drawn over to the top board to which it will adhere. Remove the book entirely and place the strip of brown paper between the two boards and proceed to turn in the cloth. Note from your dis-

sected binding how the corners are cut before the edges are turned in. The bone folder is used to remove the air from under the cloth and generally to ensure sticking. The case having been made, and while still pliable, the book may be replaced ready for the next operation (Fig. 17).

The work of case making, complicated as it is, is now done by machines where quantities are large. The cloth is fed over glued rollers, the boards are placed in exact position by section feeders, the hollow is cut from a continuous roll, the edges are turned in and a cushion presses the cloth home. The output is about five hundred cases per hour and the machines may be entirely automatic (Fig. 18).

Completing the Forwarding

The operation from the stage of sewing, up to and including the covering, comprises a branch of the trade known as *forwarding*, while from the covering to the completed book, including the lettering and decoration, is known as

AUTOMATIC CASE-MAKING MACHINE

Fig. 18. *This is one of the most successful methods of bookbinding by machinery, the machine producing a perfect case. The cloth passing in from the left is glued; the boards and the hollow are automatically placed into position, and the turn-in is made. The finished case can be seen passing into the hopper on the right of the machine after a light pressure.*

the *finishing*. The work of attaching the sides to half binding, and pasting down the end-papers is carried out in either workshop according to the particular circumstances.

Having decided upon the material for the sides of half bindings, it is cut to shape in such a way that the back and corners are correctly proportioned and the edges of the leather completely covered (Fig. 19). Unevenness in the paring of the leather will show through the material and must be evened up with a sharp knife used at the start. Glue is used, as the extra water content of paste will mar the finish of the cloth and tend to warp the boards in an outward direction.

Pasting Down. This is an operation that is more important than it at first appears and especially so in the case of hand-bound books. For this reason the case binding will receive attention first as it is fairly straightforward. The last operation left the book in its case but unattached. The boards are now opened, the ends glued and reclosed and the book pressed with the pressing boards placed up to the joint but not over it. Glue is preferable to paste as there will be less stretch in the paper. The work must be kept clean, for a trace of adhesive between the leaves will cause them to stick together and the

book will be spoiled. Several hours' pressure will help to set the book firmly, and when removed a weight should be placed upon it until the moisture has dried out, or the boards will warp.

Wholesale cloth binders employ machines for the above work and the operation is known as casing-in. The backs of the cases, the lettering of which will be described later, are flat and require to be shaped to the book. For this purpose a steam pipe of the required diameter is used, except on some machines where this is done automatically. The operator on the casing-in machine feeds the books on to an arm or blade, and two rollers paste the end-papers, giving a quarter reverse turn at the joint to ensure sufficient paste is applied. The case is automatically placed over the book and set with slight pressure, after which it is removed and, if necessary, the square adjusted. Additional hands build up the presses as they leave the machines and they remain under pressure for several hours. The output of the casing-in machines is about 500 to 1,000 per hour, depending on the type of machine, and the presses are rapidly filled. The use of special clamping boards enables the books to be removed and transported while still under pressure and so releases the presses for the following work (Fig. 20).

Leather Bindings. The difference between cloth and leather which directly affects the pasting-down operation is their thickness, for whereas cloth may be folded with a sharp crease, leather merely bends. This has the effect of drawing the boards away from the joint each time it is opened and allowance must be made when pasting down the end-papers to avoid breaking. The only way to do this is to keep the book open. The little extra paper acquired by the joint has the effect of increasing the

Fig. 19. *Turning in at the corners of a full-bound leather binding.*

CASING-IN MACHINE

Fig. 20. *A complicated binding operation successfully mechanized. In the centre is a book receiving its case after the end-papers have been pasted; at the top a cased book is shown leaving the arm of the machine ready for the final pressing of the book.*

The above description of the work of pasting down does not apply to library bindings which may be pasted down shut, as for cloth work. This is on account of the French groove which gives a freedom of opening, avoiding strains upon the joint in spite of the use of thick leather, and constitutes the main advantage of this style of binding.

This completes the forwarding operation for three styles of binding, namely, the drawn-in leather book, a library style and the cloth-cased style of book.

Finishing

Book decoration, as with many other crafts, has changed during the past few years. Ornaments, that play no part in the construction, added to articles already complete are now rightly considered futile, and the elaborate corner and centre stamps and rolls are now replaced by lines carefully arranged. Book finishing has not been made less difficult on this account, for the elaborate gilt back did not require the accuracy that the plain lines demand, and might mask defects.

Forwarding also plays a very considerable part in the appearance of the finished article.

Blind Finishing. This work consists in making impressions in the covering

fore-edge margin and it becomes necessary to equalize the top and bottom margins by cutting.

If there is a waste sheet preceding the board paper it is removed at this stage, and the joint is freed from hard paste or other matter likely to injure the paper. Paste is used as it is cleaner, does not harden the joint and helps to counteract any outward warp of the boards. The work should be rubbed down well to ensure sticking, especially in the joint, and when completed left open in order to dry before any attempt is made to close the book.

material by means of heated hand tools, pallets or rolls. Hand tools are brass stamps set in handles, and as the pressure required is considerable their size is limited. A pallet is a form of hand tool, long and narrow in shape for use over rounded backs. A roll is an engraved wheel set in a long handle; it is used for covering flat surfaces (Fig. 21). The effect of blind tooling depends upon the depth of the

Fig. 21.
Showing the use of the roll in finishing work.

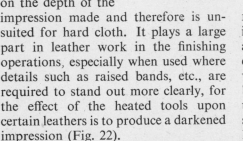

impression made and therefore is unsuited for hard cloth. It plays a large part in leather work in the finishing operations, especially when used where details such as raised bands, etc., are required to stand out more clearly, for the effect of the heated tools upon certain leathers is to produce a darkened impression (Fig. 22).

The temperature of the tools, the amount of moisture, etc., required must be tried out for every material used, as, owing to the wide range, it is not possible to lay down rules. Generally speaking the temperature is lower than that required for gold finishing.

Gold Finishing

The following is the generally adopted method of gold finishing on the average good quality leather. The cover is first marked up as a guide to the position of the tools. With experience only a few guiding lines will be needed and these are made with a bone folder assisted by the ruler and dividers. The beginner, however, should work out his pattern on thin paper and then impress the heated tools through, thus leaving an impression on the leather.

The next process is to wash the leather over with thin paste water which cleans and at the same time leaves a slight dampness; the object of the paste is to fill the pores whereby the glair

remains on the surface. The glair, which is the preparation which makes the gold adhere, is made from the white of raw eggs or albumen to which a little vinegar has been added. This, when beaten up and strained becomes quite thin and is ready to be sponged over the surface for tooling. A gold cushion, knife, book of gold leaf, tin of vaseline and a handful of cotton wool are required for the next stage which is known as laying-on.

The glair is allowed to dry and is vaselined over with a small piece of cotton wool. A firm pad of wool very lightly greased by contact with the hair will enable the gold leaf to be picked up and brought into contact with the leather until the area is covered. The result should be an unbroken layer of gold covering the surface which is to be tooled.

A gas finishing stove is required to heat the tools, and a saucer of wetted cotton wool is used to cool them down to the correct temperature. They should be cooled down until hissing just ceases, and stamped on to the prepared cover with a firm uniform pressure until the pattern is completed. The gold will stick wherever the heated tools have been impressed and the surplus may be wiped away with a rag, the remaining vaseline being removed with benzine on cotton wool. An alternative method is to use a specially prepared india rubber which retains the surplus gold.

The process is the same for nearly all ordinary book covering materials, involving only slight variations of temperature to suit the particular work. Even the most experienced finishers are at a loss sometimes when handling new surfaces, which present special problems.

Lettering

The process of lettering is naturally the most important side of the finisher's work. It is required to be easily read from a fair distance, and so clear, well-spaced type free from decoration is required. There are two distinct methods for lettering miscellaneous volumes, one making use of individual hand stamps and the other employing brass type and holders. The former method is used for larger books, and although for smaller books it has certain properties, the necessary experience is difficult to acquire, and type has become more popular.

Hand Lettering. The following rules apply to hand lettering the title of a book. The wording is decided by the title page and should be as brief as possible, a draft being made at the time indicating how it might be displayed. Its position and the size of the letters is decided by the amount of space available, avoiding any crowding. The cover is prepared and laid over with gold as explained in the previous chapter.

The necessary marking up is done on the gold leaf itself, for which a length of thread and a pair of dividers are required. The thread drawn across the gold will produce a clear line and this should be used to indicate the top of

each line of lettering. By means of the dividers find the centre of the back, marking the gold above each line, leaving the space below the line untouched. Count the number of letters in each line, allowing the space between two words as one letter, and measure off on the dividers the average space between the centre of the letters (Fig. 23). Mark these off on the gold from the centre so that the position of every letter is indicated. The complete alphabet is placed round the stove and the individual letters impressed one at a time until the panel is completed, after which the gold may be cleaned off.

Type. Hand lettering requires a considerable amount of concentration on the part of the operator as no alteration is possible when once the tools are struck. With type set up in a holder, an impression may be made and the lettering inspected before being used. Two or more lines may be set in the same holder provided they are separated by a brass space of at least half an inch. The panel is marked up with thread as before and

Fig. 22. *The correct method of holding the finishing tool.*

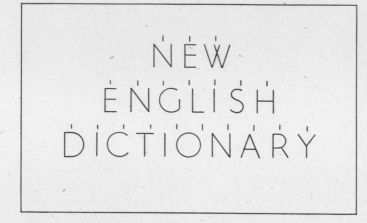

Fig. 23. *Hand-lettering. The marks for the letters are equally spaced, but the finisher must make due allowance for variation in the width of the letters. It is important that the first and last letters in each line should be correctly centred under the marks.*

centres are found, but instead of the individual letters being marked, half the length of the line is marked from the centre. By this means the heated holder is impressed across the book a line at a time, and when complete the gold may be cleaned off and the type distributed.

Rolls and Fillets. Owing to the heavy pressure required the size of hand finishing tools is limited, but rolls enable larger areas to be covered. One or two lines in the form of rolls are known as fillets and no finishing shop is complete without them. The more elaborate designs have only a limited use today. The chief difficulty with rolls occurs at the corners, and is usually overcome by running them right off the board, but is not entirely satisfactory; fillets may be correctly mitred by means

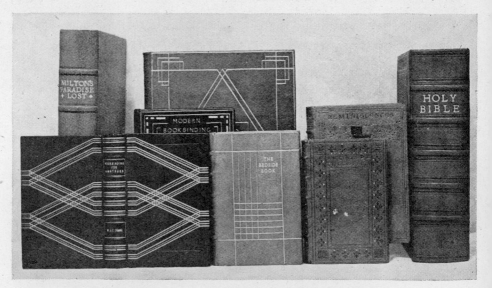

EXAMPLES OF MODERN LEATHER BINDING
A selection of modern bindings in full leather carried out entirely by students of technical schools and displaying an excellent standard of design and craftsmanship.

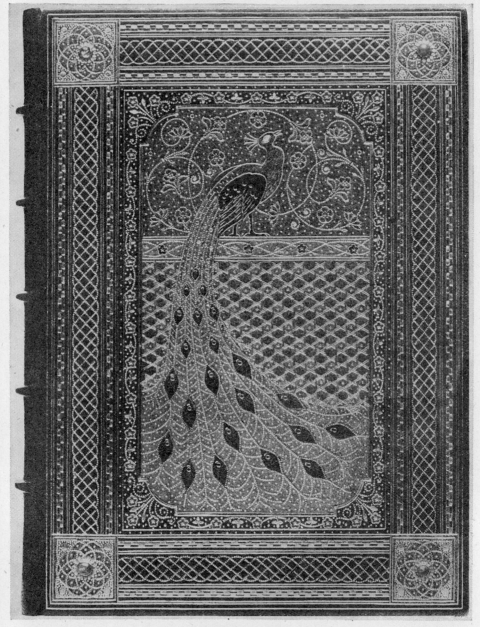

HAND FINISHING

An example of "extra" gold finishing with coloured leather inlays. Executed by E. H. Turner from a design by the author of this chapter, it represents an excellent example of advanced finishing technique, combined with fine tool cutting. The modern tendency in book decoration is towards simplicity of design and the avoidance of unnecessary ornament. It will be seen that in the above example the ornaments form an intrinsic part of the design.

AUTOMATIC BLOCKING PRESS

Fig. 24. *Cloth cases are automatically fed into the machine from the chute on the right. The gold foil passes between the block and the work in a continuous ribbon, and the impression is made; the finished cases are carried away by the rollers shown on the left.*

of hand tools of the same line thickness.

Finishing in General. Bookbinding designs being in a state of transition, the author has avoided an elaborate description of the ordinary trade pattern and is leaving the learner to work out his own ideas. Display of lettering should receive first consideration, to be followed by arrangement of lines and sample tools. Blind and gold finishing may be used together provided the latter is used sparingly. Solidarity and brilliancy of gold are obtained by careful attention to the preparation, which allows cooler tools to be used, and clean finishing by careful glairing, if necessary by painting in instead of sponging over the whole of the surface. Calf is a very porous leather and should be prepared with a coat of thin size, to be followed by two coats of gelatine.

Polishing. Certain leathers may be polished with a special iron set in a handle. The face of the iron must be kept clean, by means of a knife board, used at a temperature about the same as that used for tooling. All polishing is done by moving the iron with a circular motion; it must not be allowed to stop or serious darkening will result.

Varnishing. Bookbinder's varnish is a very quick-drying spirit preparation. It is very thin and is applied by means of a very small piece of cotton wool. It dries in one minute and so the cotton must never be allowed to go over the same place twice or the first coat will be disturbed.

Cloth Books. These are lettered only, as hand tooling beyond a few cross lines is out of place. The preparation is one coat of glair only. A little colour is added to the book by the use of leather lettering pieces which may be tooled on or off the book, the former being preferable.

Pressing. The final pressing given to leather bindings is most valuable, and the use of polished nickel plates gives an extra finish to the work.

Blocking Machines

The blocking machine is generally used for all stamps that are too large to be impressed by hand. It may be used in conjunction with hand finishing for arms, etc., but in publishers' work it entirely replaces the hand work. As the pressure increases in proportion to the area, the machines require to be of massive construction. They consist of the bed or plate which is adjustable—but once set must be firm enough to take the whole weight—the plate to which the blocks are attached, the heating box and the lever to bring the block down on to the work. The design or pattern, including the lettering, takes the form of a brass engraved plate or block. Blocking can only be carried out on flat surfaces and as the cloth case is flat when it leaves the case-making machine, it may be blocked on both boards and the spine in one operation (Fig. 24).

Owing to the heavy pressures that may be applied and to the positive action of the machine, very little pre-paration of the material is required, often the dampness left by the glue in the case making being sufficient. If this is not enough then a thin coating of size may be used. Laying on the gold becomes an important operation owing to the expense of this material and the large quantities required. A slight blind impression of the block on the case will serve as a guide for the gold. Card templates may be used instead. Oil will hold the gold, but only a very small quantity is necessary, and a soft rubber is used for cleaning off in the final stage. This rubber is finally assayed for the gold it contains.

Although the blocking machine is itself rapid and efficient, the preparation of the cover, the laying on and cleaning off of the gold have to be carried out by hand. The introduction of ribbon gold entirely dispenses with these operations. The invention consists in replacing the gold leaf by depositing the metal on a thin plastic film which is supplied in reels to any desired width. When the foil is placed between the cover and the block it acts as a transfer. The pressure and heat cause the gold to adhere to the cover leaving the surplus attached to the paper. The foil contains its own glair preparation and the surplus gold may be recovered fully. In modern power blocking machines the feeding of the cases and the ribbon is entirely automatic. The machines have an output of several hundreds per hour.

Substitutes for Gold Leaf

Gold is expensive and there is still no real substitute for it. Other metals are sometimes used which are excellent in colour and, being within a thin plastic film, are protected from the atmosphere so that they remain untarnished for several years although not indefinitely. As soon as this medium breaks down the metal rapidly begins to tarnish.

CHAPTER THIRTY-TWO

STATIONERY BINDING

ACCOUNT-BOOK CONSTRUCTION. STANDARD QUALITIES OF BINDING. RULING. SEWING AND FORWARDING. TRIMMING. COVERING MATERIALS. GLUING. LOOSE-LEAF BINDING. INDEXING. ACCOUNT-BOOK FINISHING. MISCELLANEOUS STATIONERY.

THIS branch of the trade deals with account books and in general all binding work connected with the business office. It is sometimes known as vellum binding from the vellum tapes upon which account books are sewn.

While it is not so easy to find an account book for dissection as it is with letterpress binding, the learner is well advised to obtain one or two if possible, as they form a very helpful means of acquiring the knowledge where technical classes are not available. A fair-sized and well-bound book should be selected for the purpose.

How Account Books Open

First of all notice how the book opens. The hard millboard hollow has a spring action, and while it grips the book firmly closed, when levered off the back has the effect of throwing up the sections so that the book opens quite flat.

An examination of some of the end sections will show how certain leaves have been strengthened with linen.

Notice how the end-papers are constructed and that they are strongly sewn through the cloth or leather joints. The blank leaf of each end is pasted direct on the first leaf of the book forming a "stiff-leaf" where page one starts on the left-hand page.

Commence dissection by cutting down the leather about two inches from the joint and by cutting across about one inch from each end. Lifting this leather will expose the board, the joint and the spring back. A split board has been used into which has been inserted the following: the cloth holding the spring back, the leather back linings, a card stiffener used to throw off the spring back, and the webbing tapes.

Now cut through the cloth holding the back, and through the leather at the head and tail; this will enable the spring back to be opened, revealing the back linings and the sewings.

The dissected binding should be retained for study in conjunction with the details that follow. In connection with the information to be given it is pointed out that the reader is assumed to have read the sections dealing with letterpress binding; therefore operations common to both branches of the trade will not be described in full.

Three Standard Qualities

Three standard qualities of account-book bindings will be described. Each quality will be to a definite specification and the terms "extra," "half-extra" and "common" are used in the trade when ordering. The specifications are:—

Extra. Hand-made paper for the book, six sections taped at each end, made ends, leather joint, stout webbing strips, hand sewn, rope millboards, split boards, spring back, back lined all along with calf, covered with calf or hide.

Half-extra. Machine-made paper tub

sized, four sections taped each end, made ends, cloth joints sewn on, sewn thread, webbing slips, back lined between tapes with leather, spring back and split boards of grey millboard covered with calf or roan.

Common. Writing paper for book, machine sewn on tapes, cloth joint, back lined canvas or sheepskin, strawboard for boards, covered with sheepskin or buckram.

Writing papers differ from those used for printing in many respects, as they are required to serve an entirely different purpose. The surface is not so smooth and the paper is less absorbent, tubsized papers being used for all but the cheapest work. The dimensions of writing papers differ from printing papers, being a few inches smaller although the names are much the same.

Ruling

The enormous demand for ruled paper in the stationery trade has created a supply of high-speed ruling machines, and the technical skill required to operate them makes ruling a complete trade of its own.

The Pen Machine. As its name implies the paper is drawn under a series of pens. It is the oldest method of ruling and is still considered to produce the best work. Its comparative simplicity and low initial cost make it the most economical machine for short runs and for standard ruling, the complete sets of pens being kept in stock for immediate use. A piece of flannel in contact with the pens supplies the ink which is a water stain, and one or more colours may be used on one pen shaft, and one or more sets of pens may be used at one time according to the nature of the ruling. The sets of pens may be lowered or lifted in any position on the paper by means of adjustable cams at the side of the machine and worked in conjunction

with a release gate at the feeding end.

The Disk Machine. Metal disks built up as desired upon a shaft take the place of pens in this type of machine. These shafts are set round a cylinder over which the paper passes ; the continuous rotary action in conjunction with an automatic feed allows the machine to be run at high speed. The cylinder with the disks and cams forms a compact unit and by using a pair the paper may be ruled on both sides. While the hard disks do not take so kindly to the paper as in the case of the more flexible pen, careful adjustment and attention to the composition of the inks produce good work with the added advantage of greater output, especially for long runs.

Standard Rulings are as follow: "feint only" such as used for exercise books; "feint and margin" contains one red down line on the left-hand side of the page; "feint and common" contains a date and a cash column; "double cash" contains two cash columns; the ledger, day-book and the journal all contain cash columns with a stopped heading. All the smaller books are ruled (and sometimes bound) more than one up.

Folding and Taping

Complicated folds such as are used in letterpress work are not required when all the leaves in a book are the same. The number of sheets to a section may be four, six or eight according to the thickness of the paper, and these are counted off and folded together either by hand or on the section folding machine.

The End-papers. A pair of accountbook "made" end-papers requires four folded sheets, two of which may be ruler's wastes. These are joined together in pairs by a strip of strong cloth and lined with marbled paper.

When dry they are folded and further strengthened on the outside with cotton —note that the cloth is not placed centrally but that the board paper side is made wider in order to cover the joint (Fig. 1).

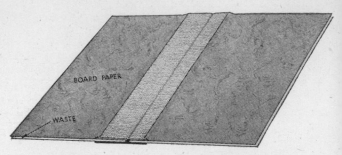

Taping. The first few sections of account books have to withstand considerably more wear as compared with the rest of the book, especially if there is an index. Compensation is made by strengthening certain sheets by lining the folds with cotton. The sheets so treated are usually as follows: the outside of the last section, the inside of the outer sheet of the next section, and so on alternately for four sections at each end of the book.

Fig. 1. *The account-book "made" end-paper.*

Sewing and Forwarding

Account books require to be strongly sewn for they are usually large and extensively used; also the spring-back binding places considerable strain upon the back sections (Figs. 2 and 3).

Linen thread is used for sewing and heavy webbing for the tapes, special attention being given to the kettle stitches. Sewing frames are not needed but are preferable, as the position of the tapes is not important provided they are fairly equally distributed; and no saw cuts are used as these would slacken the grip of the thread upon the paper. Sewing machines are used for the lighter books only.

Gluing up. Due to the general hardness of writing papers and the thicker thread used in sewing, a considerable swelling in the back is likely to occur. Much of this should be hammered out before gluing as too much round weakens the binding. A flexible variety of glue should be used; this may be obtained specially prepared for the purpose, or by adding a few drops of glycerine to ordinary glue. The brush is applied between the tapes only as these have to be pulled tight after pressing, which would be impossible if fixed with glue.

The fore-edge is now ready to be trimmed in the guillotine and presents no difficulties provided a watch is kept on the pence column of the ruling to be sure that the proper allowance has been made. The other two edges of extra and half-extra bindings are not cut until the books have been rounded and pressed, owing to trouble with the swelling. The flexible glue enables the book to be hammered into its rounded shape without the sections starting forward or the back breaking, which must be avoided. The pressing serves the double purpose of setting the book firmly and sticking the stiff leaves together, an operation undertaken at this stage.

Account books commence at the left-hand page and to provide for this the two leaves are glued together at each end-paper, and wherever there is a change in the ruling such as the index, etc. Thin glue is used to avoid paper stretch and risk of set-off of the ruling. The slips are drawn back while pressing and with large books a fair weight may be applied. Pressing should be continued for at least twelve hours for the book to become permanently solid and firm. Due to a slight reduction in the thick-

The book sewn and fore-edge trimmed.

The book cut and rounded.

The book placed between boards ready for pressing.

The back lined with leather.

Fig. 2. ACCOUNT-BOOK FORWARDING (1)

ness of the book, the webbings will be found to be buckled, but as we have taken the precaution of avoiding gluing them they may be drawn tight again. The heads and tails may now be trimmed, provided the book is shaped into a parallelogram form, in line with the diagonal direction of the knife. This is necessary in books with a rounded fore-edge owing to the tendency for paper to break under pressure of the knife when unsupported.

The Edges. While not used to a great extent in letterpress binding, marbling continues to be the method of edge treatment for account books. For the process a bath of gum obtained from a seaweed known as carrageen moss is used. Body colours ground in water are caused to float and spread on the solution by the admixture of ox gall. Patterns may be formed by sprinkling or by the use of coarse combs, etc., which are transferred to the edges of books by dipping. An alum solution sponged over the paper will cause the pattern to be picked up, after which surplus gum is washed away. The time taken to prepare the bath and the technical experience required to operate it make the process uneconomical for small quantities of work, but when once prepared and when the demand is sufficient, books can be marbled very cheaply.

Sprinkled edges are a cheap and easy substitute for marbling, and the use of different colours may form a means for the identification of the various stock rulings. Coloured ruling inks are suitable, the spray being ejected from an ironbound glue brush by beating against a heavy rod.

For very large quantities the use of the aerograph spray is clean and highly efficient.

Back Linings, etc. The stiffener is a piece of thin millboard about two inches wide and just long enough to be covered by the slips. It is glued on to the waste sheet of the end-paper, level with the joint, and the slips are stuck down on to it. Its purpose is to stiffen the joint to enable the hollow to be levered off as the book is opened. Common account books are not stiffened at this stage of the forwarding.

The best materials for lining the backs are rough calf or seal; both leathers are strong, pliable and able to adhere

The spring back hollow.

Spring back hollow attached.

The split board.

The boards attached.

Fig. 3.   ACCOUNT-BOOK FORWARDING
(2)

firmly. Of the cloths, moleskin or strong soft canvas is quite good; but hard-glazed cloth or leather is not suitable, whatever its strength, as it breaks away from the sections with use. Extra bindings are lined over the whole of the back and two inches over the side in one piece; half-extra bindings are lined from off-cuts of leather between the tapes only. Common account books are lined with canvas. These linings should be pasted on as the softening effect of the moisture makes for closer contact, but the sections themselves are glued with strong but flexible glue all along the back.

The Spring Back Hollow.   This is built up of very thin boards cut to size, glued together and inserted between brown paper attached to wooden rollers. A stock of these rollers is kept and one selected whose thickness is the same as the book. Little difficulty will be experienced with the strawboard hollows of the cheaper styles, but large ones of millboard may require to be heated to soften them before rolling. The backs should be removed before becoming too dry and hard, and the edges bent by means of a strong folder or lifted gently with a hammer over a hard ridge so that they grip the book, after which they may be allowed to harden on a flat surface between boards to keep them in shape. The attachment to the book consists of a lining of canvas on the inside; the canvas projects sufficiently to enter the split of the board. The above remarks apply to extra and half-extra work; common account books have the hollows placed into position when covering.

The Boards. Best rope millboards are used for extra books built up from thinner boards to the required thickness with an extra thin board for the split. Thicknesses up to $\frac{3}{8}$ in. are used for large ledgers, etc., and as boards of this weight cannot be cut by any bookbinding machine, the thinner components are reduced to a near size before being glued together; the final trim, provided that it is not more than $\frac{1}{8}$ in., is done with the guillotine. Glue should be used to reduce the dangers of warping, but if paste is used for the thin split, the result will be a slight inward pull which is an advantage. For half-extra bindings machine millboard may be used with a strawboard split, but for common account books strawboards with no split are used in accordance with the specification.

The width of the squares should be about equal to the thickness of the boards with a little extra for the fore-edge. The groove at the back, i.e. the distance from the edge of the hollow to the board, should be about equal to a fore-edge square for the usual covering material, but may be increased with very thick leather.

Boards are attached by gluing the split and inserting the flange already prepared, leaving the small pieces at the head and tail outside to allow the cover to be turned in. Press the book under a fairly light weight at first, increasing to a heavy pressure when all danger of the boards slipping out of position has passed. Boards with no split are simply glued to the waste leaf of the end-paper, leaving sufficient flanges at the head and tail for turning-in purposes.

Covering Materials

Calf is a thicker leather than that used for letterpress books and is dressed on the rough side. Its wearing qualities are excellent and it always has been a popular leather for extra work. It must be worked clean for it cannot be washed afterwards.

Hides are skins from full-grown animals and are naturally very large. They are reduced to a workable thickness by the leather dresser.

Pigskins have all the desired qualities, being very strong and durable and owing to their size enable large covers to be cut.

Vellum. Calf vellum, while rather difficult to work, is the most durable of all covering materials and if kept free from damp and moisture does not perish.

Sheepskins are suitable for half-extra bindings provided they are the full thickness leather. Split sheepskins are only suitable for pocket-books.

Forels are split sheepskins dressed like vellum which they sometimes resemble. They are not suitable for anything larger than a hand book as they easily tear.

Buckrams and leather cloths vary in quality, but the best wear as well as do many leathers.

Canvas Cloths. As appearance is of secondary consideration, these materials are very useful for cheap account books as many are very strong and they stick well.

Cloth. Ordinary bookbinder's cloth is not strong enough for heavy work but is useful for the smaller books and for joints.

Covering account books, although the same in principle as letterpress binding,

The book covered: half bound.

The book covered: full bound.

Fig. 4. ACCOUNT-BOOK FORWARDING (3)

involves a number of differences that require explanation. The work is heavier and the full thickness of the leather is retained, paring being confined to the edges only. Ample turn-in should be allowed or covering will be difficult and the edges of the boards will be weak. The leather must be well set into the back groove and tied round with rope or thick string; back covers of boards are cut and shaped to allow this to be done (Fig. 4).

Account-book heads are set to a special shape, which is formed by making that portion of the millboard soft by wetting and breaking with a hammer, so that it may be moulded underneath the leather. Full thickness of leather must be retained at the corners of the boards either by the special method illustrated in Fig. 4 or by the use of rounded corners, a practice extensively used for loose-leaf work.

Cloth sides of half-bindings are apt to peel off with use when the books are heavy, and precautions should be taken to ensure they adhere firmly by the use of fairly strong glue and, if possible, using a material with a rough side.

Gluing Down

Only in cases where the leather is exceptionally thick is it necessary to trim out and fill in the inside of the boards, but it may be done with extra bindings. If the boards show an inclination to warp outwards, as may be the case with vellum covered books, a thin strawboard lining counteracts this tendency. The actual sticking down of the end-papers is a straightforward operation, as it is only necessary to glue them, close the book, insert cardboard "fences" between the marble papers, and press. You will remember that in the case of the common account books the stiffener was omitted, it being a simple matter to place a piece of thin card on to the joint at the time of gluing down the end-papers.

Loose-leaf Binding

Books with removable leaves have serious disadvantages when used as a record of accounts, although on the other hand they have many advantages, and their increasing popularity has made them an important branch of the trade. Of the many systems in use most of them are variations of one of three methods: the metal post, the thong, or the ring (Fig. 5).

The *Post Binder*. A series of metal posts connects the boards, these being permanently fixed at the base but held by a releasable catch at the top. The paper is punched either by round holes to get over the posts, or by slotted holes, the latter having the advantage of allowing the required sheets to be removed without disturbing the remainder. These binders are strong and having a set capacity may be made with a leather-covered back. Wide binding margins must be allowed and such books are always made oblong for this reason.

The *Thong Binder*. Flat thongs connect the two boards to which the sheets are held by slotted holes. These thongs may be shortened or lengthened as required by a key mechanism contained in the back board. In these circumstances a small or large number of sheets may be firmly held. This type of binder is strong and durable and generally of less weight than post binders. Here again the leaves do not open into the back and ample binding room must be given.

The *Ring Binder*. Snap rings are used and the leaves are punched with corresponding holes. This type of binder does open flat as the paper can move about on the rings, therefore less binding margin is required and upright books may be used with success. They are excellent for students' note-books, but their capacity is limited to about one inch of paper and they are unsuitable for accounts, as the leaves are not secure enough for permanent records.

Much of the work of the loose-leaf manufacturers is done in the engineers' workshops with the binder left to do the making-up, ruling, cutting, indexing, etc.; case-making forms most of the work for the ring binders, and some intricate covering is involved in the larger account books.

Indexes are extensively used through-out the stationery trade, being essential to the ledgers and other important account books.

The one-letter index has one leaf allotted to each letter of the alphabet and as I and J are placed together and X is omitted twenty-four leaves are required.

The two-letter index contains two letters to each leaf, therefore twelve only are necessary. This form is used for all the smaller account books where the number of entries is insufficient to justify the larger index.

The cut-through index has all the leaves of the book allotted to the letters

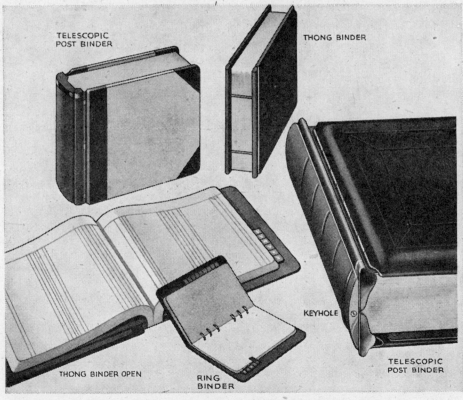

GROUP OF LOOSE-LEAF BINDINGS

Fig. 5. *The loose-leaf system of binding for account books and other forms of stationery is increasing in popularity. Most methods of loose-leaf binding are variations of one of three methods illustrated above: the telescopic metal post, the thong, and the ring.*

in proper proportion to their use as initials to surnames. A study of a small directory will reveal a very marked variation in the number of leaves required for the different letters, and the learner is advised to make out for himself a scale giving proportionate leaves for a series of totals. A useful approximation may be obtained as follows: count the total number of leaves in the book to be indexed and divide by twenty-four, which gives the average for each letter. Allot this number to the following letters: A, D, E, F, G, IJ, K, L, N, P, T; give half as many again to: B, C, H, M, R, S, W; and half the average to: O, Q, U, V, XYZ; which gives the required total.

Cutting the Index. Miscellaneous indexes are cut by hand for which purpose a pointed knife, a straight edge and a sheet of thin zinc are required. Divide the length of the book into twenty-four parts and mark the divisions on a cardboard scale together with the number of leaves allotted to each letter. Cut the leaves one letter at a time according to the scale; special self-inking wheels are used to print the letters, but failing this a set of hand tools from the finishing shop may be used. Alternate red and black impressions is the usual practice and printing ink is very convenient for this.

Cut indexes are not only used for important ledgers, etc., but for a large number of smaller books in commercial stationery, and for this work an indexing machine is a necessity. This machine uses a shaped cutter which stamps out the letters starting with Z and working upwards to A. It is adjustable to a wide range of sizes, produces a clean cut and is an economical necessity where quantities of one size are required to be indexed. The printing of the letters is a separate operation for which the self-inking alphabet wheels are used.

Tab Indexing. The ordinary cut index is useless for loose-leaf bindings and tab projections are necessary. The set of twenty-four tabs may be prepared in one piece on a strip of folded cloth, leather or vellum, which is glued halfway, leaving a split for attachment to the leaf. The letters are printed or blocked on the strip and afterwards cut up. The tabs are attached to the loose leaves in a complete series down to the fore-edge with the letters projecting, whereon the contents may be distributed.

Account-book Finishing

Most of the work of the account-book finisher is lettering, and the practice of using leather lettering labels or pieces saves much of the handling of heavy account books. Split roan leather is used for these pieces and a special method is used for preparing them. A large piece of millboard is bees-waxed over one side and a piece of leather pasted on. When dry it is ready for tooling as required, the use of bees-wax enabling the pieces to be cut round and peeled off without damage. When finished, the leather is marked up, prepared and lettered in gold exactly as described for letterpress work, the edges being outlined with a two-line or a narrow floral roll. When removed from the board the piece requires to be neatly edged round with a paring knife and it is ready to be glued to the book. Paste must not be used as it disturbs the gold.

Some of the extra large letters used on account books will be found difficult to strike, but a fairly deep blind impression made before the gold work and two coats of glair painted in should prove effective.

The blind tooling to be seen on account books is carried out in a direct manner upon the leather without previous preparation except for rough calf for which a special method is used.

Flush Binding. This is the term given to books whose boards are cut flush with the edges. In general, however, the term is used to include all the less expensive forms of binding included in stationery work. The importance of this work must not be underrated, for it forms by far the larger portion of the trade and the production requires as much technical skill and ingenuity as the more expensive bindings.

A brief description of the operations in their correct order for a quarter-flush binding is as follows: sew on the tapes, edge on single folded ends, glue up, paste on boards direct to the end-paper leaving a groove along the back, cover quarter leather or cloth with a tight back, marble paper sides, trim the edges.

A superior binding results if the covers are turned in, but the order of operation requires to be modified as follows: sew on tapes, single folded ends, glue up, attach the boards by lightly tipping them on to the end-papers, cut flush cover either quarter- or full-bound, turn in the covers, paste down the end-papers.

The paper-covered book is unpretentious but may be very attractive. It is used in both letterpress and stationery binding. One method is as follows: sew without tapes, single folded ends edged on, glue backs and draw over paper cover, glue down the cover, press in batches and shape up the backs while in the press. A quicker way would be to glue the cover and draw it over the book, but in this case the covers would curl outwards when dry. It can be proved by a simple test that when two pieces of paper of equal thickness are pasted or glued together the final curl will be towards the sheet with the adhesive.

Perforating. The pin perforating machine produces a clear round hole. Its low initial outlay and the fact that it is readily adaptable to varied short runs make it popular in the smaller work-shops. It employs a long bar with its series of pins with corresponding holes in the platen, and the paper is laid by hand to set gauges. The pins do not continue along the whole length of the bar, and so stop perforations may be made. According to the thickness of the paper two or three sheets may be perforated at one time but care must be exercised or the paper will be weakened.

Corresponding rotating spindles that are adjusted to the number of cuts are used on the rotary perforating machine. While the quality of the perforation is not so good as that of the pin machine, it is very fast and all the cuts in one direction are carried simultaneously. Its rotary character and its compactness make it suitable for direct attachment to the printing or ruling machine whereby the two operations are continuous.

Numbering. When the pages of an account book are numbered consecutively it is said to be paged; but where each opening is given a number it is said to be folioed. The work is best undertaken after the edges are cut and for this purpose the page numbering machine is used. Manifold books may be numbered after binding only when the figures occur at the top corner of the leaf, otherwise the work must be done in sheets.

Manifold books consisting of folded sections cannot be numbered until they have been interleaved and folded, but with books of single leaves the work is much simplified. Books without folds in the back cannot be sewn in the usual way; they must either be wire stitched through the side or stabbed with holes and sewn with thread. They do not open at all well, but on the other hand they are very strong and very economical to produce; the cost of perforation and interleaving is much lower and, by means of numbering boxes which can be set up with the type, the leaves can be numbered as they are being printed.

CHAPTER THIRTY-THREE

INSTALLATION AND MAINTENANCE OF MACHINERY

OBSOLETE MACHINERY. INSTALLATION PROBLEMS. EFFICIENT RUNNING. ELECTRICAL EQUIPMENT. ILLUMINATION. IMPORTANCE OF LUBRICATION. HEATING AND VENTILATION. ELECTRO-DEPOSITION. AIR CONDITIONING. POWER TRANSMISSION. ERECTION AND TESTING OF MACHINERY. BREAKDOWN REPAIRS. FUTURE DEVELOPMENTS.

MECHANICAL plant for the printing and allied trades is designed to produce its quota of machine-set ens, of metal plates, of sheets of printed matter, or of bound copies, at a definitely determined output with a minimum amount of preparation.

There are many examples of apparently efficient mechanical plant still doing good work, but which might otherwise be considered as having long outlived their useful lives. It is indeed questionable if it is a paying proposition to retain such machinery as a part of the operating plant.

The majority of machines can be credited with a fairly definite term of years of effective life; but when this term has been served, the machine becomes redundant to the plant, and should be broken up.

Having studied the existing state of the engineering trade, the purchaser can plan for a period of perhaps five years, on the assumption that such period will elapse before there is any outstanding upheaval in either structure or method of production.

The prospective purchaser should then thoroughly investigate the possibilities of the most suitable existing plant which is available. By securing machinery which will not only serve the immediate purpose, but also allow for a surplus of productive capacity when necessary, he will avoid the risk of disappointment and failure. He should go even further by requiring, from the designer and manufacturer, a unit which will give results beyond his probable requirements. A system of progressive study would avoid the unfortunate bottle-neck which so often mars the economic running of a printing plant.

Failure to secure satisfactory results from mechanical plant is rarely due to any deficiency in the machinery itself. It can be allocated usually either to lack of vision on the part of the purchaser or to the mishandling of the production problem.

Housing of Machinery

Sometimes an opportunity to acquire a machine at a low price, or in order to satisfy the desire for ownership, has led to the introduction of plant which, although first-rate when in its own useful sphere, not only fails to fulfil requirements, but may also create serious difficulty for other departments.

The housing requirements of the machinery to be installed should take priority over any other consideration, and it must be definitely decided that the plant laid down will receive this priority call upon the design and layout of the factory. Of course, heating, ventilation and lighting must be adequate for the processes intended. The function of the works should be one of service to the plant.

Nothing can be more detrimental to efficiency than cramming well-designed precision machinery into various odd corners and makeshift building extensions. This not only adds to the wear and tear, but nullifies the efficiency and sets up an insidious time-lag on production.

A lag, however slight, introduced at any point will remain a permanent trouble. In the continuance of even a minor drag there is always the possibility that it will not remain an isolated case, thus forming a still greater deterrent to production.

Granted that new plant to be laid down is to fit in with the general plan, the main problem will be the ever-present temptation to permit congestion.

Exclusion of Dust

During the installation of machinery, dust should be rigidly excluded; all structural alterations must have been completed already. It may appear to save time by rushing the installation so as to bring a machine quickly into productive use, but any attempt to do so is liable to produce dissatisfaction at a later date.

Having determined the type of plant required, it is essential that provision be made for duplication of units both in design and size. One of everything, although to a certain extent comprehensive, will not work as efficiently as, say, a reasonable duplication of mechanical composing machines, or of printing presses of exactly the same

constructional details for multi-colour work.

For a study of purchase problems, we need only consider the position of firms possessing a clear view of the nature and quantity of the goods which are to be produced. The standard requirements of these firms will influence the creation and supply of the mechanical aids available in the general market. The justification for the supply of machines and accessories can only exist by service to the demand.

It is, of course, superfluous to tell the average printer not to install a typesetting machine, or a quad flat or rotary press, when the anticipated business will consist of miscellaneous matter down to bill-heads and similar small jobs. This exaggeration in a modified form is, however, too often -observed.

Although many printing firms have made organized and successful endeavours to advance and progress with the times, many plants still convey the impression that those responsible have suddenly lost all interest in the development of their plant.

In such cases an accurate system of production graphs taken over a very short period, would look rather more like that taken from a seismograph where violent and erratic subterranean disturbances were recorded, than that of a normal business with slight fluctuations tending always in the direction of a steady rise.

Composing Machines

The mechanical composing machine, of either the single-cast or line-casting model, has been designed to cast and eject a clean-cut metal output from the ingots supplied to it. To enable such a machine to give the designed productive efficiency and to work without mechanical stress, it is obvious that

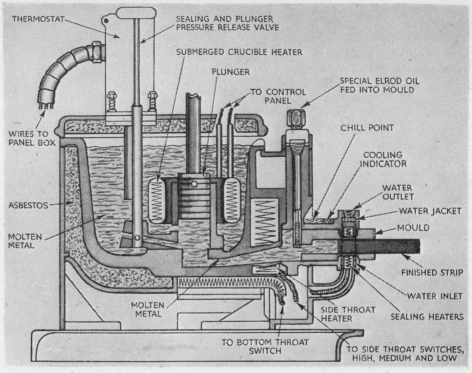

THERMOSTAT

SEALING AND PLUNGER
PRESSURE RELEASE VALVE

SUBMERGED CRUCIBLE HEATER

PLUNGER

TO CONTROL
PANEL

SPECIAL ELROD OIL
FED INTO MOULD

WIRES TO
PANEL BOX

CHILL POINT

COOLING
INDICATOR

WATER
OUTLET

ASBESTOS

WATER JACKET

MOULD

MOLTEN
METAL

FINISHED STRIP

WATER INLET

MOLTEN
METAL

SIDE THROAT
HEATER

SEALING HEATERS

TO BOTTOM THROAT
SWITCH

TO SIDE THROAT SWITCHES,
HIGH, MEDIUM AND LOW

THERMOSTATIC CONTROL OF METAL HEATING

Fig. 1. *The diagram shows clearly the method employed in controlling the heating of metal for the Elrod type-caster. A similar apparatus is used for other type-casting machines.*

every attention must be given to the quality of the metal supplied and its correct working temperature.

Many of the troubles experienced by the users of these machines may be said to be due either to the quality of the metal supplied or, as is more often the case, to faulty maintenance and incorrect heating of the metal.

An automatically-controlled electrically-heated crucible with variation in heat limited to plus or minus 3 deg. F. should always be fitted. This system of heating has many advantages over the use of gas or oil as the heating agent, notably a minimum of metal losses and the absence of obnoxious fumes. Heat is confined to the actual point where it is required to do work,

and less liability placed on the human element. Fig. 1 shows the method of thermostat-controlled heating as applied to the Elrod caster.

The mechanical composing unit demands something more than just a place for erection plus motive power. For efficient service the unit requires the class of work for which its particular design is most suited. Good lighting is essential, and an uninterrupted outflow of the product to the point where it will be utilized must be aimed at.

Proof Presses

There are efficient proof presses for every branch of the trade: letterpress, offset-litho and photogravure, from the smallest hand-power to self-contained electric power models. The latter show a high standard of efficiency, and many printers are now equipped with first-rate models. Although the cheaper models are fairly suitable for ordinary composing room use, it is unwise to expect from these the high standard required for outgoing proofs of blocks or author's copy—particularly for the blocks—where it is essential that every detail should be brought out.

Printing Machines

When considering the purchase of a printing machine for a definite output, it is advisable to look to such features as speed under normal working conditions, and sufficient weight and strength where it is required—this will mean a clean impression, correct register and lack of vibration. All gearing and bearings should be so designed that they may be attended to without interfering with the main structure.

Machine design in general, after an experimental period of saving in weight and constructional costs, has, with the exception of certain moving parts, returned towards weight, it being generally recognized that modern high speeds, combined with increased accuracy, demand a balanced weight and stability in construction.

Bookbinding Machinery

Finishing and bookbinding machinery, with the exception of guillotines and wrapping machines, belong to the light high-speed class, and, as the work to be done consists of piercing or bending a very small area of paper or card, only a sufficiency of metal to overcome this resistance, and to resist shock, is embodied in the construction. As machinery of this type is not heavy and the units are fairly mobile, it can be installed with little trouble.

There is here an exceptionally wide choice of mechanical aids and systems, all being capable of the greatest efficiency in handling light, medium, and heavy outputs. Capital outlay is not relatively high and in some cases units may be added to units without loss of efficiency, gathering and stitching machines being remarkable examples.

The troubles experienced with wire-stitching machines can usually be attributed to the stitching wire, and not to the machine. Folding machines, properly adjusted to the thickness of stock, rarely fail to do good work and the chief essential maintenance concerns the gripping rollers and bearings.

Guillotines are very sensitive to any uneven foundation, or failure to damp out floor vibration. Many seemingly unaccountable fractures could well be attributed to the machines being mounted on an unsuitable foundation.

Electrical Equipment

Electricity, with its outstanding advantages for power and lighting, plays an important part in every factory. Managers today rightly appraise as valuable assets the health and contentment of those whom they employ, and some firms who have specialized in this direction—particularly with lighting—assert that their policy has been dictated by definite commercial considerations, and that, judged by this standard alone, it fully justifies itself. Although the purchaser is often tied to one particular supply system, this need not affect efficiency.

When considering the suitability of illumination, it is essential to decide upon the relative importance of the various points enumerated below:—

(1) Illumination on the horizontal and vertical planes; (2) freedom from direct and reflected glare; (3) softness of shadows; (4) maintenance.

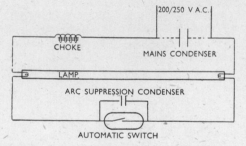

Fig. 2. *Wiring arrangement of 80-watt tubular fluorescent lamp.*

Lack of attention to (1) will seriously affect both quality and quantity of the work output. (2) and (3) Direct and reflected glare and shadows will baffle the operatives, creating an adverse psychological effect upon those working under such conditions. Neglect of maintenance (4) will eventually create deterioration and lower the general intensity of illumination.

Eighty-watt tubular fluorescent lamps (Figs. 2 and 3) are at the present time coming into popular use, the outstanding features being high efficiency, 35 lumens per watt; low surface brightness, three candles per sq. in., which provides glareless lighting; low temperature; and minimum reaction to variations in voltage.

Light is diffused from the entire surface of the 5-ft. long tube at three candles per sq. in. approximately.

Motors

Whether the supply system be direct or alternating current, there is a choice of very robust and efficient motors ranging from fractional horse-power for small plant up to the requirements of the largest rotary

letterpress or photogravure presses.

The purchaser should be careful not to underestimate the full power required for his machines at the maximum output, strong robust control gear being essential. Electrical installations, provided that such are suitable for the job and properly treated, will be found to be remarkably free from trouble, the development of local supply control and power factor correction having overcome many of the difficulties experienced at one time. Alternating current commutator motors have become available for every class of machine drive. Variable speeds may be obtained either by moving the brush gear or by induction regulation; in the latter system slip rings are omitted. In either system full automatic remote control is obtained by a pilot motor operating either the brush gear or rotating the induction regulator.

Figs. 4 and 5 illustrate a typical commutator motor with remote mechanized speed control device.

Regular expert attention will pay for itself many times over, by the resulting freedom from trouble. Special care should be given to the correct alignment of the motor to the machine which it has to serve, whether the intermediate

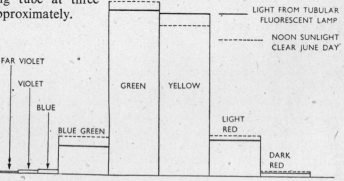

Fig. 3. *Diagram showing the close approximation of fluorescent lamp to daylight. The height of each block is proportional to the total light of that colour emanating from each source.*

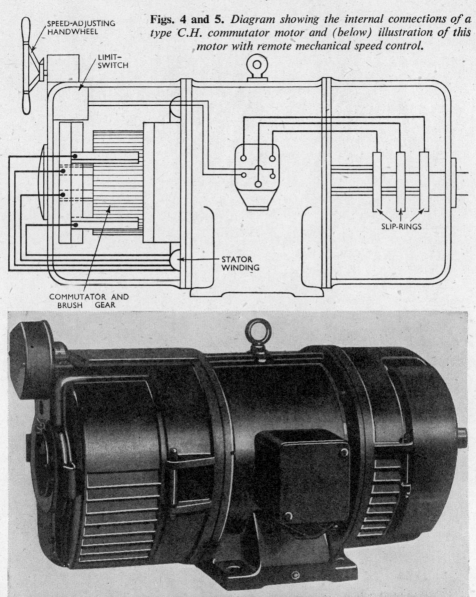

Figs. 4 and 5. *Diagram showing the internal connections of a type C.H. commutator motor and (below) illustration of this motor with remote mechanical speed control.*

SPEED-ADJUSTING HANDWHEEL

LIMIT-SWITCH

SLIP-RINGS

STATOR WINDING

COMMUTATOR AND BRUSH GEAR

transmission agent be by toothed wheel, vee, or flat belting, fixed or flexible coupling. Undue stress will be set up unless the alignment is correct. The vee belt drive has outstanding efficiency, transmitting the maximum power whilst giving the flexibility necessary to avoid possible stress.

The principal requirements in the way of heating in a printing works are for metal melting, for service to hot presses, and for bookbinders' machines. Electricity has outstanding advantages over all other methods. There are no fumes of combustion; an even heat is assured, as the elements encircle the metal pot or cover the areas to be heated; automatic temperature control is continuous and adjustable instantly to any desired temperature; pre-heating is safe and reliable.

Electro-deposition

The direct current power supply to deposition vats was originally obtained from batteries. Generator sets were soon used for large outputs and they have had about thirty years of reliable supremacy. But the sets are noisy and liable to commutator and brush troubles. They are also subject to vibration, and are apt to circulate dust.

This system is now seriously challenged by the rapid development of the metal rectifier (Fig. 6). Equally reliable, it has the enormous advantage of requiring no maintenance. It is peculiar in that efficiency is maintained at a steady value, being the same whether the output is 500 or 5,000 amps, varying only with the output voltage, all power being available for the electrochemical reactions which are involved in deposition.

Lubrication

The useful life of a machine, whether mechanical or electrical, depends upon proper and consistent lubrication. The lubricant is the film which actually carries all moving parts. The delicate film introduced must possess the essential working body so as to provide, under the most severe strain, a constant coating to all the bearing surfaces, while keeping fluid and clean, without residue. The value of a lubricant depends mainly upon its film-forming capacity and suitable viscosity for the machinery employed.

All rubbing surfaces, whether flat or revolving, when in motion create friction; friction creates heat; the general effect of heat is to diminish the elasticity of metals, and finally to remove it altogether; and excessive heat will cause the rubbing surfaces to seize.

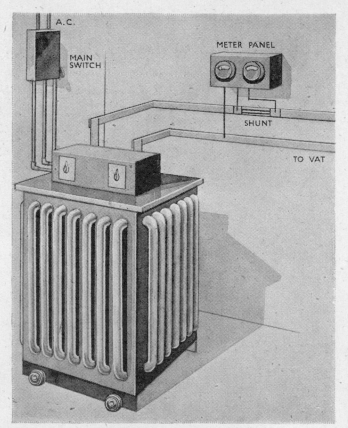

METAL PLATING RECTIFIER

Fig. 6. "*Westlite*" *low-voltage plating rectifier and transformer for electro-deposition, showing meter panel and leads to the vat.*

The amount of friction depends principally upon the pressure per sq. in. between the rubbing surfaces.

For example, smooth iron and brass in motion with dry surfaces will heat and seize with a pressure of 60 lb. approximately per sq. in., but with a fair lubricant will stand pressure up to 600 lb., the pressure being in one direction only and not pressing equally from all sides.

There is a lubricant for every class of machinery and manufacturers usually recommend the use of one particular brand of lubricant for their machines. This is recommended only after a very careful investigation based upon experience and backed by the laboratory tests of the refiners, having due regard to the work to be done. Both manufacturer and refiner have a reputation to maintain, so the advice of either should not be discarded without a perfectly sound reason. The question of cost should not be regarded as a sound reason—"the best for the job is always the cheapest" in the end. The right place for the lubricant is in the bearings of the machine and not all over the machine or on the floor.

The lubricant must be rigorously guarded against contact with foreign matter. Until needed to perform its useful work, the proper place for all lubricating agents, whether liquid or solidified, is in the container.

Printing Machine Stresses

All printing presses, whether platen, flat-bed or rotary principle, and their auxiliary plant, are constructed to resist the strain set up whilst the impression is being taken, and also to control the stoutest stock to the point of delivery after printing.

Designers of such machinery have worked upon the principle of uniform velocity transmission, gained by equally spaced teeth meshed with similar teeth; and the teeth of a rack formed relative to a pitch plane in place of a pitch circle when used to convert a rotary to a linear motion.

A reasonable margin of safety is allowed, limited to the understanding that the pressure load resistance will be evenly distributed over the contact areas.

With presses, the endeavour has been to limit variation of impression to 1/10,000th part of an inch, and any exaggerated variation from the even distribution of load would tend to throw the moving parts concerned out of balance, causing undue wear or, perhaps, a fracture of one or more of the parts called upon to receive the excess strain. The method of adjusting the impression is shown in Fig. 7.

Uneven Formes

A common example of this risk is the uneven type forme or set of plates. Here, defects may be compensated by correspondingly uneven packing or mechanical adjustments, to give a passable impression; but the mechanical tendency would be to throw the sections concerned in opposite directions towards the final resistance of the framework. Badly-set inking rollers may also apply an uneven braking effect, which would be suddenly and unevenly transmitted to various moving parts as the contact was applied and released.

The use of ball-and-roller bearings, viz. the substitution of plain sliding friction by pure rolling motion, Fig. 8, has done much to reduce wear.

The introduction of staggered roller bearings is now common with heavy rotary presses where speeds as high as 400 r.p.m. of main cylinders can be operated under working conditions without loss of efficiency.

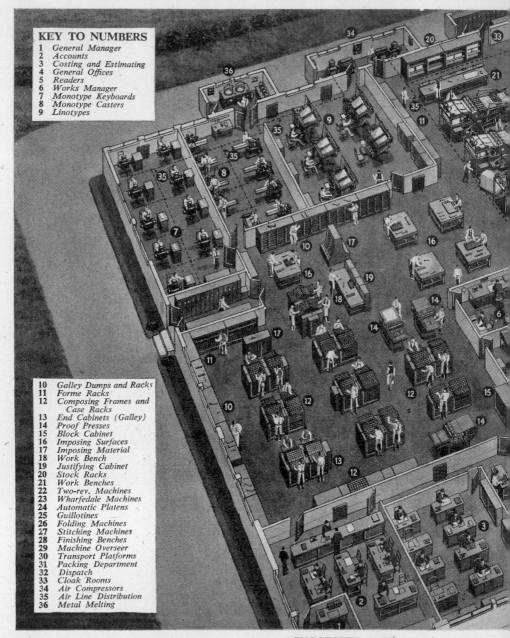

KEY TO NUMBERS

1 General Manager
2 Accounts
3 Costing and Estimating
4 General Offices
5 Readers
6 Works Manager
7 Monotype Keyboards
8 Monotype Casters
9 Linotypes

10 Galley Dumps and Racks
11 Forme Racks
12 Composing Frames and
      Case Racks
13 End Cabinets (Galley)
14 Proof Presses
15 Block Cabinet
16 Imposing Surfaces
17 Imposing Material
18 Work Bench
19 Justifying Cabinet
20 Stock Racks
21 Work Benches
22 Two-rev. Machines
23 Wharfedale Machines
24 Automatic Platens
25 Guillotines
26 Folding Machines
27 Stitching Machines
28 Finishing Benches
29 Machine Overseer
30 Transport Platforms
31 Packing Department
32 Dispatch
33 Cloak Rooms
34 Air Compressors
35 Air Line Distribution
36 Metal Melting

SUGGESTED LAYOUT PLAN FOR

A general impression of a layout designed to give rapid and labour-saving transit to the production department from the office, whence the order or copy is passed to the works manager. He will plan, and forward to the department concerned. The job then takes its course through the various stages to the final point of delivery. Works buildings vary in

LETTERPRESS PRINTING WORKS

structure, and it may be convenient and economical to modify the layout slightly: for example, it would be possible to accommodate stereotyping and block-making plant. The ideal layout is one in which all departments are at the same level, permitting uninterrupted progress from the office, through various sections of the works, to the point of delivery.

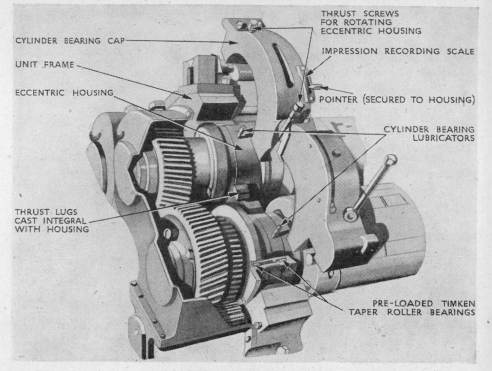

CYLINDER BEARING CAP

UNIT FRAME

ECCENTRIC HOUSING

THRUST LUGS
CAST INTEGRAL
WITH HOUSING

THRUST SCREWS
FOR ROTATING
ECCENTRIC HOUSING

IMPRESSION RECORDING SCALE

POINTER (SECURED TO HOUSING)

CYLINDER BEARING
LUBRICATORS

PRE-LOADED TIMKEN
TAPER ROLLER BEARINGS

GOSS ECCENTRIC HOUSING

Fig. 7. *Showing a modern method of adjusting the cylinder impression on a rotary printing press. This adjustment can be made to within one ten-thousandth part of an inch.*

Air under mechanical control is in general use with modern printing plant, notably for retouching, etching, electro-deposition, composing machines, paper feeding and control, anti-set-off devices, copy and message carrying, pressure lubrication and ink supply, heating installations, ventilating and cleaning plant, and the removal of waste.

With the exception of air-cushioning to printing presses and instances where usage makes it essential that the equipment must be a self-contained unit, it is necessary to install some form of independent air-pumping plant.

This type of plant is notoriously noisy and should therefore be installed in a distant part of the factory, or better still, in a well ventilated compartment

with an abundant air supply free from dirt, otherwise the tendency will be to create a partial vacuum in the room.

For general usage an adequate volume of compressed air available at a steady pressure is essential, and the best service is obtained from a system of centralized air plant. Air service from a remote source to meet the majority of requirements can be installed with efficiency and cleanliness, and an absence of local compressors, electric motors and floor plant which would otherwise interfere with the normal work which is carried on.

Full provision should be made to cover the maximum demand; a reasonable future development; loss of pressure due to distance and friction in pipes; thus protection and economy are realized by means of automatic balancing control.

Ducting liable to the interference of vibration or excess heating should be fitted with flexible canvas joints, thus allowing for expansion.

With anti-set-off installation, clean compressed air is used to atomize a chemical mixture and direct fine globular particles either continuously or at rapid intervals upon the surface of freshly printed stock, these minute particles being sufficient to form an air pocket.

The service piping should show a slight upward rise from pressure supply point to allow possible condensation to flow back for drawing off.

Where pipe drop line joins main service line, an inverted U connection should be fitted to keep condensation away from the distribution gun.

Power Transmission

The principal agents for power transmission in the order of general use are belting, vee belt, chain, link, direct

gearing, coupling and friction, each of which may have a specified use. Of these, the most popular in general use is the vee belt which is rapidly gaining favour both for main and subsidiary driving. Its principal advantages are minimum slip, maximum power, and economy in floor space due to the short centres required; the governing rule for centres being (a) not less than the diameter of the larger pulley; (b) such that the arc of contact on the small pulley is not less than 102 deg. Vee belts with their wedge action have a positive grip. This ensures transmission of the full load noiselessly at all speeds.

Ordinary flat belting can at its best only rely upon the amount of friction set up between two flat surfaces, the efficiency of this friction being subject to every fluctuation in load and to atmospheric conditions.

Chain transmission, when properly applied, gives the minimum centres; is definite in action and allies gear ratio with the strength of a flexible coupling. This type of transmission is expensive and only suitable in specific cases.

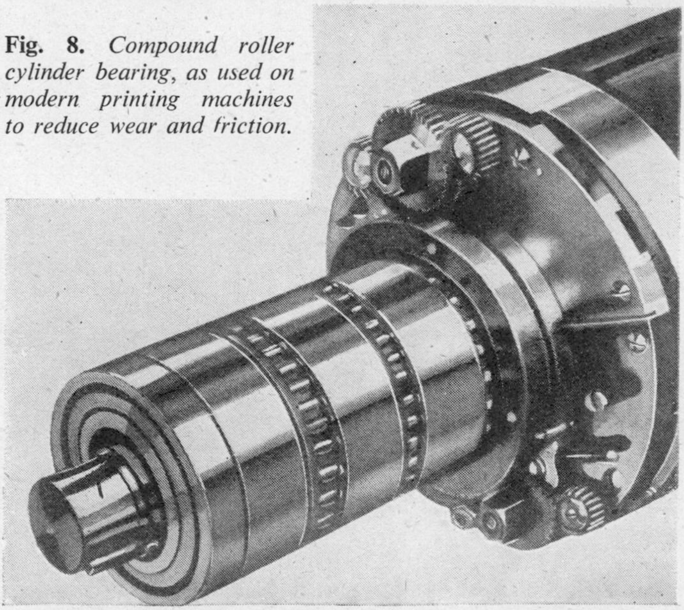

Fig. 8. *Compound roller cylinder bearing, as used on modern printing machines to reduce wear and friction.*

With the pinion and spur direct drive the action is definite, but noisy, and fails to damp out the fluctuating strains set up during the operational working of the machinery.

Automatic Platens

To be fully efficient the great majority of printing works must depend upon the general use of the automatic press, ranging in design from the smaller platens to the largest sizes practicable. Almost every make of platen machine can, with the incorporation of modern fitments, become a self-contained fully automatic unit.

With the exception of certain continental designs, platen presses vary but little in general principle. The Heidelberg, with its unique gripper action, differs from the general principle of direct forward feed to the impression; as does the Lagonda, with its feed direct across the platen from left to right.

The modern Auto-Thompson handles the paper feed straight down the platen, and is guaranteed to perform work at 3,000 to 4,500 impressions per hour. Chain driven geared inking is also fitted.

The Auto-Falcon is constructed with the paper feed as a separate unit, built to co-operate with semi-automatic features of the machine. The type-bed has a radial movement and the printed sheet stripped from the forme in the natural way.

Auto-Peerless and Auto-Sterling are both parallel impression machines with self-contained register device fitted. The Sterling has a wheel-away feed and delivery as a separate unit.

Vertical Job Press

Outstanding features of this machine are vertical operation; vertical reciprocation of the type-bed; impression-cylinder also reciprocating in a like manner, but in contrary motion to it.

The type-bed and the cylinder, through the frame on which the latter is mounted, are geared together and receive their reciprocating motion from a common source, being effected by a direct-acting crank. Type-bed and cylinder are directly connected with each other during the operational period through a gear on the end of the cylinder and a rack extending the whole length of the bed. Synchronized movement is secured by moving up and down continuously in opposite directions, and being approximately the same weight, they act as counterpoises and balance each other.

The advantages from this construction are mainly a saving in power; no shock absorbing devices are required. The actual motion-speed of the press is comparatively slow, though the normal production-speed is high.

Flat-bed Printing Machines

Stop-cylinder Machines. The best known and most widely used is the Wharfedale pattern. Of robust construction with powerful inking distribution these machines are practically foolproof, and require little adjustment when changing over to fresh jobs. When fully automatic, a pile-paper feeder is usually fitted and pile delivery makes the unit thoroughly self-contained. The reciprocating bed movement is given by a crank acting through rolling wheels and the printing cylinder is geared direct to the bed.

From the year 1851 to the present day is a long time, but many original principles remain, and have also formed the basis for a number of machines of continental design.

Two-revolution Machines. With this design the principle of continuous motion is followed and utilized to the fullest extent possible, the machine retaining the versatility of being able to handle all styles of movable formes and varied weights of paper stock. These machines are equally efficient whether for single- or two-colour, or perfecting.

When fitted up as a fully automatic unit, a highly consistent productive efficiency is maintained. The reciprocating parts are controlled by means of the reversing gearing, and movement

TWO-REVOLUTION MACHINE TRANSMISSION UNITS

Fig. 9. Four instructive illustrations showing the principle of the two-revolution machine and the method by which the cylinder is thrown out of action during the return of the bed. (Above, left) Gear displaced laterally by Spence bed motion to the lower rack during non-printing travel. (Above, right) Gear in upper rack during printing travel. (Below, left) Ball and socket gear reversing the bed. (Below, right) Ball and socket universal coupling.

of bed motion by a pinion meshing with the rack (Fig. 9).

The efficient working life of flat-bed machines, of either stop-cylinder, continuous drum cylinder, or two-revolution design, may be largely influenced by the effectiveness of the air cushioning heads or buffers. These are so designed as to produce automatically the air pressure required to balance the stress on the general structure due to the reversal of heavy reciprocating parts, i.e. type-bed and rack, or type-bed and rack hanger with component parts.

When the machine is moving slowly much less pressure resistance is required than when it is running at high speeds. It is obvious that too much compression would result in excessive power being required to overcome the resistance set up; whilst too little would fail to check the advancing weight, the tendency being to strip the bed from its gearing. In the former case, undue pressure must be applied to those parts actually in mesh on the pressure side; and, in the latter, a great strain is thrown upon all gearing which must recover its momentum.

Manufacturers have endeavoured to make foolproof the system of cushioning, by fitting automatically balanced heads timed to function as the speed of the press fluctuates.

Rotary Machines

Production by rotary methods is applicable to every class of printing. It is as consistently efficient from the simplest and smallest ticket machine up to multiples of units for the largest sizes of newspapers, periodicals or cartons, in one or more colours, as it is for litho offset, photogravure or letterpress work; where a speedy or continuous output is required, or where it is desirable to embody certain ancillary mechanism for continuous operations to the production.

The general principle in every case is to utilize to the full the perfection of pure rolling motion.

For jobbing or general work it may be desirable to incorporate printing, slitting, numbering, gumming, interfold folding, folding or perforating mechanism; or an all-size cut-off from reel-fed supply, the cut-off being adjustable to a pre-determined length suitable to the size of job required. In this case the advantage of rotary production may be found in (1) economy in cost of reels as against reams of stock; (2) adaptability of stock to varied sizes; (3) combination of two or more operations after printing from multiples of plates; and (4) speeds up to 14,000 cylinder revolutions per hour and continuous output.

Periodical and Newspaper Machines

Machines for the production of magazines and periodicals are required to operate at similar speeds, production being to a definite time limit and cut-off to a fixed size.

Variable speeds to sections or units, cover printing units, slitting, collating, folding and wire-stitching mechanism may be incorporated; the product being counted and delivered in multiples of any set quantity, usually dozens or quires.

Machines for the evening and daily press make the most severe demand upon design and structure, requiring a very high standard of construction and balanced mechanism to withstand the strains set up by rapid acceleration to maximum speed and retaining such speed at its peak over a period. At the same time they must remain unaffected by either almost instantaneous stoppage or frequent and rapid variations in speeds.

It is obvious that in order to secure the designed results from this class of machinery, particularly the newspaper press, every care should be taken to ensure that nothing disturbs the rhythmic motion. The following points must, therefore, be noted: impression absolutely parallel with gears properly in mesh; packing and plates to the set limits, with the latter evenly planed to fit the carrying cylinders; inking rollers even; folding mechanism balanced.

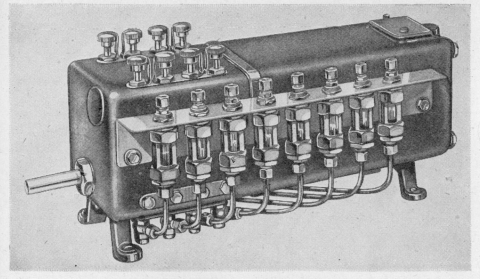

MECHANICAL LUBRICATOR

Fig. 10. *The simple working of this mechanical force-fed lubricator unit makes it very suitable for practically all types of printing machines. Mechanical lubricators are now coming into general use. The importance of regular lubrication cannot be over-emphasized.*

Parts unprotected by some form of plating are liable to corrosion and must be carefully watched; particularly plate-carrying cylinders and their integral mechanism.

A great demand is made upon the lubricating system and most modern presses have an efficient system of forced application where considered necessary. An example of a mechanical lubricator is shown in Fig. 10.

Always Query Trouble

If trouble is suspected with any type of machine, do not attempt to continue running it under power. Once the starting torque is overcome all machinery, whether mechanical or electrical, should settle down to rhythmic motion.

There is one golden rule which should be strictly adhered to : "Safety First." Always turn the machine over by hand without using undue force; unless the fault is due to the lubricant breaking down under speeds, any undue strain will be easily apparent to the touch.

If unable to allocate the source of trouble, first disconnect from the driving power and test again. This will exonerate either the machine or the motive power. Should the trouble be with the machine, various parts must be isolated and tested by a competent person until the source is discovered.

For the efficient and rapid transportation of materials to the various processing departments and the outlet of the finished product, mechanical control should be utilized to the greatest possible extent. This will lessen the strain on operatives, avoid damage and wastage of valuable material, and save considerable floor space.

The stack and trucking system can be used by the majority of printers and carton makers when flat stock is handled; also power-operated and gravity conveyors for the larger plants.

The problem of heating and ventilation is usually treated as merely relating to the comfort of the operatives, and may or may not receive that degree of attention to which it is entitled; too little interest being taken in the scientific development as an essential factor to problems of production.

Heating and Ventilation

During cold weather, for instance, it is possible for bearings in mechanical plant to wear as much during the first few minutes of a warming-up period as in several weeks under normal working conditions. The effects on inks and other materials used by the printer are well known. The correct solution is so vital to efficiency that a competent heating engineer should always be consulted.

The efficient works require the conditions of domestic heat and ventilation where the average operative is comfortable in a temperature of 60 or 70 deg. F., and given the number of air changes per hour which will enable him to carry on with routine processing without physical discomfort. Where certain processes require varied heating conditions, care should be taken to confine these to the process concerned.

The quantity of heat required for heating air depends on the specific heat of air, and the co-efficient for air is, therefore, the number of B.T.U.s required to raise the temperature of 1 cub. ft. through 1 deg. F; this may vary from ·02 to 2·00 according to the construction of the building.

Ventilation is defined as the process and practice of keeping an enclosed space supplied with proper air for breathing. It is generally considered that the air of a confined space where people are working should not contain more than one part in 1,000 of carbon dioxide.

Electrical, steam, hot water and Plenum systems under thermostatic control are equally reliable, but vary in flexibility, and the choice of installation will rest largely upon local conditions. The principal systems are:—

The *Plenum* or *fresh-air ventilation system* (Figs. 11 and 12). In this system a centrally placed fan draws in air and discharges it through a system of ductwork at points located within the enclosure to be warmed. The system can be fitted with means for warming the air by incorporating electrical elements or otherwise heated tubes, air filters or air washers, or both.

Where an air washer is installed, a measure of air cooling in summer is possible; and it is also feasible to embody in the one installation suitable devices by means of which air may be conditioned, not only as regards temperature but with respect to purity and humidity.

The *unit system*, in which case each individual heat emitter or flood heater is provided with its own heat generator. These may be suspended on tilting brackets giving the advantage that heat is controlled directionally and, as the unit is self-contained, no demand is made upon the floor space.

A *central heating system* in which steam or hot water, generated by central boiler plant, is circulated by piping throughout the building. This system is installed in many works and may be fed by electricity, gas, oil, or hard fuel boiler plant, or used in conjunction with a Plenum system.

Advantages and Disadvantages

This type of installation occupies a considerable amount of valuable space; heat losses are by no means negligible; piping and radiators harbour dirt; oil fuel and hard fuel themselves create a considerable amount of dirt. There is, however, the advantage that steam

Fig. 11. *Plenum floor type ventilator.*

or hot water, with the aid of reducing valves and suitable calorifier equipment, may be made available for various useful purposes in addition to heating.

The correct location of automatic thermostatic control is essential with either of the above systems. It should be placed where it will be subject to the average temperature of the area to be warmed, avoiding locations near doors, windows and heating units.

Erection of Machinery

Before leaving the makers, machines have, in the majority of cases, passed through the fitting and erecting stage, also a severe running test; and makers, naturally, prefer the

installation to be carried out by their own staff. When an installation is undertaken by the purchaser the fact that the machine has already passed a running test must be kept in mind, and careful handling should mean a straightforward job. It is necessary to keep a firm level foundation and ensure protection from dirt. Machine-finished faces should fit perfectly and be carefully cleaned, bolts gradually tightened up, keeping the tension even. No attempt must be made to use the bolts as a screw to draw heavy parts into position. Make sure that the bolt clearance is evenly distributed before the final tightening up is carried out.

An average equipment of tools should consist of at least two sets of chain blocks and falls; a travelling runner; two 1-ton jacks; chain and wire slings; a good spirit-level; mercury or brass plumb-bob; set of fox wedges; lead

PLENUM VENTILATING SYSTEM

Fig. 12. *Showing the air-duct system of the Plenum (fresh air) ventilating and heating units as installed in printing works.*

hammer; piano wire; comprehensive set of spanners; some stout timbers; clamps; oilcan; plus the usual set of small tools. Scrapers, die nuts and taps should only be used to remove burr.

Breakdown Repairs

Fracture may be due either to the remote but not unknown possibility of a flaw in the materials, or to shock, and it is with the latter that we are usually concerned. Any elastic structure subject to shock will deflect until the product of the average resistance developed by the deflection and the distance through which it has been overcome, has reached a value equal to the energy of the shock. The effect of a shock is, therefore, to a great extent dependent upon the elastic property (the springiness) of the structure subjected to the impact.

A clever engineer can devise emergency repairs for almost any type of breakdown, but should first consider the following questions: the reason why the fracture occurred; what other parts have been affected by the shock; the total stress to be carried by the repaired part; the most effective type of repair; effect of the repair upon the balance of any other moving part; if the repair is subject to variation of temperature; which combination of stresses—tensile, compressive, torsion, bending, traverse, lateral or shearing— will be imposed upon the repair.

Welding and Bolting

In the majority of cases where heavy parts are concerned, welding or building up will give an accurate and lasting job with almost equal strength and elasticity to that of the original structure. Plating, bolting or clamping together will require the additional material to compensate for the weakness of the fractured part.

Gears may be repaired with screwed-in studs or sections cut and dovetailed. When properly meshed and balanced, the result is a good job.

Personal supervision is a vital factor in the efficiency of an installation. The attendant should watch the behaviour of all units, keeping an itemized record of each, entering breakdowns and repairs and generally noting the behaviour under load. In this way a close check can be kept on the working of the plant.

In a large installation it is possible to have a certain amount of uniformity as regards horse-power and type of motor, a minimum variation being aimed at. This will allow for interchangeability of motors and a stock of spare parts to be carried.

Future Developments

From the above résumé of the work of the printer's engineer the importance of his position in the efficient running of a printing works will be realized. Every department is dependent in greater or less degree on the engineering staff for its smooth running with absence of breakdowns.

But the engineer must not be content with the routine work of keeping things running; he must also be a man of vision who can watch the trend of mechanical invention and keep himself fully abreast with all the developments and inventions which will undoubtedly take place in the near future.

These developments are likely to include: alternating current supply service which will bring the induction regulation type of variable speed into more general use; increasing use of the metal rectifier, with saving in current up to about 20 per cent; development of plastics in various processes involving the installation of small handy moulding presses; and finally, ever-increasing speed production by machine makers.

APPENDIX

TECHNICAL EDUCATION
IN THE PRINTING TRADE

THE following alphabetical list of Schools of Printing in the British Isles, and of Technical Schools in which instruction is given in various branches of printing, is based on information which has been kindly supplied by The British Federation of Master Printers.

I. PRINTING SCHOOLS AND TECHNICAL COLLEGES WITH PRINTING DEPARTMENTS

Aberdeen: School of Printing. **Birmingham:** Central School of Arts and Crafts. **Bristol:** Merchant Venturers' Technical College. **Edinburgh:** Heriot-Watt College. **Glasgow:** Stow College of Printing. **Leeds:** College of Technology. **Leicester:** College of Arts and Crafts. **London:** The London School of Printing and Kindred Trades; School of Photo-Engraving and Lithography (Bolt Court). **Manchester:** Municipal College of Technology.

II. TECHNICAL SCHOOLS GIVING INSTRUCTION IN VARIOUS BRANCHES OF PRINTING

Aylesbury: Hazell, Watson & Viney, Ltd. **Bath:** School of Art. **Batley:** Technical College and School of Arts and Crafts. **Belfast:** College of Technology. **Blackburn:** Municipal School of Art. **Bolton:** Municipal School of Art. **Bournemouth:** Municipal College of Art. **Bradford:** College of Arts and Crafts. **Brighton:** School of Art. **Burslem:** School of Art. **Cambridge:** Cambridgeshire Technical School. **Cardiff:** Technical College. **Cheltenham:** School of Arts and Crafts. **Colchester:** School of Arts and Crafts. **Cork:** Crawford Municipal Technical Institute. **Coventry:** Municipal School of Art. **Derby:** School of Arts and Crafts. **Dublin:** Municipal Technical School. **Dudley:** School of Arts and Crafts. **Dundee:** College of Art. **Gloucester:** Municipal School of Arts and Crafts. **Guildford:** Technical College. **Halifax:** School of Art. **Harpenden:** Technical School. **Hertford:** William Baker Technical School. **Huddersfield:** Technical College. **Hull:** Municipal Technical College. **Ipswich:** School of Arts and Crafts. **Keighley:** School of Arts and Crafts. **Limerick:** Municipal Technical Institute. **Liverpool:** City School of Art. **London:** Camberwell School of Arts and Crafts; Central School of Arts and Crafts; Chiswick Polytechnic School of Art; Hornsey School of Art; Junior Technical Evening Institute; North-Western Polytechnic. **Maidstone:** School of Arts and Crafts. **Mansfield:** School of Art. **Newcastle-on-Tyne:** King Edward VII School of Art. **Norwich:** City Technical College. **Nottingham:** University College. **Portsmouth:** Southern College of Art. **Rochester:** Medway School of Arts and Crafts. **St. Albans:** School of Art and Technical Institute. **Sheffield:** College of Arts and Crafts. **Southampton:** School of Arts and Crafts. **Thanet:** School of Arts and Crafts, Margate. **Tunbridge Wells:** Technical Institute. **Walsall:** Municipal Technical School of Art. **Watford:** School of Art. **Worcester:** School of Arts and Crafts. **York:** Technical College.

INDEX

(Figures in italics refer to illustrations)

ACKNOWLEDGMENTS

The Publishers wish to express their thanks to the following for valuable assistance in connection with the preparation of this book:—

Adams Bros. & Shardlow Ltd.; Aeraspray Mfg. Co. Ltd.; American Type Founders Co.; Ault & Wiborg Ltd.; Autotype Company Ltd.; T. Barnes (Burman Cooper Ltd.); Bentley & Jackson Ltd.; Bertrams Ltd.; British Federation of Master Printers; A. J. Bull, M.Sc., F.R.P.S. (Principal: London School of Photo-Engraving and Lithography); William Caslon & Co. Ltd.; F. W. Clulow, Ph.D., F.R.I.C.; W. F. Colley (Birmingham College of Arts and Crafts); R. W. Crabtree & Sons Ltd.; Croxted Manufacturing Co. Ltd.; Dawson, Payne & Elliott Ltd.; The Elm Press; F. C. Errington (Principal: Leeds School of Printing); R. B. Fishenden; Fry's Metal Foundries Ltd.; B. H. Green; Hall & Kay Ltd.; Harrild & Sons Ltd.; R. Hoe & Co. Ltd.; H. T. B. Ltd.; Hunter-Penrose Ltd.; Imperial Chemical Industries Ltd. (Dyestuffs Division); Intertype Ltd.; W. Lewis, M.A.; Linotype & Machinery Ltd.; Lorilleux & Bolton Ltd.; Lowe & Brydone Ltd.; Manders Printing Inks Ltd.; George Mann & Co. Ltd.; Masson Scott & Co. Ltd.; Monotype Corporation Ltd.; Stanley Morison; Odhams (Watford) Ltd.; PATRA (Printing and Allied Trades Research Association); Frank F. Pershke Ltd.; George Philip & Son Ltd.; John Ratcliffe & Sons Ltd.; Sheridan Machinery Co. Ltd.; C. W. Shortt & Co. Ltd.; Martin J. Slattery & Son Ltd.; J. Cameron Smail, O.B.E., F.R.S.E. (Principal: Heriot-Watt College, Edinburgh); Smythe-Horne Ltd.; Soldans Ltd.; Stephenson, Blake & Co. Ltd.; Stevens, Shanks & Sons Ltd.; Strachan & Henshaw Ltd.; W. E. Thirkettle (Principal: London School of Printing and Kindred Trades); T. C. Thompson & Son Ltd.; Timsons Ltd.; Usher Walker Ltd.; Victory-Kidder Printing Machine Co. Ltd.; Waite & Saville Ltd.; Waterlow & Sons Ltd.; H. Watton (Lake & Sons); B. Winstone & Sons Ltd.